PALS
6.18

Programming Systems
and Foreign Affairs Leadership

Programming Systems and Foreign Affairs Leadership

An Attempted Innovation

FREDERICK C. MOSHER

AND JOHN E. HARR

A STUDY PREPARED FOR

THE INTER-UNIVERSITY CASE PROGRAM

New York
Oxford University Press
London 1970 *Toronto*

Foreword

When this study was commissioned by the Inter-University Case Program, we hoped that it would shed new light on at least one of three aspects of American government that concern social scientists and analysts of public affairs. Now, thanks to the ability of the authors and the cooperation extended by officials and experts, the finished study can be commended to the reader on all three grounds.

First, this is a case study of an inside effort at introducing a major administrative change, one that would have affected all Washington agencies with overseas operations. This innovation aspect will have special significance for those concerned with the dynamics of organizational change, governmental modernization, and high bureaucratic politics. The authors' account of the persistent efforts of the innovators, who were based in a staff unit of the State Department, is abundant in tragic drama. Although experienced in the back ways of Washington executive branch relationships and artful in tactics of support building, the innovators had the formidable task of winning acceptance for their proposal from the White House, from agency leaders of cabinet and sub-cabinet rank who were preoccupied with important and urgent affairs, and from suspicious senior Foreign Service professionals. One source of tragedy in this aspect of the study is the audacious imbalance between the meager authority of the innovators and the magnitude of the changes they wanted their innovation to achieve.

At its second level of significance, this is an important study about the world of foreign affairs administration. It is also about new efforts to improve the ability of the American government to conduct its extensive foreign affairs activities coherently in a world shrunk by modern awareness of the interdependence of things and by advances in transport and communication. These factors have led a growing number of domestic agencies—for example NASA and the Departments of Agriculture, Commerce, and Labor—to expand their operations abroad, thus joining the foreign aid and information agencies, the intelligence services, and the Departments of Defense and the Treasury. Aiming at the most direct achievement of their particular functional purposes, these agencies have seldom prized the values of working through, or under the coordination of, the Department of State in Washington or U.S. ambassadors abroad. Nor have some Foreign Service careerists believed that they should concern themselves deeply with matters outside of traditional diplomatic functions. Presidents Eisenhower, Kennedy, and Johnson all sought to strengthen the role of ambassadors as directors of all U.S. government activities in their countries, but progress was sometimes slow, and in Washington there was no similar preeminence for the Department of State *vis-à-vis* other agencies. (The conflict late in 1969 between the Department of Transportation and the State Department for top responsibility in negotiating airline route agreements indicated that the classic problem continued to exist in the Nixon administration.) The innovators in this study wanted to introduce a computerized country programming system that would, they believed, give the State Department a stronger managerial potency indispensable for coordination of all U.S. government activities in any given country.

Third, this is a uniquely revealing study of the administrative and intellectual politics attending the development and attempted installation of a major governmental programming system. Such programming systems have become increasingly important in "big government" since the much-publicized use of systems analysis and programming systems by former Defense Secretary Robert McNamara. The authors describe the progressive experimentation that went into the development of the proposed State Department country programming system. They portray in detail the different resistances and criticisms encountered by those working for the introduction of the system, and the tactics adopted to overcome these difficulties. A highlight of this aspect of the study is the description of the collision between the sponsors of two major trans-governmental programming systems: those who had developed the State Department country programming system and those in the Bureau of the Budget who were working to introduce the PPB (Planning-Program-Budgeting) system promulgated by President Johnson and designed to work on an agency basis. In describing the conflicts and negotiations between the proponents of the two systems, including appeals made to prestigious external authorities in universities and so-called "think tanks," the authors present an intimate view of some of the politics of the programming systems world that has been notably lacking in the literature.

In all three aspects, this story is fullest in its portrayal of the actions and perspectives of the innovators. White House officials, cabinet secretaries, and historic eminences are glimpsed in action, but usually from the purposeful, below-stairs viewpoint of the innovators.* Both authors, as noted in the biographical accounts on the dust jacket, were participants in some of the events described in their study. Their participation was on the side of the innovators—Mr. Harr employed directly in the innovation effort for a considerable time and Professor Mosher appearing sporadically as an authoritative

---

* For a fuller picture of the setting in which the case takes place, the reader may turn to John P. Leacacos: *Fires in the In-Basket* (World Publishing Co.: Cleveland, 1968), chapters XI and XII.

adviser, consultant, or member of a high-level expert committee. However, the authors have worked hard to present both a full and an objective account. They have interviewed every important figure willing to speak with them. (Almost all were.) An early draft of the study was sent to all the major actors, and the present version owes much to the willingness of many of them to respond with additional data, criticisms, and corrections. Former Secretary of State Dean Rusk was not available for interviewing and did not comment on the draft.

Some of the research for this study was supported by funds made available to the Inter-University Case Program from the Albert Schweitzer Chair established at Syracuse University by the State of New York. We wish to express our thanks to Professor Dwight Waldo, holder of the chair. Other funding came from contributions of over sixty universities to the Inter-University Case Program.

> EDWIN A. BOCK
> President, Inter-University Case Program
> Professor of Political Science, Syracuse University

May 1970

Contents

Glossary of Abbreviations

ACORD   Action for Organizational Development, a program developed under Crockett for T-Group training and organizational change

AFSA   American Foreign Service Association

AID   Agency for International Development

ARA   Bureau of Inter-American Affairs in the Department of State

BOB   Bureau of the Budget

CAP   Country Assistance Program, annual programming document employed by AID

CASP   Country Analysis and Strategy Paper, a comprehensive programming initiative generated in the Latin American Bureau of State in 1966

CCPS   Comprehensive Country Programming System, the initial system set up by the State Department group

CFO   Component Field Organization, organizational elements utilized by CCPS (later changed to Component Programmed Organization, CPO)

CIA   Central Intelligence Agency

CISR   Center for International Systems Research, set up by Crockett in 1965

DCM   Deputy Chief of Mission, second-in-command in overseas embassies

DOD   Department of Defense

EA   Executive Assistant, new position in U.S. embassies created by State Department programming group

ECA   Economic Cooperation Administration, the first major U.S. foreign-aid agency, predecessor to AID

EROP   Executive Review of Overseas Programs, the study of selected missions directed by the President in 1965

FAMC   Foreign Affairs Manual Circular, State Department method for issuing and maintaining official administrative pronouncements

FAPS   Foreign Affairs Programming System, the revised version of CCPS, developed during the winter of 1965-66

FAS   Foreign Agricultural Service of the Department of Agriculture

FSO   Foreign Service Officer (career category)

FSR   Foreign Service Reserve Officer (temporary category)

IFAPS Integrated Foreign Affairs Programming System, the expression utilized and recommended by the Hitch Committee

IRG   Interdepartmental Regional Group, created by NSAM 341 for each of five regions of the world

MOP   Management by Objectives and Programs, slogan expressing concepts central to the reorganization of the administrative area of the Department of State by Crockett in 1965

MPS   Management Planning Staff in the administrative area of the State Department

MUST   Manpower Utilization System and Techniques, developed by the management group within the State Department

NASA   National Aeronautics and Space Agency

NPP   National Policy Paper, prepared by W. W. Rostow's planning staff on individual countries

NSAM   National Security Action Memorandum, a directive of the President in the national security area (NSAM 341 was the directive of March 4, 1966, that provided for State Department leadership over almost all foreign affairs.)

OCB   Operations Coordinating Board, an interagency group established to coordinate and assure implementation of decisions of the National Security Council; abolished by President Kennedy in 1961

OMP   Office of Management Planning, the enlarged version of Barrett's Management Planning Staff (MPS), set up in 1965

PAS   Program Analysis Staff, established on paper in 1965 by Crockett, intended to become top-level analytical staff of the State Department

PPBS   Planning-Programming-Budgeting-System

RAND   Nonprofit research corporation, established initially by the Air Force, engaging in contract research in a number of fields, headquartered in Santa Monica, California

SIG   Senior Interdepartmental Group, created by NSAM 341

SRI   The nonprofit Stanford Research Institute, loosely associated with Stanford University, with headquarters in Menlo Park, California

USIA   United States Information Agency

USIS   U.S. Information Service, the overseas elements of USIA

Chronology of Key Events

February 1961	President Kennedy dissolves OCB.
May 1961	Kennedy letter gives ambassadors managerial responsibility.
1961-62	McNamara-Hitch programming system installed in Defense.
1962	Walt W. Rostow develops NPP concept in State.
December 1962	Herter Committee issues its report.
Spring 1963	Barrett writes memorandum proposing programming system.
May 1963	Barrett idea tested in Colombia.
June 1963	Barrett becomes staff aide to Crockett.
July 1963	Task force formed in ARA to carry on programming system.
August 1963	System is revised, given name: CCPS.
September 1963	Field experiments occur in Dominican Republic and Venezuela.
December 1963	CCPS installed in Colombia; first "total country program" book is produced.
January 1964	Team is switched from ARA to Crockett area, under Barrett; CCPS is revised, computerized.
February 1964	Crockett and Rostow form alliance; describe CCPS effort to Secretary Rusk.
March 1964	Mexican and Ethiopian installations of CCPS seen as very successful; plan for balance of 1964 set.

December 1964	By end of year, CCPS installed in 30 U.S. embassies, 20 officers serving abroad as "Executive Assistants."
January 1965	Major revision of CCPS occurs in conference of Executive Assistants and Barrett staff.
February 1965	Crockett certifies to Rusk that CCPS is ready to be made operational; Rusk's response is to appoint committee.
March 24, 1965	Barrett briefs Bunker Committee on CCPS.
March 25, 1965	President Johnson calls for country program review—EROP.
April-June 1965	EROP is launched in 13 countries.
June 1965	Crockett reorganizes administrative area of State.
August 25, 1965	President Johnson announces intention to achieve "planning-programming-budgeting system" (PPBS) for federal government.
September 1965	Washington review of EROP country submissions occurs.
Fall 1965	General Taylor begins study of foreign affairs coordination.
October 1965	Budget issues Bulletin 66-3 instructing each agency to create its own PPBS.
November 1965	Fruitless effort by State and Budget groups to write final report for the President on EROP begins.
December 1965	Rift between State and Budget groups widens.
January 1966	Major revision occurs on basis of EROP; name of system is changed from CCPS to FAPS.
February 1966	Budget opposes State's plans for total regional use of FAPS in Latin America for next budget cycle.
March 4, 1966	Taylor's work culminates in issuance of NSAM 341.
March 6, 1966	Crockett and Rostow state their case strongly in memorandum to Rusk.
March 7, 1966	Crockett-Rostow appointment with Rusk aborted, memo not officially sent.
March 8, 1966	Crockett meets with AID Administrator David Bell; Hitch Committee idea is born.
March 9, 1966	Crockett-Barrett rift occurs in "Black Wednesday" meeting.
March 11, 1966	Barrett calls off elaborate Latin American plans.

March 14, 1966	Hitch receives lengthy briefing in California.
March 14-16, 1966	Conference of Executive Assistants takes place.
April 1966	Hitch visits Washington, sees Rusk.
May 1966	Hitch Committee is organized.
June 8, 1966	Budget Director Schultze writes "ten questions" letter to Rusk.
June 13, 1966	First meeting of Hitch Committee occurs.
September 17, 1966	Second and final meeting of Hitch Committee occurs.
September 22, 1966	President Johnson announces appointment of Nicholas Katzenbach as Under Secretary of State.
September 1966	Barrett staff, under Robert Bonham, begins collaboration with Latin American bureau in CASP project.
October 5, 1966	Hitch report is delivered to Secretary of State.
December 1966	Katzenbach assumes responsibility for Hitch report, writes letter thanking members.
January 1967	Katzenbach reaches agreement with Thomas Schelling to be high-level head of systems effort; Schelling to join full time in June.
January 30, 1967	Crockett's resignation becomes effective.
Spring 1967	Barrett staff begins to thin out as it becomes clear there will be no linkage between Katzenbach and previous efforts.
May 1967	Schelling withdraws; Barrett programming staff notified it will be abolished.
June 1967	Programming staff extended to September in order to finish first-cycle collaboration on CASP.
Summer 1967	Barrett leaves Department of State.
July 1967	Ferment among middle and junior FSO ranks becomes visible when "group of eighteen" takes over control of American Foreign Service Association.
August 1967	Jackson Subcommittee begins study of PPBS in foreign affairs.
September 1967	Programming staff abolished; Robert Bonham joins Katzenbach staff as sole survivor of past efforts.

*Programming Systems
and Foreign Affairs Leadership*

Introduction: The Setting

IN THE WINTER of 1962-63, a small group of individuals in the U.S. Department of State undertook the development and installation of a system to program American activities of all agencies in individual foreign countries. This later came to be known as the Comprehensive Country Programming System (CCPS), and still later, with further modifications, as the Foreign Affairs Programming System (FAPS).

On August 25, 1965, President Johnson announced "that we would begin to introduce a new planning-programming-budgeting system in Government." The announcement was first made in a Cabinet meeting, then in a press conference. Thus was begun a new thrust (some have called it a revolution) in federal management, the full impact of which may still lie ahead. It is commonly known by its initials, PPBS.

Seven months later, in March 1966, the President issued another directive, National Security Action Memorandum No. 341, known as NSAM (pronounced *nasum*) 341, which delegated to the Secretary of State the responsibility for "overall direction, coordination and supervision of inter-governmental activities of the United States Government overseas."

These three actions—the State Department initiative and the two presidential directives—provide major punctuation points in the story that follows. The underlying purposes of their sponsors were basically compatible, but in origins, interpretation, and application the three actions were divergent and brought to a head quite different concepts of federal administration of international activities. This study describes the issues seen by the protagonists in these three actions—especially the events as they developed from 1962 through 1967. It is a problem case. No neat answers have yet appeared, and very probably the definition of acceptable answers may consume some years in the future. The story treats the technical and methodological aspects of programming and budgeting, whether CCPS or PPBS, only peripherally. The primary concern is the political and administrative implications and obstacles of bringing about major change in a system of government such as that of the United States. These aspects seem to have been minimized in the mushrooming literature about PPBS in recent years.

PPBS AND ITS ANTECEDENTS

There is little consensus as to how PPBS differs from earlier concepts and principles about budgets and planning. Budgetary improvement has been a central element in governmental reform at all levels for at least the last 60 years. Its continuing themes have included greater rationality and objectivity in reaching decisions; greater budgetary authority for the executive branch; clear association between what is to be done (program) and what is to be spent; orientation toward the future rather than the past; and consideration of long-range effects in making today's decisions. The PPBS "new look" in budgeting that swept the Pentagon in 1961 included all of these elements; some it extended, some it absorbed implicitly.

Budgetary reform has characteristically come in waves, each with a distinctive approach. The first wave in recent times was begun by the New York Bureau of Municipal Research, which started its work in 1906 in cities and later extended its efforts to states and federal government. Its emphases, partly in response to widespread municipal corruption, were upon accountability, honesty, accuracy, and improved technique in public accounting. Yet even in this first wave the underlying idea of program budgeting—that what is to be spent should be tied with what is to be done—was clearly present. Soon other municipal research bureaus sought to apply the same theme in other cities, and it is generally true that budgetary reform during the first third of this century began with city governments. Later this reform movement penetrated many state governments. Its most notable federal expression was in the reports of the Taft Commission on Economy and Efficiency, issued in 1912 and 1913. It is significant that the Commission was chaired by Frederick Cleveland, then Director of the New York Bureau of Municipal Research.

The Taft Commission's vigorous recommendations about a national budget were ultimately given expression in the Budget and Accounting Act of 1921, which may for convenience be considered the starting point of the second budgetary reform wave. This effort, initially led by the first Budget Director, Charles G. Dawes, sought to establish the authority of the President over the budget; to provide an effective staff arm for this purpose (even though the Bureau of the Budget was then formally a part of the Treasury Department); and to achieve hard-headed, tough-fisted, businesslike efficiency in carrying out the essential activities of the government.

The third wave of budgetary reform was initiated by the 1937 report of the President's Committee on Administrative Management (the Brownlow Committee), which led to the establishment in 1939 of the Executive Office of the President, the Bureau of the Budget becoming its central and strongest element. During the period that followed, the budget process and the organization that superintended it— the Bureau of the Budget—emerged as principal instruments of executive policy and management. The review and approval or disapproval of administrative proposals for legislation, on behalf of the President, were centered in the budget organization, as were the study and review of organizational plans. Clearly the intent at that time was a rational linking of policy planning, program organization, and budget.

The fourth wave followed World War II, impelled by the reports of the first Hoover Commission in the late 1940's; the Commission had been sparked by James Forrestal, then Secretary of Defense. The first Hoover Commission—specifically, Hoover himself—is said to have coined the phrase "performance budgeting"; it stressed the linkage of budgeting with programs and activities, performance reporting, the rationalization and simplification of appropriation structures, and a number of other things. Its concept of "performance budgeting" was essentially comparable with what was then known as "program budgeting," and some at the time thought the latter designation more appropriate.

The fifth wave came in the 1950's and may have been started by the second Hoover Commission. It proposed its version of program budgeting, but its main emphasis was upon the modernization of accounting practices, accrual accounting, and allocation of costs to programs and activities. It was typified by the expression the Budget Bureau made for some years its standard terminology: "cost-of-performance" budgeting.

The sixth wave, which broke over the Pentagon building in 1961 and is beating on other agencies today, was an updated and extended version of program budgeting, now widely referred to in federal circles as PPBS. Its distinctive emphases included: systematic linkage of objectives with plans with programs with budgets; stress on outputs in relation to inputs; planning ahead a good many years beyond the next budget year; quantitative measurement of consequences and accomplishments; consideration of alternatives —both alternative programs (means) and alternative objectives (ends); more intensive analysis of projected programs and their alternatives by trained and skilled systems analysts;

and the extensive utilization of modern techniques and computers for the handling of enormous quantities of data toward the reaching of the most rational decisions. Like performance budgeting, PPBS is linked with the Department of Defense, where it began, and with the name of its former Secretary, Robert S. McNamara. Its principal architect was Defense Comptroller Charles Hitch, who brought the ideas for the system as well as some of its key personnel from the RAND Corporation.

All but one of the reform waves described above brought into budgeting a somewhat different kind of person, with distinctive training, background, and orientation. Most of them also brought a somewhat new way of thinking, a new bag of tools, and a new glossary, even though the language of federal budgeting has never suffered from oversimplification. A very rough sketch of the kinds of leaders associated with each wave might appear as follows:

Wave	Approximate Beginning Year	Types of Leaders
I	1906	Public-spirited, progressive reformers
II	1921	Hard-headed military officers, experienced in logistics from World War I
III	1939	Persons trained and experienced in public organization and management
IV	1949	Same as III
V	1955	Accountants and men with business experience
VI	1961	Economists with emphasis on research and systems analysis

Every wave except IV has occasioned contests between the old and the new and inevitably some personal and professional rivalries.

This brief review of budgetary reform is presented primarily that the reader may judge in broader historical perspective the problems and the progress of the contemporary wave, PPBS, and more specifically the story that follows. All the reform efforts succeeded in leaving some permanent additions to governmental planning and budgetary processes. Each built on previous reforms. None was totally effective.

THE DEFENSE DEPARTMENT MODEL

To a considerable degree, the last three budget reform waves were stimulated in and by the Department of Defense. This is perhaps explained in part by the sudden rise of defense expenditures to a position of dominance relative to the rest of the national government. It may also be explained by the fact that many people, including several recent Presidents, have believed that much, if not all, of Defense resembled very large corporate businesses and should be operated according to the same principles and practices. Many of the innovations proposed for the government as a whole over the last 20 years have been transfers of private business ideas by way of the Department of Defense.

The concepts of PPBS apparently go back to World War II, particularly to certain analytical studies and programs for critical materials. Subsequently, the RAND Corporation, which had been established by the Air Force as a semi-independent research organization, launched a program of research on air equipment and weapons systems. In 1954 the RAND staff's David Novick issued a brief report on a program-budgeting system for the Department of Defense. Later comparable studies were undertaken in other areas of Defense and in the fields of atomic energy and natural resources. In 1960 Charles Hitch and Roland McKean, both of RAND, published *The Economics of Defense in the Nuclear Age*,[1] which proposed intensive economic analysis (associated with the budget process) of possible new programs, with emphasis upon very expensive weapons and equipment systems.

When Robert McNamara was appointed Secretary of De-

---

1. Charles J. Hitch and Roland N. McKean, *The Economics of Defense in the Nuclear Age* (Cambridge, Massachusetts: Harvard University Press, 1960).

fense by President Kennedy in 1961, he chose Hitch, theretofore head of the Economics Division of RAND, to be his Assistant Secretary (Comptroller). McNamara gave Hitch full backing to install a program-budgeting system along the lines drawn by previous RAND studies, and this became the heart of the McNamara revolution in Defense management. Hitch brought with him from RAND a number of men imbued with the new program-budgeting approach and methodology, hired some economists from the outside, and developed a number of others, civilian and military, already in the Department. The "whiz-kids" of Defense earned the respect of some in Congress and many in the executive branch, including the President.

The projected extension of the PPBS approach to the rest of the national government presented, and still presents, a tremendous challenge. This arose partly from the paucity of prior study and experience in applying the approach to the civil activities of government. The RAND Corporation had been at work on defense problems for many years before 1961, and when Hitch moved to Washington he could bring with him a bag of rather sophisticated tools and a trained body of carpenters skilled in the use of those tools. Except in one or two fields, nothing similar had been developed for the civilian side of government. Secondly, the Defense Department presented almost unique organizational advantages for the installation from above of a new management system. Its mission was relatively clear cut, definable, and identifiable with the organization. There were relatively few overlaps in its central activities with other organizations and authorities. Its fifteen years of organizational consolidation were marked by three major developments: the National Security Act of 1947, which established the Department with a weak Secretary; the National Security Act Amendments of 1949, which provided the Secretary with a greater degree of budgetary authority; and the Executive Reorganization Plan of 1958, which further strengthened the Secretary and the Joint Chiefs of Staff at the expense of the three service departments. By 1961 the legal authority of the Secretary of Defense over the entire military establishment was firm and unquestioned. PPBS and the proposals growing out of it could be directed from a single office at the top. Further, PPBS was a device that could give substance and meaning to the wording of the precedent legal authorizations.

A third factor, perhaps more important, resided in the person of the Secretary of Defense. A strong executive and an able administrative politician possessing amazing capabilities of intellectual grasp, analytical ability, and memory, McNamara was also attuned and sympathetic to the PPBS approach through prior education and experience.

A fourth advantage of Defense derived from the relatively simple structure and procedure of the appropriations process for that Department. Over the years prior to 1961, Hitch's predecessor, Wilfred McNeill, had developed a single-cost category system applying to all the services and necessitating a degree of interservice compatibility. The military budget was submitted and defended as a single entity, it was reviewed by only one set of subcommittees in each house of Congress, and it produced a single basic appropriation bill. Congressional authorizations to the Defense Department in many fields, particularly research and development and procurement, were extraordinarily broad in comparison with comparable authorizations to most other governmental agencies, leaving large areas in which the Department could effectively analyze and choose among alternative courses of action with substantial confidence that its decisions would stick. And the appropriation items themselves were, and remain, broad and enormously large—averaging better than $1 billion apiece— to permit a substantial degree of current-year flexibility.

Finally, a very large share of the Defense budget was directed to research, development, and procurement of *things* —especially large "hardware" items of equipment and weapons systems. Each category of *things* could be related to fairly precise objectives. Each was quantifiable; its costs could be roughly estimated, its effectiveness predicted within a reasonable margin of error. By 1968 Defense was trying to extend the PPBS approach to other areas of expenditure, such as operations and maintenance and the costing of military personnel. But at the time of the presidential order of 1965, the most spectacular PPBS achievements concerned weapons and major equipment.

No other governmental programs present advantages for the ready application of PPBS comparable to those in the Defense Department. In few are the boundaries of mission so nearly contiguous with the boundaries of organization. Few enjoy so strong a leadership, supported by both legal authority and the commanding presence of the incumbent. Most governmental programs—however defined—involve a large number of different administrative organizations: education, more than 40; foreign affairs, more than 50; natural resources, more than 20; urban development, an indeterminable number. Most operate within the confines of myriad legislative acts and a multitude of different appropriations, developed through a variety of appropriation subcommittees. In only a handful of governmental programs are the choice and procurement of equipment and other things more than incidental to primary objectives.[2] A large share of expenditures on federal programs consists of grants and loans to foreign countries, to other units of American governments, and to private agencies, where the federal "seed money" is matched and the accomplishments depend upon the activities of others. The larger part of direct federal spending in most agencies is for people, not things. And the principal objectives of most federal programs are social; they concern people: their economic well-being, their education, their so-

2. Perhaps the best example is the National Aeronautics and Space Administration (NASA). Others probably include the Atomic Energy Commission; some of the construction programs, like the Bureau of Public Roads; some of the research programs, as in Agriculture; and the Post Office.

cial adjustment, their health, their housing—the most difficult areas to reach precise, agreed definitions of objectives and measurable criteria of results. Here is an arena where political feedback—through administrative, legislative, party, and nongovernmental channels—is continuous, as are the possibilities of political intervention.

For these many and diverse reasons, the Department of Defense could offer only the most general of guidelines for the application of PPBS in the majority of civil agencies. Its aims and principles, and some of its techniques, might be transferable. But its application would involve new complexities and new kinds of difficulties. Leaders in most federal agencies are now endeavoring to sketch blueprints of PPBS appropriate to their fields of activity. The story that begins in Chapter II describes the early phases of that endeavor in one difficult field—foreign affairs.

THE MANAGEMENT OF FOREIGN AFFAIRS

In highly general terms, the problems of foreign affairs today are like those of other public affairs: they are carried on in an era of rapid and accelerating change; they are necessarily responsive to a technological and cybernetic revolution; they can be politically volatile; they are bureaucratically divided among a large number of different organizations, each with its own political, legislative, and clientele support and opposition. Such generalizations, however, should be interpreted judiciously. In the 1960's there were both changes and long-standing traditions in the conduct of U.S. foreign affairs that were not necessarily compatible with the proposed new rational programming and budgeting systems. The drives of the Kennedy and Johnson presidencies in foreign affairs administration are central ingredients of this case. An understanding of them requires at least a thumbnail sketch.

Until the 1930's the American posture in international affairs was substantially isolationist. The roles of the State Department and its Foreign Service were principally those of observers and reporters, negotiators on occasion, and protectors of Americans and U.S. interests. The missions of the War and Navy Departments were to protect the nation's shores and secondarily to protect U.S. shipping and private investments abroad, especially in Latin America. The Departments of Agriculture and Commerce promoted and assisted American agricultural and business interests overseas. But in the main the U.S. government approached its foreign responsibilities as an observer. It was "reactive" rather than initiatory.

Its assumption of manifold overseas responsibilities just before, during, and following World War II found the United States government organizationally, attitudinally, and culturally unprepared. It met the problem with typical pragmatism: new agencies, separate and autonomous; new leaders and personnel from other than diplomatic backgrounds; *ad hoc* and usually temporary programs and budgets. The new programs dwarfed the older ones, particularly those of the traditional foreign affairs agency, the Department of State, whether measured in terms of dollars, personnel, or impact. In 1939, there was an integration of two of the older overseas programs, Agriculture and Commerce, into the Foreign Service. A similar integration into State of information and cultural programs occurred shortly after the war. Both of these ingestions were resented by career officials steeped in traditional notions of foreign affairs and gave the State Department organizational indigestion for many years. In the postwar period new undertakings such as foreign aid were usually begun outside of the jurisdiction of the Department of State.

Today, almost every significant agency of the national government is interested in, and is doing something about, one or many different problems overseas. In organizational terms, there is no pattern and no logic about *how* they are pursuing their interests. Some work through, and rely upon, the Department of State (e.g., the Labor Department). Some conduct their activities with virtual autonomy (e.g., Agriculture); some are legally part of State but for most operational purposes work separately (e.g., AID); some utilize State Department facilities and personnel but have considerable influence and control over what is done and who will do it (e.g., Commerce). Most have their own budgets, their own appropriations subcommittees in Congress, and their own reviewers in the U.S. Bureau of the Budget. A consequence of this large-scale development is that most of what the U.S. government *does* overseas is done by, most of what it *spends* overseas is spent by, and most of its *people* overseas (under whatever personnel label) work for, agencies other than the Department of State. Not including military forces, U.S. expenditures for foreign affairs in recent years have been running nearly six billion dollars annually, a significant amount but less than one per cent of the Gross National Product. Of this total, the State Department itself accounts for less than one-twelfth; its expenditure for fiscal 1968 was less than one half of one percent of the U.S. budget and, by way of comparison, about half the total expenditure of the University of California. As shown in the table below, the big spenders in foreign affairs have been AID, the Department of Agriculture, and the Department of Defense.[3]

The Department of State has long occupied an anomalous position in the national administration. It is the oldest, most prestigious agency of the government. It is viewed by many, here and abroad, as being not only the principal policy adviser on international affairs and formal representative of the government overseas, but also, in a vague way, as being responsible for all American activities in the international arena. Yet it has another image, widely held within the federal government and particularly among its own Foreign Service personnel, which derives from its history and indeed from the development of diplomacy over two thousand years. This historic diplomatic image is that of a "staff" agency,

3. Based on U.S. *Budget* for 1968.

Estimated Payments to the Public, FY 1967

	Amount (millions)	Percent
U.S. Department of State	$ 378a	7
AID	2,415	42
Food for Freedom	1,710	30
Military Assistance	1,000	17
USIA	184	3
Export-Import Bank	128	2
Trust Funds	111	2
Peace Corps	100	2
International Financial Institutions	—336	—6
All other	30	—
	$5,720b	100

a Including $58 million for foreign information and exchange activities.
b Not including $545 million for intragovernmental transactions and adjustments.

advisory to the President, and representing him in dealings with other nations. It does not encompass "operations," nor the supervision of the operations of other agencies; nor the provision of day-to-day services to other agencies; nor direct relations with foreign peoples other than their governmental officials; nor "management" as generally understood in large bureaucracies. As will be shown, this image has been decreasingly accurate for many decades.

Over the years there have been a great variety of proposals to clarify the image of the State Department and to rationalize the entire structure of foreign affairs. They have ranged from amalgamating all foreign affairs activities in a single Department of Foreign Affairs to reducing the State Department to a small staff agency attached to the President. In between have been proposals for: a superdepartment of foreign affairs along the lines of the Department of Defense with subdepartments, of which one would presumably be State; an assistant president for foreign affairs; a sizable policy and coordinating office in the Executive Office of the President. Few officials and few observers have expressed anything but dissatisfaction with the U.S. government's organization for foreign affairs. In recent years, the alleged "sponginess" of administration in the State Department bureaucracy has been a standard target of criticism from the White House, from the seventh floor of the State Department building,[4] and from others in and out of government. But the traditional image of the elite staff department persists at the highest levels. Secretaries, under secretaries, and ambassadors have historically been chosen on the primary basis of presumed ability in foreign policy and representation, sometimes colored by consideration of party and political support, past and future. Few were chosen because they promised to make good managers in foreign affairs.

THEMES IN FOREIGN AFFAIRS MANAGEMENT TO 1961

During the decade and a half between World War II and the inauguration of President John F. Kennedy, the response to the State Department problem, in concept and to some extent in practice, rested upon two dichotomies: a clear organizational division between policy and operations in foreign affairs; and a clear division within the Department of State between substance and administration.

Policy and Operations. The first Hoover Commission, which reported in 1949, urged that the Department of State be viewed as a staff agency to the President and be restricted to policy matters and coordination. The seventh recommendation of the Commission's report on "Foreign Affairs" was explicit: "The State Department as a general rule should not be given responsibility for the operation of specific programs, whether overseas or at home." Dean Acheson, who became Secretary of State before this report was published, was Vice-Chairman of the Commission. His actions as Secretary indicated a general sympathy with this point of view. But his successor, John Foster Dulles, and President Eisenhower gave

4. The seventh floor is the locus of the offices of the Secretary, Under Secretary, Deputy Under Secretaries, and their immediate staffs.

the concept much more emphatic support. In the first place, the "primacy" of the Department of State in policy matters was repeatedly and vigorously reaffirmed in legislation, executive orders, and public statements. Second, some of the significant "operating" responsibilities of the Department were removed to other agencies. Its technical assistance activities were transferred in August 1953 to the new Foreign Operations Administration. The same month, its information program was transferred, by another reorganization plan, to the United States Information Agency. A year later, its agricultural responsibilities and personnel were transferred to the newly reestablished Foreign Agricultural Service. Most significant of all was the establishment, also in 1953, of the Operations Coordinating Board, an interdepartmental committee, chaired by the Under Secretary of State, with its own staff. It was charged with the responsibility "to provide for the integrated implementation of national security policies by the several agencies."

The policy-operations split, of course, never became anywhere near complete and clear cut. The vast majority of State Department personnel were still in "operations"—in administration or consular work or drafting routine reports or handling foreign visitors to the United States. In fact, one of the Department's most historic and traditional areas of activity—consular work—is ninety-nine percent "operations." On the other hand, the heads of the other agencies—in Defense, or Agriculture, or FOA, or USIA—could hardly divorce themselves from policy questions even if they wanted to. Some, including many of the future leaders of the Kennedy administration, thought the dichotomy aggravated rather than solved the problems of coordination in foreign affairs. But it did provide a convenient and simple rationale for living with them.

Administration and Substance. Parallel with and to a degree mutually supportive of the policy-operations dichotomy was a clean division *within* the Department of State be-

tween "substance" and "administration." The placement
upon the Department of presumably complete responsibility
for foreign-affairs policy matters brightened the image of the
Foreign Service as an elite corps. But elitism was threatened
from another direction. The tremendous growth in size,
scope, and complexity of American activities overseas during
and following World War II had been accompanied by an
even faster growth of administrative activities, such as personnel, budget and finance, buildings, communications, housing,
utilities, etc. This was particularly true in the Department
of State, since it was called upon to provide administrative support for many of the other agencies operating overseas. The management of these activities and the relating of
them to the traditional "substantive" role of the diplomat
became issues of major internal conflict within the Department. Partly in defense of its historic elite posture, the FSO
corps relied upon a clear distinction between what was "administration" (or management) and what was "substance."
The latter was usually defined to include representation, negotiation, reporting, and, more recently, foreign policy. In
fact, "substance" within the Department of State means ap-
proximately diplomacy plus foreign policy.[5]

If great numbers of administrative personnel had to be
absorbed within the Department's myriad organizations at
home and abroad, their acceptance had to be on terms that
would make them clearly subordinate to the elite Foreign
Service Officer corps. To the FSO's administration is an instrument of substance, not its superior nor its equal. Most
of the "old-line" FSO's avoided administrative assignments
and tried to keep it clear that administrators were technicians, necessary but largely irrelevant to the real work of the

5. A representative definition of the traditional diplomacy is: "the application of tact and intelligence to the conduct of official relations between the
governments of independent states." (Sir Ernest Satow, *A Guide to Diplomatic
Practice,* 4th edition. New York: David McKay, 1957, p. 1.) The historic
meaning of diplomacy does not include policy making. Diplomacy is an instrument of policy, not its originator.

Department. The fear that administrators might "take over" or "move in on" the territory of the substantive officers was keenly felt by some—probably the majority—of FSO's. Retired Ambassador Ellis O. Briggs, an extreme example, referred to "administrative types" as "glorified janitors, supply clerks, and pants-pressers" who "yearn to get their fingers in the foreign affairs pie. . . ."[6] Another retired ambassador, Henry Villard, wrote: "In the State Department, the administrators are no longer the servants of the policy makers—they are rapidly becoming the masters."[7] Still another, Charles W. Thayer, quoted an unnamed FSO approvingly: "They [professional administrators] seem to forget that they are essentially valets. Instead of pressing our pants, they are trying to wear them." Thayer went on to note that they were "unfamiliar with the objectives, problems, and methods of diplomacy. Yet, instead of confining their efforts to administrative problems, they rashly injected themselves into the substantive work of diplomacy."[8]

Between 1945 and 1961, the Foreign Service was the subject of many studies, mostly by outside groups—on the average, one every two years. They included a study (unpublished) by the Bureau of the Budget in 1945; a study within the Department that led to the Foreign Service Act of 1946; the study and report by the first Hoover Commission in 1949; a study and report by the Secretary's Advisory Committee on Personnel (the Rowe Committee) in 1950; a study for the Bureau of the Budget by the Brookings Institution in 1951; a study and report of the Secretary of State's Public Committee on Personnel (the Wriston Committee) in 1954; a study (unpublished) by a White House Task Force under the direction of the President's Adviser on Personnel Management (the DuFlon study) in 1955; two studies for the Senate

6. Ellis O. Briggs, *Farewell to Foggy Bottom* (New York: David McKay, 1964), p. 29.

7. Henry Villard, *Affairs at State* (New York: Thomas Y. Crowell, 1965), p. 36.

8. Charles W. Thayer, *Diplomat* (New York: Harper & Row, 1959), p. 274.

Foreign Relations Committee in 1959, one by the Brookings Institution and one by Syracuse University. The large majority of these were critical of the elite corps and recommended its enlargement by adding to it personnel from other categories in the State Department and/or personnel from other foreign-affairs agencies. Only two of the studies had appreciable results: the departmental study which led to the Act of 1946; and the report of the Wriston Committee, which led in the mid-fifties to the induction into the Service of about 1,500 persons from other personnel categories in the Department. A great many of those were engaged in administrative and consular work, and, in the minds of a good many FSO's, their absorption was an adulteration of the corps and caused a major decline in its professional quality.

Most of the studies cited above were perceived as products of "administrative types," and the response of the corps was defensive—both toward the recommendations and toward the "types" who authored them. By 1961, this defensive posture had engendered suspiciousness toward new initiatives by "administrative types" or in management generally. And the dichotomy between substance and administration was applied, after the Wriston program, not only between the FSO corps and other categories of personnel but also within the corps itself. The Wristonized "administrative types" would be "together but not equal."

For the most part, the sharp distinction within State between "administration" and "substance" was recognized and accepted on both sides. Most in administrative positions viewed their roles as clearly circumscribed, and few would venture into areas of "substance" where they might be characterized as trying to "wear the pants" as well as "press" them. The consequence was a built-in resistance by both substantive officers and administrative officers against unification into overall *management* or an encompassing *executive*.

The Changing Role of the Ambassador. One trend that developed during the postwar years ran counter to the two dichotomies discussed above: the growing reliance upon the ambassadors overseas to coordinate and superintend the activities of agencies other than the Department of State in their countries. To the extent that such enlargement of responsibility was effective, it forced the ambassadors and some of their embassy staffs more and more into both administration and operations. Division and fragmentation in Washington would be partially balanced by integration and unification in the field. Though the Department of State in Washington was (ideally) concerned only with policy, the ambassadors overseas, as the President's representatives, should have responsibility for coordinating the field activities of all agencies. Of course, most of the ambassadors then and now were career Foreign Service officers, and most of their senior staffs were, too.

The problem of the ambassadorial role in the postwar years grew principally from the relationship between ambassadors and the mission chiefs of the Economic Cooperation Administration under the Marshall Plan. Initially, the latter officers were autonomous and co-equal with the ambassadors. Gradually the need for better coordination drew increasing attention and response from Washington. In 1951, the Mutual Security Act directed the President to "prescribe procedures to assure coordination among representatives of the United States in each country, under the leadership of the Chief of the United States Diplomatic Mission." Early in 1952, President Truman issued an executive order, directing that the ambassador coordinate all activities under the Mutual Security Act of 1951 and exercise "general direction and leadership of the entire effort."

President Eisenhower reaffirmed the policy and extended the coordinating responsibility to cover USIA. Later, in 1956, he instructed the ambassadors to exercise leadership and supervision over the representatives of *all* agencies whose activities significantly affected American operations. And in the closing weeks of his administration, another executive order asked the ambassadors to exercise "affirmative responsibility" in coordinating the activities of other agencies. But the listing of activities to be so coordinated significantly excluded intelligence and military operations.

Thus evolved during the fifties the concept of ambassadorial leadership crossing agency lines. With it developed the concept of the "country team" wherein the heads of most American agencies in any given country and the chiefs of the principal embassy sections are intended to work as a coordinated and unified body under the leadership of the ambassador, acting not alone as chairman but as a "little President." The effectiveness of the country team and of ambassadorial leadership varied from country to country and from ambassador to ambassador. It was, on the whole, less impressive than the wording of the directives would lead one to expect. Only a few of the ambassadors were inclined to manage the total American program, to "interfere" in activities of other agencies.[9] Few had experience in this kind of work,

9. The terms "other agencies" and "other agency," as used throughout this study, mean all agencies of the federal government, other than the Department of State, which carry out activities in foreign countries or which have interests in international relations. They cover almost all the significant agencies of the government, although the degree of involvement of many is slight and peripheral. They may, for convenience though without precision, be categorized as follows:

military agencies, including strategic planning and negotiation, intelligence, and military assistance;

foreign affairs agencies, whose primary or exclusive purposes are in foreign affairs, including AID, CIA, Peace Corps, USIA, and others;

attache-type activities of agencies whose primary purposes are domestic but which have continuing interests and/or continuing activities overseas in their substantive field of jurisdiction, such as commercial, agricultural, scientific, cultural, labor attaches and many others;

extension abroad of domestic activities, such as NASA stations, overseas research programs of many agencies, regulatory activities (such as customs, narcotics, civil aviation, apprehension of criminals, immigration), services to American citizens (such as veterans and others), etc.

The variety of organizational, budgetary and personnel arrangements for these many activities almost defies description; and it is nearly impossible to draw a clear line between the third and fourth categories above. These diffi-

nor were they armed with staff or managerial tools that could help them much. In spite of the vigorous messages from Washington, their actual authority in the field was limited by agency directives. And two programs of great importance in some countries—intelligence and military—were specifically excluded.

In spite of these limitations, ambassadorial leadership and the country team spirit grew significantly during these years. There was increasing communication among agency representatives and increasing mutual understanding. The Jackson Committee could report in 1963: "The field is refreshingly free of interagency strife. In general, the deep jurisdictional clashes evident in Washington are absent."[10]

Drums Along the Potomac. In fact, much of the coordinative effort in the field was effective in spite of Washington; and most of its weakness was because of Washington. Along the Potomac there was no country team, no regional team, no single world team. Rather there were fifty or more satrapies, each, directly or indirectly, managing its own overseas ventures. Most had their own budgets, their own support and opposition in Congress and outside, their own legislation, their own subcommittee of the House and Senate Appropriations committees. The agencies together covered the full spectrum of public visibility from the covert programs of the Central Intelligence Agency (CIA) to the United States Information Agency (USIA), the very purpose of which was exposure. They varied enormously also in their popularity ranking and in the clienteles that might support or attack them. But most shared the quality of political volatility, even when their activities were shrouded in secrecy.

culties are very germane to this case. See Robert E. Elder, *Overseas Representation and Services for Federal Domestic Agencies* (New York: Carnegie Endowment for International Peace, Foreign Affairs Personnel Study No. 2, 1965).

10. U.S. Senate, Committee on Government Operations, Subcommittee on National Security Staffing and Operations, *Administration of National Security: Basic Issues*, 88th Congress, 1st Session, 1963, p. 11.

The older foreign affairs agencies and the international programs of domestic agencies had over the years developed and pretty largely solidified procedures, timetables, and practices for preparing and administering their budgets. Some had developed systems to relate their programs and their budgets, but here too there was wide variation. The foreign-aid program in its alphabetical metamorphosis from ECA to AID had evolved a massive procedure for country programming and had located in every major overseas mission a program staff for the purpose of planning and projecting various types of assistance within the various sectors of the host country. During the period of this case, these were known as Country Assistance Programs (CAP's). Military assistance programs were developed through entirely different organizations and procedures, beginning with the U.S. military groups in individual countries, processed up through the appropriate regional joint military commands and on finally to the Pentagon building. The USIA developed its Country Plan system as early as 1953. These plans were largely narrative expositions of what the field staff proposed to do during the coming budget year. On the other hand, the Department of State had virtually nothing in the way of forward planning machinery except in the policy field. Its policy planning was largely *ad hoc,* directed to specific issues, and in no way linked to ongoing programs and budgets.

Two general observations about these developments are warranted. One is that none of the agencies had developed what would now be recognized as a sophisticated systems analysis approach and few had systematically related their forward programs with their budgets. The second is that there was almost no machinery or opportunity for relating, comparing, and evaluating the programs and budgets of the different agencies at the country, regional, or world level. During the Eisenhower years, the OCB might conceivably have performed in such a role, but its time was largely consumed in following up on specific *ad hoc* determinations of the National Security Council. It was never involved in the day-to-day processes of programming and budgeting.

The Bureau of the Budget had, in the late forties, organized an International Division to bring together in one unit its resources that were focused on foreign affairs. This division reviewed the estimates and reports submitted by the more important foreign affairs agencies. It could and sometimes did raise specific questions pointed to interagency problems. But the differences in the content, classification, and timing of agency submissions, together with the limitation of its own staff resources, precluded any systematic, comparative review of the related programs of different foreign-affairs agencies.

"THE KENNEDY ROUND"

The new administration of 1961 promised a New Frontier in foreign affairs as in other governmental fields. Its impetus for change was undoubtedly strengthened by the disaster of its first significant initiative—the Bay of Pigs. President Kennedy and his assistants attacked and very largely overturned the policy-operations dichotomy. They challenged the substance-administration dichotomy though with less immediate and less resounding results. They endeavored to extend and hasten the growth of ambassadorial authority in the field. The efforts described in this case were an extension of all three of these administration objectives.

The assault on the idea of separation between foreign policy in the State Department and operations in other agencies was quick and decisive. Almost immediately Kennedy abolished the Operations Coordinating Board, making it clear that the task of supervising the implementation of foreign affairs decision making should be the responsibility of the Department of State. In his statement of February 19, 1961, accompanying his order to abolish the OCB, the President said:

I am today issuing an Executive order abolishing the Operations Coordinating Board. This Board was used in the last administration for work which we now plan to do in other ways.
This action is part of our program for strengthening the responsibility of the individual departments.

First, we will center responsibility for much of the Board's
work in the Secretary of State. He expects to rely particularly
on the Assistant Secretaries in charge of regional bureaus, and
they in turn will consult closely with other departments and
agencies. This will be our ordinary rule for continuing coordination of our work in relation to a country or area.

In the words of McGeorge Bundy, the President's assistant on
national security matters: "We have deliberately rubbed out
the distinction between planning and operation. . . ." In a
wide variety of statements and actions, the administration
made clear its intention that the Secretary of State and his
Department should exercise authority over almost all aspects
of foreign affairs, both policy and operations. The AID program received the most thorough overhaul in its history in
the Foreign Assistance Act of 1961 which created the Agency
for International Development *within* the State Department.
One of its regional bureaus, Latin America, was later brought
together physically ("back-to-back") with the corresponding
bureau of State, and the offices of Assistant Secretary of State
for Inter-American Affairs and the AID director of the Alliance for Progress were vested in the same person.

Pursuant to the new President's objectives, a number of
new agencies were created: the Peace Corps, the Arms Control and Disarmament Agency, the Office of the Special Representative for Trade Negotiation. All were placed within
the Department of State or related to its Secretary as the
nominal boss. In this early period of the Kennedy administration, there was little doubt of the President's intention
that the Secretary of State and his Department take charge.
On the other hand, the new President and his advisers did
not appear to start with a realistic appreciation of the ob-

stacles to such a take-over. These obstacles are painfully illuminated in this case.

The attack of the Kennedy administration on the substance-administration dichotomy was more verbal and persuasive—less active and less directive. Necessarily, it was indirect, and probably a good many of the administration leaders were not aware of what they were really attacking. The principal leadership in the Department of State was divided between political appointees and the career Foreign Service. If the Department was to "take charge" of American foreign affairs, the political appointees and the upper levels of the Service must all "take charge," each in his appropriate sphere of assignment. They would have to be executives as well as policy framers and diplomats. The split between substance and administration could hardly survive in such a situation, for management, by definition, involves the application of available resources to objectives.

The efforts of the new administration to imbue State with action-oriented, aggressive, managerial spirit pursued three main tactics. The first was through direct political appointments to the top positions in Washington and to the critical ambassadorships in the field. It was exemplified by the early appointments of Dean Rusk, Chester Bowles, George Ball, Mennen Williams, Averell Harriman, Roger Jones, Harlan Cleveland, and others in Washington; and of Kenneth Galbraith, Lincoln Gordon, Samuel Burger, George McGhee, and others in the field. The President's talent search was conspicuously successful in producing men of outstanding intellectual quality: imaginative, energetic, and articulate. Unfortunately, only a handful brought much experience in the hard business of translating objectives into action through large, complex organizations.

The second tactic was simply exhortation, and one of the leading exhorters was Secretary of State Dean Rusk. As early as February 20, 1961, he spoke to the policy-making officers of the Department about its new role as the leader of change:

The recent Executive Order which abolished the Operations Coordinating Board bore witness to the fact that the Department of State is expected to assume the leadership of foreign policy. In consequence, an enormous responsibility falls upon us here not only in developing policies but in seeing that they are carried out. . . .

Power gravitates to those who are willing to make decisions and live with the results. . . . On this particular point the Department of State is entering, I think, something of a new phase in its existence. *We are expected to take charge.* [Emphasis added.]

Later, on May 31, 1962, President Kennedy in an address to the Foreign Service Association stressed the changing and challenging responsibilities of the Foreign Service job:

This is the great period of the Foreign Service, much greater than any period that has gone before. . . . But it places the heaviest burden upon all of you. Instead of becoming merely experts in diplomatic history, or in current clippings from the *New York Times,* now you have to involve yourselves in every element of foreign life—labor, the class struggle, cultural affairs and all the rest—attempting to predict in what direction the forces will move. . . . Those who cannot stand the heat should get out of the kitchen. . . . Personally, I think the place to be is the kitchen, and I am sure the Foreign Service Officers of the United States feel the same way.

These statements, and many others like them, did not specifically attack the substance-administration dichotomy; yet all by implication were addressing themselves to the managerial totality of the role of the State Department and its individual officers. The most direct confrontation with the issue came in the 1962 report of the Committee on Foreign Affairs Personnel (the Herter Committee) when it expressed its conviction that: "the tendency within the [State] Department to view what is called 'administration' as separate, subordinate, and of little relevance to the foreign policy function must be corrected."[11]

The expression, "new diplomacy," which became popular during the early years of the Kennedy administration, had a different meaning than the "new diplomacy" of Woodrow Wilson—"open covenants openly arrived at." It connoted the application of varied skills, knowledge, techniques, and re sources to the achievement of American goals overseas. The new diplomat would be an activist rather than an observer, an achiever rather than simply a cultured representative, an executive as well as a negotiator.

The third tactic was to modify the systems of operation in the Department, an effort that was principally pursued by subordinate officers several echelons down. It included: the modification of the personnel system and particularly the promotion criteria in the Foreign Service; the study and recommendations of the Herter Committee and the subsequent efforts to implement them; the effort to develop explicit statements of American objectives in individual countries under Walt Rostow, after he became chief of the Department's Policy Planning Council; the establishment of the Latin American Policy Committee (LAPC) by Assistant Secretary Edwin M. Martin; the effort to develop a graduate academy for foreign affairs personnel; the effort to develop a programming and budgeting system, as described in this case; the effort to develop a manpower utilization program. Most of these were longer term than presidential appointments and public exhortations. Most were initiated and pursued by departmental appointees rather than from the White House itself or even from the top of the Department.

Not long after his inauguration, President Kennedy undertook to strengthen the position of the ambassadors *vis-à-vis* other U.S. agencies in their countries. He was prompted to this partly by the fact that the new AID legislation would

11. In *Personnel for the New Diplomacy*, 1962 (New York: Carnegie Endowment for International Peace), p. 10.

nullify the Mutual Security Act and presumably the executive orders that President Eisenhower had issued to implement it. He was prompted partly by the evident lack of communication between the intelligence community, principally the CIA, and the rest of the foreign affairs community, so dismally exemplified in the Bay of Pigs fiasco. He felt that a personal letter to each ambassador would have more immediate and direct impact than an official, bureaucratic order. So on May 29, 1961, was issued the famous Kennedy letter to the ambassadors, which remains today, in 1969, the principal basis of ambassadorial influence with regard to other agencies. The letter was initially drafted by Presidential Assistant Ralph Dungan, not the Department of State. The key sentences were:

> In regard to your personal authority and responsibility, I shall count on you to oversee and coordinate all the activities of the United States Government in _____.
>
> You are in charge of the entire United States Mission, and I shall expect you to supervise all of its operations. The Mission includes not only the personnel of the Department of State and the Foreign Service, but also the representatives of all other United States agencies which have programs or activities in _____. I shall give you full support and backing in carrying out your assignment.

The President acknowledged the right of the representatives of other agencies to communicate with their Washington headquarters and to appeal for higher review of any decision by the ambassador in which they did not concur. He excepted the military forces operating in the field, but not military aid and military intelligence. For the first time, all intelligence activities, including the CIA, were covered under ambassadorial surveillance. In the words of Arthur Schlesinger, Jr., the President sought to "end the faceless system of indecision and inaction" among State, Defense, and the CIA.[12]

It should be emphasized that there was no comparable presidential message to the Secretary of State or to the Department's regional assistant secretaries or its country desk officers, other than the somewhat vague message accompanying the order that abolished the OCB. We would stress, too, that there was little guidance about machinery; as to how, for example, the ambassadors were to "oversee and coordinate" other agencies.

The chapters that follow principally concern the efforts to develop and install a programming and budgeting system that would be centered in the Department of State and that would comprehend most undertakings of all U.S. agencies overseas. It was born in the milieu of the Kennedy administration and was seen, by its authors at least, not alone as consistent with the Kennedy objectives in foreign affairs but as an essential instrument to their achievement. It would, they hoped, facilitate effective mergers of policy planning with operations, of administration with substance; it would make it possible for the Department of State to "take charge" in a responsible executive manner; it would strengthen the hand of the ambassadors in their relations with other agency representatives abroad. But, as has been noted in many places before, there can be a good deal of distance between formal directive and action, between rhetoric and changed behavior.

12. Arthur M. Schlesinger, Jr., *A Thousand Days: John F. Kennedy in the White House* (Boston: Houghton Mifflin, 1965), p. 427.

I

The Development of a Design: CCPS
(December 1962-March 1965)

THE NEED for better coordinated direction of American foreign affairs activities was no new discovery of the Kennedy administration. Nor was it an especially novel idea to try to satisfy this need by utilizing programming techniques and budgeting innovations. Such proposals had been advanced soon after World War II with the initiation of the Marshall Plan and later during its implementation by the ECA. In the late 1950's the Bureau of the Budget had conducted and contracted for major studies dealing with the organization and coordination of foreign affairs agencies.

One of the first acts of the Kennedy administration was to launch the Labouisse task force of 1961, which prepared the legislation that revamped the foreign-assistance program and created the Agency for International Development (AID). Further impetus in the early Kennedy period was provided by the widely heralded success of the McNamara "revolution" across the Potomac, the central features of which were economic analysis and the systematic linkage of planning, programming, and budgeting. Could not a similar approach be used in foreign affairs?

The man who was to sponsor the State Department's programming effort, William J. Crockett, showed an early interest in the subject, accumulating thoughts and ideas during many years of service abroad as an administrative officer for AID and State. When he became Assistant Secretary of State for Administration, early in 1961, he prepared a list of changes and improvements he regarded as needed in the Department of State, and prominent on this list was a new method of linking plans, programs, and budgets. In the fall of 1962, he followed this up with a memorandum to his superior, Deputy Under Secretary for Administration William Orrick, proposing a programming system for foreign affairs.

Richard W. Barrett, who was to supply much of the creative energy for the programming effort under Crockett's leadership, also developed an early interest in the subject in his years of experience with the Bureau of the Budget. Others were displaying interest as well. As early as May 1961 Roger W. Jones, who then was Deputy Under Secretary for Administration in State, wrote Under Secretary Chester Bowles a memorandum pointing out that the Department was "flying blind" in regard to the totality of foreign-affairs budgets and operations. In August 1962 Jones left the Department to become Special Adviser to the Director of the Budget, David Bell, but his interest in foreign affairs problems continued. He wrote Bell a memorandum in which the key statement was that ". . . if the State Department does not take the initiative in pulling together a foreign affairs budget, then the Bureau of the Budget should do it." Jones quoted Bell's response as follows: "I'm taken with your idea of pulling together foreign affairs budgets even if we can't appropriate that way." Subsequently, Jones rather quietly supported the development of a programming-budgeting system in foreign affairs and encouraged the efforts to establish such a system. In the light of later events, this early interest in the Bureau of the Budget in foreign affairs programming and budgeting is significant.

THE BEGINNINGS

During the Kennedy years, the first public recommendation for programming in foreign affairs appeared in December

1962 in the report of the Committee on Foreign Affairs Personnel, known as the Herter Committee after its Chairman, the late former Secretary of State Christian Herter. This 12-man committee had come into existence a year earlier at the suggestion of Secretary of State Dean Rusk, seconded by the heads of AID and USIA. The Committee was nongovernmental in auspices, support, and membership. It was established under the leadership of the Carnegie Endowment for International Peace and notably its president, Joseph E. Johnson, and received substantial grants also from the Ford Foundation and the Rockefeller Brothers' Fund. None of its members were currently occupying official positions in the government, but most had earlier held high offices in or related to foreign affairs agencies.[1]

Given the unhappy history of most previous reform efforts, the Herter Committee recognized that its personnel recommendations were not likely to take effect unless they were cast within a broader framework. The framework was found in the Kennedy administration's somewhat hortatory emphasis on the "new diplomacy" and the leadership role of the Department of State. The Herter Report became the closest thing to a blueprint on how the State Department could assert its responsibility for leadership over the whole spectrum of foreign affairs activity.

The first recommendation of the report, *Personnel for the*

1. The Herter Committee members were: Christian A. Herter, Chairman, former Secretary of State; Don K. Price, Vice Chairman, dean of the Graduate School of Public Administration, Harvard University; George V. Allen, retired career ambassador and former Director of USIA; Kenneth B. Clark, professor, City College of New York; Carlisle H. Humelsine, former Deputy Under Secretary of State for Administration; Joseph E. Johnson, president of the Carnegie Endowment for International Peace; Milton Katz, director of International Legal Studies, Harvard University, and former ambassador; James A. Perkins, vice-president of the Carnegie Corporation; James Rowe, former assistant to the President and Chairman of the Advisory Committee on Personnel to the Secretary of State; James Hopkins Smith, Jr., former director of the International Cooperation Administration; Arthur K. Watson, president, IBM World Trade Corporation; and John Hay Whitney, publisher of the *New York Herald Tribune* and former ambassador to Great Britain.

New Diplomacy, laid the cornerstone for the balance of the report:

The capacity of the Department of State to assist the President in providing leadership and coordination in foreign affairs must be strengthened. The Department's responsibility should embrace the formulation of foreign policy, *the development and coordination of foreign affairs programs, and the planning and marshaling of the resources needed for their implementation.* [Emphasis added.][2]

The next two recommendations made specific proposals designed to bring this about. Recognizing the overload on the Secretary and the Under Secretary of State, the second recommendation proposed the establishment of a new position of Executive Under Secretary of State, to be third in rank and to play the principal executive role in assuring interagency coordination of policy, personnel, programs, and resources. The third recommendation proposed the institution of a system

whereby *foreign policy objectives are translated into programs of action to be undertaken in each area of foreign affairs activity, projected as far into the future as is feasible,* and used as a basis for estimating future personnel and other needs in foreign affairs [Emphasis added.][3]

The 38 other recommendations that followed dealt more specifically with personnel matters. During the spring of 1963 they became the basis for an elaborate structure of interagency task forces, and on a number of the recommendations action was subsequently taken or sought. But no task forces addressed these first three, which the Herter Committee had regarded as of fundamental importance. On the first, which sought a strengthening of State's leadership role, little was

2. *Personnel for the New Diplomacy,* p. 10.
3. *Ibid.,* p. 13.

done.[4] The second, to establish an Executive Under Secretary, was rejected by Secretary Rusk for reasons he did not make explicit, and was not further considered. The third, advocating a foreign affairs programming system under State Department leadership, provided the springboard for a good part of the activity described in this case. Several committee members were interested in the subject, as was the staff. At different times during 1962, both Crockett and Barrett independently discussed the idea of a programming system for foreign affairs with Frederick C. Mosher, staff director of the Committee, as did Melbourne L. Spector, then Executive Director of the Bureau of Inter-American Affairs in State. Spector later was instrumental in helping Crockett and Barrett get started on their programming effort.

Barrett, who turned 40 years of age in 1962, had spent ten years with the Bureau of the Budget. Early in the Kennedy administration he left the Bureau and served on the Labouisse task force that overhauled the foreign-aid program to create the new Agency for International Development. For a time he was assistant personnel director for AID under Spector.

Barrett met Crockett at a social function and later was offered a job by Crockett at about the same time that a job offer came from the White House office of Ralph Dungan. Dungan's main areas of interest, as assigned by the President, were Latin America and presidential appointments. Barrett went on State's payroll, but was assigned to Dungan's office to work on recruiting policy-level executives for the Kennedy administration.

Throughout these experiences, Barrett developed the reputation among those who came in contact with him as a man of restless energy, creative intellect, and forceful personality. His interest in programming techniques became focused on

4. More than three years later the presidential directive known as NSAM 341 gave official sanction to this general idea, but it did not grow out of the Herter recommendation. (See Chapter III.)

foreign affairs while he was a member of a Bureau of the Budget task force that in 1959 made a study of operations and management in the U.S. Embassy in Rome. The multiplicity of agency operations there, the unclear authority of the ambassador, and the lack of conditions favoring lateral coordination and communication convinced Barrett that some overall programming system would be extremely useful. The conviction was strengthened by Barrett's knowledge that the Rome Embassy was comparatively well managed and much less complex in a programmatic sense than the large missions in the underdeveloped countries.

Over the next few years Barrett actively discussed the programming idea with others. A frequent response was enthusiasm in theory, but pessimism as to the practicality of making it effective. Against it were arrayed not only the normal obstacles to major change in bureaucratic life, but such additional complicating factors as the strong traditionalism of the State Department, the conservatism of the Foreign Service, lack of interest in or acceptance of management concepts in State, the centrifugal pressures of the many federal bureaucracies, the extreme geographic scatter in foreign affairs, and the complexity and intangibility of much of modern foreign policy and operations in contrast to the hardware and logistical base of the Pentagon.

James Frey, who was later to play an important role in the story, remembered one meeting late in 1962 with Barrett and Ralph Dungan, in which Barrett presented his ideas to Dungan. Frey, who had worked for Barrett in the Bureau of the Budget, then was an assistant to Dungan principally on foreign aid and Latin American matters. Barrett had written a conceptual paper for Dungan explaining his ideas on foreign affairs programming, and Frey had arranged the meeting for a Saturday morning. Although very much in favor of reforms in the State Department, Dungan expressed concern that a programming system such as that outlined by Barrett might be too static, that it might be too cumbersome and inflexible to respond to fast-changing situations. Barrett and Frey argued that any well-designed system would have to be dynamic and that good planning and programming had to be a continuing, flexible process. Dungan advised Barrett to continue developing the plan and to seek an opportunity to test it in a small-scale way. He thought the Latin American regional bureau in State might be a good place to experiment, and he suggested that Barrett see Edwin M. Martin, assistant secretary in charge of the bureau, which was known as ARA in the organizational shorthand of the State Department.

Barrett and Melbourne Spector, chief management officer of ARA under Martin, were old friends, and Spector was an enthusiastic supporter of the idea of comprehensive programming in foreign affairs. The two men developed a plan to select one Latin American country for a test of a programming system. A small team would be assembled to canvass all documentation available in Washington on U.S. operations in the selected country. Based on this survey, a set of input and output categories would be distilled, intended to cover all overseas operations regardless of agency base. The team would then go to the selected country to gather fresh on-the-scene data, organized according to new categories, to see how viable they were and whether the results would be of interest to the ambassador and other decision-makers.

Early in 1963, Barrett made minor revisions in the paper on programming he had prepared for Dungan. He and Spector met briefly with Martin in the latter's office, and left the paper for his consideration. In the paper, Barrett described the problem as follows:

> The Department of State has often been criticized for its inability to apply accepted management principles to the business of foreign affairs. Its critics have charged that the Department is so preoccupied with day-to-day matters that it has little time to anticipate or influence future events. . . . There is considerable evidence to support the conclusion that the old practice

of doing business "off the cable" is in fact an outmoded and ineffective method of operation. Effective management requires a definitive work program to provide a basis for allocating resources, monitoring performance, and appraising results.

The memo proposed development of a "country programming system" to "provide the Ambassador with the action-forcing process he needs to focus the total spectrum of U.S. programs on a set of agreed-upon objectives and goals." The purpose of the system, in Barrett's view, was to provide "a much-needed management tool" that would "assist the Department and its officers in discharging the enormous managerial responsibilities inherent in the new diplomacy."

A short time after the paper was transmitted to Martin, Spector asked Barrett to manage the logistics for Vice-President Johnson's trip to the Dominican Republic for the inauguration of Juan Bosch as President. During this adventure, Barrett had an opportunity to discuss the programming proposal with Martin, who also made the trip. Meeting in the residence of U.S. Ambassador John Bartlow Martin, Barrett and Assistant Secretary Martin explored the idea.

It was not an accident that the activity first started in ARA. During the turbulent growth in U.S. foreign affairs after World War II, Latin America had been a relatively neglected region. Many Foreign Service officers avoided assignments to Latin America, regarding it as a backwater area. This situation began to change perceptibly toward the end of the Eisenhower administration and dramatically so at the beginning of the Kennedy administration with the creation of the "Alliance for Progress" and the occurrence of the Bay of Pigs disaster. By 1963 ARA had become infused with energy and readiness for experimentation, a mood that was heightened under the keen leadership of Assistant Secretary Martin. After President Kennedy had abolished the OCB and had stressed the coordinating role of the Assistant Secretaries of State, it was generally expected that the regional bureaus would form interagency policy committees. Martin, in forming the Latin American Policy Committee (LAPC) in 1962, was the first to do this. His lead was followed by the new African bureau in 1963. The other three regional bureaus did not form such groups until directed to do so in 1966. Another example was the "back-to-back" movement in ARA whereby its officers and AID personnel working on common countries or problems were located near one another. In isolation, this innovative mood in ARA would by no means be regarded as daring and radical; it seemed so only in comparison with the other regional bureaus in State.

Having secured Martin's blessing, Barrett and Spector set to work to form a task force, select a country for experimentation, and make the necessary arrangements. A snag developed over financing. With three-fourths of fiscal year 1963 nearly over, ARA was in the perennial position of State Department bureaus: it was desperately short of funds. At Spector's suggestion, he and Barrett went to see William J. Crockett, who, as Assistant Secretary of State for Administration, was responsible for the overall State Department budget.

Crockett had started his working career as a bank clerk in Nebraska. He had entered the foreign affairs field in the late 1940's as a specialist in administration, serving overseas with the foreign-aid program. He had moved over to State, entering the career Foreign Service officer corps laterally. Serving successively as head of administrative sections in several U.S. embassies abroad, Crockett established a reputation, unusual in the State Department, as a highly action-oriented executive who regarded rules and regulations as opportunities to be used and tested, rather than as rigid constraints on action. He also possessed a warm, easygoing personality and considerable political skill. These qualities proved to be a potent combination when Crockett was assigned to Washington in 1960. He became head of the State Department's Office of Budget and then moved up to become Assistant Secretary for Administration. In these latter assignments, he developed close relationships with the chairmen of the committees and subcommittees in the House of Representatives that were of crucial importance to the State Department. He also became well known to Vice-President Johnson and his key staff members by managing and participating in most of the Vice-President's overseas trips.

Along with Roger Jones, then Deputy Under Secretary of State for Administration and Crockett's superior, Crockett played an important role in setting up the Herter Committee. He and a key subordinate, Personnel Director Herman Pollock, maintained close liaison with the Committee's staff. But, a few months before the Herter Report was released, Jones was replaced by William Orrick, a San Francisco attorney who had been an active supporter of the Kennedy presidential campaign and subsequently a high official in the Department of Justice. Orrick, in launching the task force studies to implement the Herter report, worked directly through Pollock, and Crockett was not an active participant. However, as noted earlier, the task forces concentrated their efforts almost exclusively on personnel matters. The third recommendation, proposing a programming system, was neglected.

This background partly explains the hospitable reception Spector and Barrett were accorded when they asked Crockett for money to carry out the pilot programming project in Latin America. Crockett provided the funds, and he advised Barrett to be sure to acquaint Walt W. Rostow with his plans.

In late 1961 Rostow had come over from the White House staff to be Counselor of the State Department and the head of its Policy Planning Council. He did so with definite ideas about developing systematic methods for comprehensive policy planning. A start in this direction had been made by George McGhee in 1961 when he was serving as Deputy Under Secretary of State for Political Affairs. State Department Policy Guideline Papers had been drafted for every foreign country with which the United States conducted diplomatic relations. Rostow saw these as inadequate for several reasons. One was that they were not based on extensive analysis of the situation in the host country. Another was that they were State Department rather than foreign affairs papers: as a rule they addressed only political issues, not purporting to cover the whole range of multi-agency operations in the host country. Rostow's intent was to assign to one man the responsibility for creating a major policy paper on a selected country. He would establish his own interagency group and make an in-depth study of the country situation, from which would be derived objectives and lines of action for all U.S. components operating in the country. Once completed and signed by the Secretary of State, the paper would be authoritative and binding on all agencies. It would be known as a National Policy Paper (NPP). The preparation of each paper would be a tremendous job, so it was decided to focus only on those countries of major importance and concern.

Barrett approached his interview with Rostow with some trepidation. He was only vaguely familiar with Rostow's approach, since it had made little impact at that time. Less than a dozen papers were in stages of early drafting, and the methods were being tested. Barrett had spent enough time in the State Department to believe that most officials close to "policy" tended to be negative about anything that smacked of operations or management. However, he found Rostow to be emphatic about the need for developing country programs that would be complementary to, rather than competitive with, his NPP's. The idea offered promise of overcoming what he saw as another inadequacy in previous State Department policy planning efforts. Developed in an "ivory tower," there was little machinery to give them operational meaning. Together, Rostow and Barrett envisioned a continuing interplay between the policy papers and systematic program information, to keep both fresh and relevant. This was the beginning of a Rostow-Crockett-Barrett alliance to develop a comprehensive programming system in foreign affairs.

The rationale for the alliance was that Rostow's NPP's for

selected foreign countries could provide the base (American objectives) for programs of action, which in turn could underlie allocations of resources (i.e., budgets). The objectives would provide the statement of the outputs that programs and budgets were to produce. It then became possible to visualize a logical system in which the interconnected elements were:

> *plans* (from the NPP's)
>> to
>>> *programs* (of action)
>>>> to
>>>>> *budgets* (allocations of resources)

Essentially, the concept was PPBS, although that expression had not yet won general currency. But the adequacy of Rostow's NPP's to provide the bases for realistic programs was untested, as was the adequacy of Barrett's programming approach to provide the bases for budgets. Major and difficult problems were to be the linkages, the *crosswalks,* between plans and programs and between programs and budgets.

THE FIRST TRY: COLOMBIA

Colombia was selected for the first experiment because it appeared relatively stable and yet had a large and interesting program mix. Moreover, the U.S. Ambassador there, Fulton Freeman, was thought to be a progressive, open-minded career officer. Barrett made a brief trip to Bogotá in March 1963 to discuss the project with Ambassador Freeman. By coincidence, Assistant Secretary Martin was passing through Bogotá at the same time. The three men met at breakfast in Freeman's residence, and he approved the experiment in Colombia. On Barrett's return to Washington three men were recruited to join him on the project team. One, Robert G. Cox, was a mid-career Foreign Service officer with extensive Latin American experience. The other two, Karl Matthiason and Irving Rosenthal, both officers of AID with varied experience in program planning and management, were loaned to the Department for the experiment. Barrett and Cox also had served in AID, the latter as assistant to the coordinator of the Alliance for Progress. AID was by far the largest and most important U.S. government operator and money-spender in Colombia, as in most developing nations. Barrett intended from the outset to involve agencies other than State in the building of comprehensive programming and to construct the system using techniques and information already developed within the agencies concerned.

The four-man team spent most of April in Washington, amassing and studying all the data it could find on U.S. operations in Colombia. From this immersion in the policy, program, and budgetary information of all agencies active in Colombia some important facts emerged. One was that the existing data bases for most agencies did not link activities to objectives. Some agencies, such as State and USIA, were centrally budgeted so that there was no way to manipulate existing data bases to produce total U.S. expenditures in a given country. Dollar costs were not a reliable indication of real or potential impact, i.e., influence on events in the host country. Activities that could be linked to foreign-policy objectives represented only a portion, perhaps as little as half, of U.S. activities in a given foreign country. From these facts, the team concluded that the first need was a comprehensive data base. This would require on-the-spot data collection (in the formative stage of the system at least). They also concluded that the data base should include the use of time (personnel) as well as dollars as indicators of activity, and that support and administrative (nonpolicy) costs, as well as output-oriented program costs, should be reported.

These conclusions were fortified when Barrett discussed the experiment briefly with personnel of the RAND Corporation in Washington and with Charles J. Hitch, Comptroller of the Department of Defense and author of the programming system there. There was interest in both quarters, but both declined to help on the ground that the first step was creation of a data base, before systems analysis would be useful. Both said they wanted to stay in touch.

From its month of studies, the four-man team derived the rudiments of a system. Inputs were to be expressed in dollars and man-years. For the output side of the "grid" or "matrix," the team developed categories at several levels of aggregation. At the highest level were five "program packages": *Influencing, Assistance, Reports, Special Services,* and *General Support.* The first two were meant to capture the bulk of substantive program operations. *Influencing* referred to the traditional diplomatic activities and information programs, and *Assistance* to the totality of the aid programs. *Special Services* included such activities as consular affairs and commercial services. These five aggregations were broken down at the next level by techniques or sectors. For example, the most important of the aggregations, the first two, were divided into such techniques as official relations, contacts, exchange of persons (all reflecting the importance attached to personnel), dissemination of information, and the various types of economic assistance.

Finding of a suitable name for the system-to-be occasioned much discussion. Barrett and his colleagues finally decided on "Comprehensive Country Programming System" (CCPS). It was descriptive, but unwieldy, and later exposed the group to jibes about using the "Cyrillic alphabet." Moreover, as Barrett later commented, "information" would have been a better word than "programming," at least during the early stages of development.

The team spent three weeks in Colombia, starting late in April 1963. The entire U.S. Mission[5] in Colombia was di-

5. The term "Mission" with a capital "M" was defined by the State Department group as the totality of all U.S. Government activities taking place in a given country that had any direct tie to the diplomatic mission under the control of the ambassador. It will be so used henceforth in this case.

vided into identifiable organizational components, for reporting purposes. For example, the Economic Section in the
embassy constituted a component, as did the entire AID mission, the public affairs office (USIS), and each of the three
consulates. Each member of the Barrett team was assigned a
number of component units. Working with available documentation and interviewing staff members of each unit, a
picture was obtained of the unit's activities according to the
input and output categories of the system.

The team did not finish the laborious job of compiling all
the data, but the information was sufficient in some areas to
allow for a review session with the Ambassador and key staff
members. As expected, the data produced no shocking revela-
tions, but did contain a number of minor surprises: for example, the inordinate amount of time the Mission spent in
taking care of official visitors from Washington and the dominance in reporting activities of military reporting. It was
generally agreed that the data provided a fresh and useful way
of looking at the total Mission operation and a potential base
for more effective management. However, no NPP had been
completed for Colombia by Rostow's unit, and the Barrett
group did not attempt to link its tentative system with other
U.S. policy statements about that country.

There was not much enthusiasm in AID. Barrett arranged
to discuss the Colombia experiment at a meeting with David
Bell, former Director of the Budget, who had now become
Administrator of AID. Also present were Hollis B. Chenery,
Bell's Assistant Administrator for Programs, and William O.
Hall, a career FSO serving in AID as Assistant Administrator
for Administration. By coincidence Bell and Chenery had
visited Colombia while the team was at work, and Barrett had
discussed the project briefly with them then. During the later
meeting, Barrett recalled that Bell examined some of the
Colombia figures briefly and commented: "They don't do
much for me." Hall was concerned about possible repercussions over the use of a term like "influencing" to describe

major U.S. activities in foreign countries. Chenery was mildly supportive. The coolness of the AID response should be judged in light of the effort and experience of that agency in the development and analysis of country programs to govern its own operations. Begun many years earlier, this programming effort had been greatly stimulated during the Kennedy period with the acquisition of accomplished economists such as Bell, Chenery, and others, both in Washington and the field. In fact, AID at the time probably had more skills and sophistication in programming and analysis than any other agency in foreign affairs.

Orrick had left the Department of State, and Crockett was sworn in to succeed him as Deputy Under Secretary for Administration on June 10, 1963. This position ranks fourth or fifth highest in State, depending on seniority, but the label of "administration" connotes housekeeping, the opposite of substance, and thus influences most incumbents to act conservatively. Yet, for one seeking change and willing to take risks, it can be extremely influential, particularly since it immediately controls personnel and the budget. Crockett was disposed to use this influence in the service of a long agenda of possible changes and innovations aimed generally toward more active State Department leadership in foreign affairs. Prominent but not dominant in his thinking was the programming system. Crockett brought Barrett over from the White House as one of his two chief staff aides. One aide was to concentrate on day-to-day crises and problems; the other, Barrett, was to concentrate on long-term innovations.

DEVELOPMENT AND EXTENSION

Although Barrett on his return from the Colombia test was optimistic about the CCPS approach, the experience had reconfirmed his expectation that full development of the system would require a long pull, measured not in months but in years.

There could be no thought of installing the system by fiat

as McNamara had done in the Pentagon. For one thing, the tools were not ready; there had been no pre-development such as RAND had done for the Defense system. There was no body of persons with systems training or experience in State. Legally, the other foreign affairs agencies were a good deal more independent of the Department of State than were the military departments under the Secretary of Defense. Finally, Crockett's power within State, though considerable, was far from conclusive. It was sufficient to protect and support the development of the system but not to make it the official and accepted agency way of doing business.

These considerations dictated Barrett's ideas of long-term strategy. There would be continuing cycles of developing, testing, and refining the system until its sponsors were confident that it was ready for presentation to the Secretary of State with a recommendation that he direct that it be made operational in the foreign affairs community at large. Up to this point, field installations of the system would be made only in countries where the ambassadors invited it or consented to it. Concurrently with the development work would occur the training and building of a staff capability in the systems field and an effort to promulgate an understanding of the approach as widely as possible in the foreign affairs community.

The members of the team returned to their original assignments. Since Barrett was now in a staff role himself, it was decided to set up a small task force in ARA under Spector's wing. A former member of the Herter Committee staff, John E. Harr, was recruited by Spector in July 1963 to head the programming task force. Several weeks later two young Class 8 Foreign Service Officers were added, Geoffrey Harris and James Taylor. Harris was to be a major contributor to the effort for nearly two years. Taylor was to leave in a few months but would return 1½ years later.

The group set to work on the project and consulted almost daily with Barrett. The basic assumptions and goals were articulated in an oral and visual presentation that was used frequently in the ensuing months to brief groups and individuals in the various foreign affairs agencies. The first assumption was that the foreign country, or, more accurately, the total U.S. Mission in each foreign country, was to be the basic programming unit. The foreign country was the place where the action occurred, and most of the foreign affairs agencies were organized in Washington on a geographic basis. Moreover, in consequence of the Kennedy letter, the ambassador provided a natural focal point. Later, the individual country programs would provide the building blocks for regional programs. One could progressively install the system in all of the countries of a region, and then their programs could be integrated on a regional basis, including the incorporation of Washington overhead costs.

Over the next few months the categories of the system and methods to be used were explored and debated. For example, there was argument on how to handle the manpower question. One view was that expenditure of time should be accounted for in gross terms; the other, that it was necessary that it be relatively detailed, since the utilization of personnel was uniquely important and the time of one officer might be spread over several categories of activities. The latter view prevailed, even though it was recognized that this would make the system vulnerable to criticism as a time-and-motion study. Working time would be accounted for in man-hours and would also be expressed in dollars, using average figures for different categories of personnel, to produce the total cost of supporting a man in the field for one year.[6]

Plans were made for portraying the data in graphic terms and for creating a total country program report. It was decided to provide data for three years—the current year, the coming budget year, and one additional year ahead, the planning year. Forms were devised to ease the information-gather-

6. The theoretical basis of the CCPS in comparison with other systems efforts is discussed later in this chapter.

ing process and to facilitate aggregating and displaying the data. Provision was made in the basic data form, known as the "green sheet," to describe a program activity in narrative as well as in quantitative terms. An installation kit was developed so that the field mission could do the preparatory work and thus cut the length of a Washington team's visit to the post.

Sending Washington-based teams to the field to "install" the system seemed an obvious necessity at the outset, because of the need to gain experience for improving the system and to involve an increasing number of persons in the overall effort. Moreover, since experimentation would occur on a permissive basis, it seemed important to send a team to do the bulk of the work and avoid making enemies by imposing an undue workload on the Mission staff.

However, a gradual pattern of development and growth was envisioned that would eventually obviate the need for Washington-based teams. This included not only the streamlining of the system itself and its anchoring in an annual operational cycle but also the creation of program-planning staffs in each of the five regional bureaus and a high-level program-analysis staff to serve the top executives of the Department. An important related point, present in Barrett's thinking at the outset and repeatedly stressed, was that he and those who became associated with him considered themselves to be systems developers, not operators. The intent was that, in the line geographic units of the State Department, the interest and capability to run and use the system would develop concurrently with development of the system.

A first step in the direction of building staff capability in the line units was the creation of a new position in the field, to be called Executive Assistant to the Ambassador. The typical Executive Section in a U.S. Mission abroad consisted of the Ambassador, his Deputy Chief of Mission (DCM), and their two secretaries. Some ambassadors in the larger Missions had a staff aide, usually an overworked junior officer who monitored the paper flow and performed a variety of duties under the general heading of "bag-carrying." The Executive Assistant that the Barrett group envisioned would aid in more systematic management of the full interagency complex, including maintenance of CCPS, once installed, and the conduct of analytical and special studies growing out of it.

Some of these ideas and approaches were developed in discussions with a small, informal advisory group that Barrett assembled. It had a shifting composition, met only a few times in the fall of 1963, and then dissolved as the pace of activity on CCPS quickened. Among those who attended the meetings were Professor Richard Neustadt, then of Columbia University; Dr. William Niskanen, who was active in the Mc-Namara-Hitch systems effort in the Pentagon; a representative of the RAND Corporation; Everett Bellows, a vice-president of the Olin-Mathiesen Corporation who formerly had been a foreign affairs executive; and Roger Jones, the former Deputy Under Secretary of State, then consultant to the Director of the Budget.

In September 1963 the CCPS group tested its evolving system in the Dominican Republic and in Venezuela. These visits provided further opportunity to experiment with the mechanics of the system and to streamline the installation procedures. They also produced a method of devising a base of foreign-policy objectives where no NPP existed. The visiting team gathered all extant policy documents on the country and sat down with the Ambassador and his advisers to create a new one. In Venezuela, for example, there were seven distinct policy documents, but no one paid much attention to any of them. In the words of one officer at the Mission, "A man would have to be unemployed to read all of them." The effort to create a single overall document in a very short time was clearly an expedient, but those involved were satisfied with the results. Though not based on intensive analysis, the products were more than a cut-and-paste job, blending the best of the existing documents with the current thinking of the Am-

bassador and his staff. The least that could be said was that
the resulting paper meant something to the men in the field.
Careful to preserve an objective stance, the CCPS teams notified Rostow's office of what they were doing and described
the papers as "interim policy papers for programming purposes."

In December 1963 Harr, Harris, and Spector returned to
Colombia to do a thorough job with the newer version of the
system, since the original effort there had not been completed. Moreover, a draft NPP on Colombia had become
available in the meantime. On its return to Washington, the
team analyzed the data and produced the first Country Program Book, a 100-page document that presented the CCPS
data, organized in a number of ways—by categories of the
system, by each unit within the Mission—and summary data
for the Mission as a whole. Included were charts and graphs,
a narrative description of the main features of the total country program, and an analysis of how resources were allocated
by the various units toward the objectives in the NPP. The
latter showed some objectives toward which no resources were
being directed, as well as several cases in which substantial
resources were allocated toward objectives not mentioned in
the NPP. For the first time, a total picture of U.S. government activities within a foreign country was captured in one
document.

This sample product was merchandised extensively in
Washington by Barrett and his staff in another round of briefings and presentations in the winter of 1963-64. This was
done with Ambassador Freeman's approval, since Barrett felt
that, until the system became official for the Department as a
whole or in any entire region, the material gathered with the
permission of an ambassador belonged in the first instance to
him and should not be used in Washington without his express consent.

While the team was in Colombia, an important change occurred in the Department after the assassination of President

Kennedy. Assistant Secretary Martin was assigned as ambassador to Argentina, and Thomas Mann, Ambassador to Mexico, was assigned to Washington in a powerful triple capacity —Assistant Secretary for ARA, Coordinator of the Alliance for Progress, and special adviser to President Johnson on Latin America. Mann extended the "back-to-back" relationship between State and AID personnel to actual integration of the two agency staffs concerned with Latin America.

In the long run, AID, with its large resources, was the most important agency in which to generate support for the comprehensive programming approach, but Barrett's overtures there had been falling on unreceptive ears. (AID programming had by this time led to extremely detailed country program books with immense amounts of economic and social data.) Barrett realized that if Mann could be persuaded, there would be real possibilities for genuine involvement of AID, at least in Latin America. Crockett assigned Barrett to prepare a series of organization and management analyses and briefings for Mann. Barrett recruited James Frey on a short-term basis to come over from the White House to help him. Over the Christmas holidays of 1963 the studies were completed, and lengthy sessions with Mann took place, but in the end it became clear that he was not interested in CCPS. Mann seemed interested in the ends the system was intended to serve, but not in the means. The systems approach did not accord with his personal style.

One encouraging development occurred. Frey had been interested in leaving the White House staff, and Mann hired him as staff aide and secretary of the Latin American Policy Committee. In the latter capacity, he was viewed hopefully by the CCPS group as the advance guard of an eventual planning and programming staff capability in the home offices of the regional bureaus. But, in view of Mann's lack of interest, there was no longer any point in leaving the working group in ARA. Crockett therefore pulled it out and put it under his own jurisdiction into a new entity known as the Management

Planning Staff (MPS) with Barrett as chief. MPS's charter was systems development, with CCPS as its first priority. The switch was made with reluctance. Its significance was that the project retreated from a base inside a substantive line bureau to Crockett's more hospitable but less influential administrative area; it thus could be more easily attacked as an administrative intervention in "substance."

Despite the failure to enlist Mann and the subsequent change of location, the Barrett staff was optimistic because of the Colombia book and confident that it was on the right track. Crockett and Rostow were enthusiastic, and the mood was heightened when two more mid-career Foreign Service officers accepted assignments to the new positions of executive assistants. One was assigned to Bogotá, the other to Caracas. Negotiations were started with AID and USIA to obtain officers from both agencies for assignment to MPS so that the CCPS effort would have an interagency flavor. Meanwhile, MPS in Washington grew to six persons through the recruitment of two more junior FSO's. One of the new men, Arnold Nachmanoff, had a rare background for an FSO— experience with computers. He began to devise a computer program to handle the CCPS data. The State Department had obtained its first computer in 1962 and up to that point it had been used exclusively for routine administrative chores such as the payroll. Nachmanoff found some interest in the Data Processing Division in the development of nonadministrative uses of the computer, and his work progressed swiftly.

Crockett and Rostow decided that the time had come to apprise Secretary Rusk formally about CCPS. Early in February 1964 a meeting was arranged, the first of the few occasions that were to occur when the Secretary participated in considering a comprehensive programming system for the foreign affairs community. Crockett, Rostow, and Barrett spent 30 minutes in Rusk's office describing CCPS, the assumptions on which it was based, the ends it was intended to serve, and the current strategy for developing and refining the system in a gradual way. The Secretary listened attentively, and the three visitors had the impression that he understood and sympathized. The Secretary thumbed through the Colombia book, smiled quizzically, and asked, "Is this my Black Book?" The reference came home immediately to the three visitors. It was known that a "Black Book" was maintained for Secretary McNamara in the Pentagon. It was revised almost daily and contained the summary information from the Department of Defense programming system and other information designed to keep McNamara up-to-date on all operations at all times.

Barrett responded by showing Rusk the single page in the Colombia book that contained the summary information on the total U.S. program in Colombia. He said that when CCPS was fully operational there would be 100 such pages—for 100 countries—plus five pages of regional summaries and a one-page worldwide summary that indeed would be Rusk's "Black Book."

Rusk then asked, "What would you like me to do?" The visitors replied that the system was not ready to be installed officially, that their only purpose at that time was to describe the development effort to him. They said that they would come back to him when they judged the system to be ready.

In retrospect, Barrett was to consider this as one of a number of critical incidents in the total effort, this one being symptomatic of the tenuousness of the relationship between the sponsors of CCPS and the top leadership of the State Department. The programming group was quite happy to settle for implied endorsement of their efforts by Secretary Rusk, and did not take the opportunity to discuss the underlying problems that worried them—the lack of analytical resources within State, the lack of interest in management, the lack of involvement of State's officers above the Crockett level, and the disinterest of many of AID's leaders.

However, at the time the fact that Secretary Rusk was not negative about the project in the meeting was enough to create a buoyant mood of "all stops out." Planning and work proceeded energetically. The next two field trips were already scheduled for early March 1964—one to Ethiopia because an advance draft of a Rostow NPP existed for that Mission, and the other to Mexico because Ambassador Freeman, who had moved from Bogotá to Mexico City to succeed Mann, had requested it.

The plan that emerged for the remainder of 1964 was a compromise between Barrett's view, that at least another year of experimentation was needed before he could certify CCPS as ready to be adopted officially, and Crockett's urging that installations proceed as rapidly as possible. It was decided to go ahead with the Mexico and Ethiopia trips, which were to test both the NPP relationship and the new computer program designed by Nachmanoff and others, to make any necessary adjustments based on these experiences, and then to "freeze" the system for a year while field installations were carried on at as many posts as possible. Instead of revising the system after every trip, ideas for improvement would be stored up throughout a prolonged and active period of field work. Then a major conference would be held to revamp the system to the point where it would be ready for official adoption by the Secretary of State. The field work leading up to this major revision would be planned to expose the system to every possible kind of situation—missions in all five regions of the world, large missions and small missions, developed countries and underdeveloped countries.

With this plan in mind, Crockett wrote a letter to every U.S. ambassador, in December 1963, announcing the project and enclosing descriptive materials on CCPS. The letter stated that priorities for test installation of the system would go to (1) those Missions for which an advanced or completed NPP existed, (2) those Missions whose ambassadors were particularly interested and requested a CCPS test installation, and (3) Missions where a new ambassador was appointed. But no installation would be made without the ambassador's consent.

The top priority given to NPP countries was a product of the fact that Rostow had managed to obtain strong presidential endorsement for the NPP's. This had taken the form of a National Security Action Memorandum (NSAM) stating that completed NPP's signed by the Secretary of State would be authoritative and binding on all agencies operating in the country covered by the NPP. Since NSAM's are signed by the President, they represent a powerful vehicle for expressing presidential wishes in the national-security field, a kind of executive order with a security classification.

Both the Mexican and Ethiopian field trips were regarded by the Barrett group as highly successful. Both culminated in ambassadorial review sessions in which program choices were discussed and policy revisions proposed. Ambassador Freeman later discussed his two experiences with CCPS in favorable terms in an article in the *Foreign Service Journal*,[7] the professional magazine of the American Foreign Service Association. The computer program was also regarded as successful. In 18 minutes the computer printed out more data and correlations than three men working two weeks had been able to compile from the second Colombia installation.

Although the NPP-CCPS linkage proved to be technically workable in the Mexican and Ethiopian installations, signs of trouble appeared. In Ethiopia, the Ambassador found the CCPS installation to be a good opportunity to reopen some policy issues he felt had been buried in the NPP or handled in a way that did not satisfy him, and this raised some hackles when the Ethiopian Country Program Book was reproduced and distributed. Rostow was generous about the matter, saying that any genuine differences should be raised in the NPP-CCPS interplay, but that they should be resolved prior to publication. However, the CCPS group was encountering a deeper difficulty, having to do with the measurement of output. It will be recalled that the underlying strategy relied on the policy objectives in the NPP's to provide statements of output goals, so that the five major "program packages" and

7. *Foreign Service Journal,* July 1964, pp. 36-38.

the program elements of the CCPS were essentially neutral, descriptive categories within which specific output objectives could be fitted. The difficulty was that the NPP's, at least in this early stage of their development, were not very useful for this purpose. The extent of coverage and the level of generality varied greatly from NPP to NPP, and quantifiable objectives were almost never used. The CCPS group developed the nagging fear that it was tying the CCPS too closely to the NPP's, a fear aggravated by its inability to see any other choice. Rostow's support was regarded as indispensable, and a decision to lessen dependence on the NPP's for specific policy guidance might alienate him. The best hope was that the partnership would influence changes in the NPP's in the directions needed to make the program system workable.

Ambassador George McGhee in Bonn, Germany, was among those who responded favorably to the Crockett letter, and an agreement was made to install CCPS in the U.S. Mission there, an interesting prospect because of the large size of the Mission and the existence of several large Consulates General in Germany and the Special Mission in West Berlin. Building on this, it was decided to establish a regional unit in Bonn, from which staff members could travel to other Missions in Europe, the Near East, and Africa to install the CCPS more economically than it could be handled from Washington. Harr headed a four-man staff based in Bonn, and over a six-month period this group was responsible for ten installations in such large Missions as Germany, the United Kingdom, Italy, the United Arab Republic, and India.

During the same period, teams working out of Barrett's Washington office installed the system in another dozen Missions, primarily in Latin America and the Far East. By the end of 1964, experience with the system had been gained in 28 countries, ranging in size from Iceland to India. In 20 of them, executive assistants were already on the job. Counting the executive assistants in the field, the Barrett staff, and the

Bonn group, a total of 40 persons were working on the development of a comprehensive programming system for foreign affairs. Although the first executive assistants assigned to the field were mid-career officers, the richest vein of talent for the CCPS effort seemed to reside in the junior ranks of the FSO corps. The young officers seemed especially receptive to new ideas and were innocent enough not to worry about possible risk to their later careers in associating themselves with a radical new undertaking that might turn out to be controversial. In Barrett's view, the junior officers brought a refreshing surge of energy and imagination. From the point of view of the junior officers, the association offered them the chance to become involved in high-level problems at a young age, in contrast to spending their first several years in routine work in large embassies and remote consulates. The prospect of going out as an executive assistant to an ambassador after six months or so in the Barrett shop was especially appealing to them. Geoffrey Harris' experience was not unusual. As an FSO-8, he was placed in charge of the Ethiopian installation, where several of his team members were much his senior in age and rank. Later he directed the United Kingdom installation and remained to serve as Executive Assistant in London.

Repeated attempts to have officers assigned from other foreign affairs agencies to State's programming staff had failed. This failure probably reflected a relatively low level of interest in other agencies, a lack of sympathy in certain quarters, and Barrett's own insistence on men of high quality. To compensate, Barrett initiated the practice of inviting officers of other agencies to participate in the field trips. A Navy captain participated in the Venezuelan installation, a Bureau of the Budget officer worked in Germany, and a USIA officer worked in India. There was also resort to direct hire to bring to the effort wider experience in foreign affairs operations. Persons with experience in USIA, AID, the Pentagon, and the Bureau of the Budget were recruited to the Barrett staff. The end result was an amalgam of about two-thirds junior

FSO's and one-third older persons recruited from other government agencies as Foreign Service reserve officers.

REACTION AND DEBATE

Throughout this period of active field work in 1964, the CCPS group vacillated between optimism and pessimism. There seemed to be plenty of reasons for optimism. The support of Crockett and Rostow remained firm. Rostow began referring to the NPP and CCPS efforts as "the quiet revolution," Crockett promoted the effort at every opportunity and made its importance clear to all officers going to the field as ambassadors or DCM's. In a paper prepared for one of Secretary Rusk's staff meetings, held in March 1964, in which the "priority programs for 1964" in Crockett's area were listed, CCPS was given a prominent place. Among other things, it was promoted on the seventh floor as a major means of effectuating two organizational objectives dear to the Secretary: improving the effectiveness of the five regional bureaus and raising the status and influence of the "desk officers" responsible for handling communications in Washington pertaining to individual countries.

In his opening statement to the House Appropriations Subcommittee (in the spring 1964 hearings on the FY 1965 budget), Secretary Rusk spoke about CCPS:[8]

> During the past year we have developed, tested, and installed in selected embassies a Comprehensive Country Programming System. This system is designed to provide our Ambassadors and top management in Washington with an over-view of the complex, multi-agency programs which we are undertaking abroad in this era of operational diplomacy. It provides a means for planning and using total U.S. resources to achieve our objectives.

8. U.S. House, Committee on Appropriations, Subcommittee on State, Justice, Commerce, and the Judiciary, *1965 Department of State Appropriations*, 1964, 88th Congress, 2d Sess., pp. 5-6.

The words were provided by Crockett, but they were uttered before a congressional subcommittee by the Secretary of State. On the other hand, the CCPS group was increasingly confronted with hostility or apathy in the field and in Washington. Only a few ambassadors responded with enthusiasm— Freeman in Colombia and Mexico, Edward Korry in Ethiopia, John O. Bell in Guatemala. Most ambassadors were neutral at best; some were hostile. Some agreed to a CCPS "installation" principally because it offered a way of getting an extra man on their staffs (the Executive Assistant). Only a few of the senior Foreign Service officers were genuinely interested in the system. There was widespread tendency to criticize the details of the system, to identify it as an administrative gimmick, and to argue that systems methods were not applicable in foreign affairs where qualitative considerations dominated.

Furthermore, a few of the field officials of other agencies were hostile, refusing to participate until forced by the CCPS team through the authority of the ambassador. This happened most often with Peace Corps representatives and senior military attaches. Generally, personnel of other agencies were more cooperative than FSO's though often with ambivalence. On the one hand, some of those in the field seemed genuinely interested in any systematic approach that offered promise of relating their own efforts more coherently to the total U.S. effort. On the other hand, they feared going so far in this direction that possible loss of identity or freedom of action of their own programs might occur.

In Washington, despite more than 50 oral briefings by the CCPS group, the dominant reaction was disinterest. Few took it seriously in the regional bureaus of the State Department or in the headquarters of the other foreign affairs agencies. The CCPS group made frequent efforts to generate interest and action in the regional bureaus, but with little result. Barrett or one of his staff members would take a country program book resulting from a CCPS field trip to the desk officer for that country and show him the complete spread of information on all U.S. activities in the country. But the response was usually cool. Since most desk officers, by virtue of the traditional definition of their role, were not concerned with a comprehensive view of American activities in their assigned country, they felt little or no responsibility for AID, USIA, and other programs in the country for which they were responsible and they ended up confused by the mass of information, seeing no way to apply it.

The CCPS group even became alienated from some of the *administrative* personnel at home and abroad with whom many of the "substantive" FSO's were eager to identify. The CCPS group members came to feel that the "conventional" administrators perceived them as an outside force that threatened to upset established routines. Moreover, the administrators were quick to pick up and reciprocate the scarcely veiled contempt with which they were regarded by some of the "young Turks" working for Barrett.

The environment and the driving energy of Barrett and some of his staff set in motion a vicious circle of steadily worsening interpersonal and intergroup relationships. The more the CCPS group sensed hostility, the more Rostow's appellation of the "quiet revolution" came to have real meaning for them. They came to feel and act like "true believers," like a revolutionary cell working against enormous odds. This attitude and behavior engendered resentment and more hostility among "nonbelievers."

Barrett, for example, did not hesitate to use Crockett's authority to cut through red tape and get what he wanted quickly, whether it involved buying equipment, demanding computer time, transferring an officer from another assignment to join his staff, or making a field trip when virtually no one else in the Department could travel abroad because of shortage of travel funds. He did so because he felt himself under orders from Crockett to proceed as quickly as possible, and because he believed that the end—the development of a programming system for all foreign affairs—justified almost any means. This view was not widely shared outside of Barrett's immediate staff. The administrative officials began building up a long agenda of real and imagined abuses. They were largely frustrated, however, since they too worked for Crockett, who was supporting Barrett's group. But Crockett began to hear complaints, and for the CCPS staff almost every move involved a struggle with one or another of the administrative units in the Department.

There were also mixed feelings of optimism and pessimism within the group in regard to the system itself. As the group members saw it, every field experience produced useful ideas for improving the system, provided valuable operational experience, and drove home the conviction that the basic concept and elements of the system were right and viable. On the other hand, its operations in more than 20 countries had produced very little in the way of concrete action. Using the CCPS data strictly at the field level required a good deal of imagination and perseverence. Only in the case of the few ambassadors who were genuinely intrigued did executive assistants feel that they had support and the right environment for actively using the system. In other Missions, the impact of the initial installation and review sessions faded, and executive assistants began to feel restless and found themselves diverted to other chores. Moreover, there was no "action-forcing process" (a favored phrase of the Barrett group, borrowed from Richard Neustadt) that required the use of the system in any dialogue with Washington. Linking the system to ongoing procedures and an annual cycle such as the budget process remained a vision rather than an actuality.

Despite all these problems, the dominant mood of the State programming group by the end of 1964 was still optimistic. One reason was that most of the problems that generated pessimism had been anticipated. It was no surprise to Barrett and his crew that a major innovative thrust met resistance from the radically differing perspectives of most FSO's, the personnel of other agencies, and the administrative officials. Nor was it surprising that little in the way of important decision making had flowed out of CCPS installations. After all, the reasoning went, the system was experimental at this point, and most of the work had been at the field level, not in Washington, so that conditions for exploiting the system in Washington-field cycles of decision making did not yet exist.

Late in 1964 Barrett decided to move ahead quickly to convene a conference to consider revisions of the system based upon the accumulated experience. He hoped that it would result in a proposal to Secretary Rusk that a CCPS be formally approved. A week-long meeting was scheduled for January 1965. All the executive assistants were brought from the field to meet with the Washington programming staff at Airlie House in Warrenton, Virginia. Every aspect of the system was studied and debated at length. A great many changes resulted. For example, one of the problems was that decision-makers had been overwhelmed with data. It was decided that a small number of the most important computer reports would be produced as models, along with a check list of other available printouts, so that decision-makers could query the computer on subjects of particular interest and end up with tailor-made country program books. The five major categories were revised to the following: *Management, International Relations, Internal Development, Standard Services,* and *Administration.* Changes were also made at the second and third levels of the programming classifications. For example, Reports, formerly a first-level aggregation, was made a second-level breakout under Standard Services.

All participants regarded the conference as productive and successful, and the conviction was unanimous that the system was ready to "go operational." It was accepted that the system would continually be revised, just as the Defense Department system was frequently revised, but this could henceforth happen within the context of actual operations rather than experimentation.

THE NATURE OF CCPS

At this point, it will be useful to summarize the characteristics of CCPS. Its development proceeded from certain basic premises:

1. Except for command military operations, the system should comprehend *all* overseas activities of the U.S. government, regardless of agency, budget, or appropriations.

2. The country was the natural, basic programming unit, and functional considerations (agency programs, specific activities) should be organized and treated for programming purposes within the geographic unit rather than *vice versa*.

3. Where available, NPP's, produced by Rostow's Policy Planning Council, would provide the basic statements of objectives (the outputs or impacts to be gained by programs).

4. Since there was no existing data base crossing agency lines and in a standard format, the first step in the development of a true program budgeting system must be the creation of a comprehensive data base; cost benefit analyses and crosswalks to budgets would follow later.

5. The data had to be in such form as to. be useful both to ambassadors and other field executives in local decision-making and management, *and* to decision-makers in Washington; the device for relating the field and Washington would be the total country program, put together in the field under guidances sent from Washington, and in turn to be reviewed and approved in Washington.

6. The major purpose of the effort was to strengthen the hand of the line geographic officers of the State Department—the ambassadors and regional assistant secretaries—in their role of coordinating all overseas operations, by making it possible for them to influence the program and

budget decisions of other agencies at a relatively early stage.

7. Impact of the system on budgets eventually would occur by means of making decisions in the review of total country program packages and translating those decisions into the normal budget processes of the agencies involved; no one envisioned the possibility of changing the actual mechanics of government budgeting.

8. The system should be developed on a voluntary basis (i.e., at the request or with the consent of individual ambassadors) until it reached the stage that it could be made operational on regional and worldwide bases.

9. The system should be regarded as a tool of *substantive* management, not another exercise in *administration:* therefore, it should be attached directly to ambassadors and regional assistant secretaries, not administrative offices, and should be worked through substantive rather than conventional budget officers.

The task of creating viable categories and building a data base was very complex in itself. There were more than 100 U.S. country Missions. Each of them had a number of identifiable components for programming purposes, representing the overseas activities of a variety of different agencies in at least eight of the Cabinet departments of the federal government and a great many other federal agencies. Eventually, 70 standard components were identified, as well as a large number of subcomponents. A later CCPS computer-factored listing identified 466 different activities of U.S. agencies overseas.

The CCPS matrix consisted of a three-level classification of (1) program categories (the five major "packages"), (2) program elements, and (3) activities.[9] Against these were assigned

9. For further information about the nature of the CCPS program structure, see Appendix V.

the resources applied to each, classified in some detail between human resources and dollar resources. All these data were aggregated and cross-classified in terms of the organizational components, were expressed for each of three years in each country package, and finally were also related to appropriate policy objectives.

Thus the system as it was initially contemplated and as it had developed by the end of the January 1965 conference could produce data and projections on overseas activities along six major dimensions:

1. *time:* current year, budget year, planning year;
2. *geography:* country;
3. *organization:* component programmed organizations, aggregatable by agency;
4. *output:* policy objective, program category, program element, and activity;
5. *resources applied:* dollar obligations (augmented in some cases by expenditures) by type of resource;
6. *manpower:* man-hours by category and level of personnel.

Data from individual countries were entered into computers in Washington to produce a variety of tables showing various cross-classifications and aggregations.

THE BUNKER COMMITTEE

Based on the results of the January 1965 conference, the Barrett staff drew up a description of the revised CCPS for Secretary Rusk. Crockett submitted it, along with a recommendation and an action plan. He recommended that the Secretary formally adopt the system and a plan for putting it into operation, region by region, starting immediately in Latin America and Europe and proceeding to the other three regions the following year. Putting the system into operation in a region meant installing it in all field Missions in that region, creating a programming and planning staff in the headquarters of the region, and tying program and budget decisions to reviews held on the basis of CCPS data on an annual cycle.

This time (in February 1965) Crockett went to Rusk alone. The Secretary's reaction was not what the proponents of the system had hoped for. He said that he was concerned that any effort in the programming field for the Department of State not be "naive and overcomplicated." He told Crockett that he had decided to convene a committee of five ambassadors to study the system and advise him what to do about it. The ambassadors were Ellsworth Bunker, Chairman; Llewellyn Thompson; Douglas MacArthur, II; William Handley; and Livingston Merchant. The committee came to be known as the Bunker Committee.

The news provoked deep gloom within the CCPS staff, though not on the part of Crockett and Barrett. Crockett's support at the top level of the Department and among the senior FSO's now seemed doubtful to the staff. Rostow's endorsement had been enthusiastic but sporadic; he traveled a great deal, and he was not anchored firmly in the power structure of the Department of State. The Secretary's reaction could be read as a vote of limited confidence—the top management officer of the Department had developed a system and was now certifying to the Secretary that it was ready to be put into operation; the Secretary's response was to turn to a committee of ambassadors for a recommendation. Moreover, the CCPS staff was psychologically set to go full force in Latin America and Europe so that CCPS could be made operational in time for the coming budgetary cycle (for 1967). Deliberations by a committee, even if its report turned out favorably, would mean a delay of one year.

However, the fear was that the ambassadorial review would not turn out favorably. The group believed that the older and more traditional ambassadors in the Foreign Service were inclined to be skeptical of radically different approaches, especially those that smacked of systems and quantification. The Secretary's use of the phrase "naive and overcomplicated" seemed ample proof that some of these older and more traditional ambassadors had "reached" Rusk with critical comments about the scheme that was being hatched in Crockett's area. This gloomy diagnosis was reinforced by a somewhat scrambled reference to CCPS by retired Ambassador Ellis Briggs in a book he had just published. Briggs said that "the ravening bureaucratic termites have chewed their way into the woodwork of the Comprehensive Country Programming System, as the latest revelation of the planners is called."[10]

So convinced were some of the CCPS staff members that the Secretary's decision meant the kiss of death to the effort that they began urging a "suicide or success" strategy of going directly to all of the important contacts the group could muster in the White House and on Capitol Hill (which, when totaled, were not inconsiderable), in an attempt to force adoption of the system.

Mildly disappointed at first, Crockett came to see the Secretary's decision as a reasonable one, as a possible means of gaining substantive credibility and respectability for a management system intended for use by substantive officers. Did they want, did they need, or could they use such a tool? Crockett saw the Secretary as testing the idea with substantive officers. If they approved, Rusk would have some assurance that the effort would be worth it.

Barrett shared this view and rejected the gloomy impulses of his staff. Even more than Crockett, he wanted a clear "go" or "no go" sign from the top. In his mind, the issue was this: either the State Department's political leadership and its elite nucleus of top ambassadors were prepared to accept fully the challenge of exerting leadership over the whole spectrum of foreign affairs, including adopting the tools necessary to effectuate that leadership, or the leadership role would have to revert to the White House or the National Security Council.

10. Ellis O. Briggs, *Farewell to Foggy Bottom: The Recollections of a Career Diplomat* (New York: David McKay, 1964), p. 29.

It would be better to learn the answer now. Barrett's first choice for the leadership role was the Department of State, but if that failed, he was quite prepared to see CCPS, or something like it, adopted and used elsewhere. With this line of reasoning, Barrett viewed the Bunker Committee as an opportunity rather than a disaster.

Barrett further advised his "young Turks" that their best protection against being psychologically hurt was to assume the posture of the professional systems developer, to see themselves as management consultants called in to develop a system for a client. If the client was not prepared to use the system, that was his problem. The professionals would have done their jobs to the best of their ability.

Both Crockett and Barrett felt the Committee should include some ambassadors who had extensive experience with the CCPS. Of the five named, only Douglas MacArthur, II, had had any acquaintance with the system, and this had been an extremely limited exposure when he had served as Ambassador to Belgium. Crockett found an opportunity to discuss this thought with Under Secretary George Ball. The result was that two men were added to the Committee, Ambassadors Korry (Ethiopia) and Bell (Guatemala), both among the more positive ambassadors about CCPS. Crockett also arranged several preliminary discussions with Ambassador Bunker. He was encouraged to find Bunker, who had run several complex missions after a long business career, to be favorably disposed toward the idea of a programming system as a managerial tool.

In one of the preliminary discussions, it was decided that the first meeting should be held on Wednesday, March 24, 1965, in the conference room of the State Department's Operations Center. It would be a half-day meeting devoted strictly to information about CCPS, to be presented by Barrett and his staff. The Committee would then decide on how it should proceed with its task. The CCPS staff set to work to prepare descriptive materials for the meeting.

Ambassador Bunker introduced Barrett, who held the floor for the bulk of the March 24 meeting. He began with a discourse on the two major trends in the management of complex organizations in the United States—the growing use of systems and computers and the rising interest in human relations and participative management (the latter was an early inkling of what was to become an important concern for Crockett and Barrett). He then discussed how these trends were impinging on the complex foreign affairs establishment of the United States, and, with the aid of many charts and graphs, described at length the history of CCPS, what it was, how it compared with the Department of Defense system, and what it was designed to accomplish.

The conclusion of Barrett's speech had been carefully thought out to present the Committee with a fairly clear-cut choice, indeed to force it to make a "yes" or "no" decision rather than recommending further experimentation and study. Barrett pointed out that the CCPS effort to date had probably cost in the neighborhood of one million dollars including all salary costs. He said this was a cheap price compared to what it had cost to produce the Department of Defense system or what an effort comparable to CCPS would have cost the Department of State had it been performed by an outside management consulting firm. Yet, unless the payoff of the system clearly outweighed its cost, it would be best to kill it altogether.

Barrett then presented four levels of utility of the CCPS. They were thought to be progressive over a period of time, in that one could be built upon another as the system developed. At the first level, the system could be used as a *management information* system for program review, providing data in a new perspective on all operations, to be used randomly by executives in the field and in Washington. At this level, which was where the system then stood, it was not worth the cost in Barrett's view.

At the next level, the CCPS data could be used for *man-*

agement planning, to provide benchmarks or indicators for manpower and financial planning, for special studies, or for the development of operating norms. Some trials had been made—for example, special studies of consulates in Mexico and of administrative expenditures in Germany, and a special computer run of 18 CCPS country packages that presented an interesting picture of how FSO's spent their time. At this level, Barrett opined, the cost of the system could probably be justified, but he would vote against continuing it.

The third level of utility, Barrett said, was the "pay-off" area, the one that had been foremost in mind since the very inception of the effort. That was use of the system for *program planning and control* of all foreign affairs programs. The State Department would set program levels and guidances by the major categories of CCPS for each Mission. The ambassador and his country team, in the light of policy considerations, would construct the total country program within the guidelines for the coming fiscal year. This country program would be reviewed in Washington and, when approved, would be binding on all agencies in terms of their budget and manpower decisions. The model was not intended to be an authoritarian one, an unseemly model in any event for the State Department. There would be appeal channels and interagency dialogue along all links of the chain. State Department decision-makers would become involved at the beginning of program planning and resource allocation, instead of at the end. In Barrett's words, the whole idea was for the State Department "to get off the wrong end of the telephone." Instead of making appeals to other agencies, it would listen to their appeals.

Clearly at this level Barrett thought the system well worth the cost. The fourth level of utility would be frosting on the cake. This would be *systems analysis,* the highly sophisticated aid to top decision-makers in which CCPS information and other relevant data would be used for in-depth analyses of major problems, setting forth alternative solutions with cost-benefit studies of each. In Barrett's mind, this kind of analysis on a continuing basis would be possible only after CCPS was operationally installed as a management control system.

Nearly two hours of questioning and discussion followed Barrett's presentation. Bunker played the neutral role of Chairman, and Thompson and MacArthur were noncommittal. Merchant was absent from the meeting. Korry and Bell made several favorable comments. The only negative comments came from Handley.

As events turned out, the opinions of the Bunker Committee members were irrelevant. Developments described in the next chapter resulted in the dissolution of the Committee, *sine die*. Its first meeting was its last, and it never submitted a report.

II

The Lines Are Drawn: EROP and PPBS
(March 1965-November 1965)

PRIOR TO THE MEETING of the Bunker Committee in March 1965, Crockett, independently, had been engaging in sporadic telephone conversations with Horace Busby, an old friend and a special assistant to President Johnson who numbered among his duties the preparation of agenda items for Cabinet meetings. The official atmosphere in Washington at this time was charged with the theme of cost reduction as the President strove for funds for Great Society programs as well as for expanding the Vietnam war. Among other matters, the Crockett-Busby conversations touched on a familiar subject: eliminating duplication and waste in overseas programs, perhaps by cutting the numbers of agencies and personnel abroad and by streamlining operations generally.

In early February, Busby told Crockett that he was going to include in the agenda of a Cabinet meeting the subject of duplication and waste in overseas programs. Crockett's response was that a general discussion would probably be inconclusive and that a more specific and positive proposal would be more useful. He suggested that the President consider instructing the State Department and the Bureau of the Budget jointly to conduct an experimental review of overseas programs in a limited number of countries. The review would be systematic and intensive, covering all U.S. operations in the countries selected. It would not concentrate on cost-cutting *per se,* but on efficiency: i.e., maximizing the impact of each dollar spent abroad. Programs would be reviewed in the light of policy, and program changes would be reflected in the next budget. The budget consideration was one reason why Crockett proposed including the Bureau of the Budget in the exercise. The other reason was that Crockett had written a memorandum to the Bureau proposing collaboration in developing the programming system. (He never received a reply.)

Busby endorsed the proposal. At his request Crockett dictated over the telephone to Busby's secretary an outline of the proposed review. Crockett then informed Secretary Rusk and Under Secretary Ball that the subject might appear on a Cabinet agenda soon.

The President Directs

More than a month later the President opened a Cabinet meeting by briefly drawing attention to a press release to be issued that day. The date, coincidentally, was March 25, one day after the Bunker Committee meeting. The release contained the text of a presidential announcement of the review that Crockett and Busby had discussed. The themes of efficiency and economy were strong in the text but were cast in a positive tone. The President stressed the importance of making certain "that our people abroad and the money that we spend abroad are used to achieve the maximum support of the accomplishment of our foreign policy objectives. We must ensure that every dollar is being utilized to the fullest —and that every dollar spent is a dollar needed to accomplish our purposes."

Stressing that action was needed more than words, the message instructed the Secretary of State and the Director of the Bureau of the Budget Kermit Gordon, at that time) to "look at our operations in ten or fifteen countries" on an "experimental basis—before our next budget enters preparation."

The theme of the country program was emphasized: "The review should be on a country basis—with all U.S. agencies, all U.S. programs, and all U.S. policies being reviewed country by country." The reviews were to be tied firmly to the budget cycle, in terms that suggested joint leadership of the State Department and the Budget Bureau over all foreign affairs budgets:

> In countries where such reviews are conducted, I shall expect each agency to respect the levels established for each of our programs by Secretary Rusk and Mr. Gordon in the allocation of funds and resources for the ensuing year—and in the projection of our plans.

The President concluded on a strong note:

> I believe that this kind of country-by-country review—looking at all of our programs as they relate to our objectives in each country—can insure for us better management in the fuller utilization of all our resources. I also believe that this approach can and will materially strengthen the conduct and execution of the foreign policy of the United States.

Crockett accompanied Secretary Rusk to the Cabinet meeting. On the return trip Rusk handed Crockett the text of the President's press release, and said: "It's your baby, Bill." In turn, Crockett called Barrett in, and the two men quickly sketched a plan for getting together with the Bureau of the Budget, selecting ten to fifteen countries that had a CCPS data base, and mounting the joint review in a form that would utilize CCPS techniques. They saw in the President's directive an opportunity to test and, hopefully, prove the usefulness of CCPS.

Robert Cox, who had returned from his post as Executive Assistant in the Dominican Republic to join the Barrett staff, immediately coined an acronym for the project: PROP, standing for "Presidential Review of Overseas Programs." Several weeks later word filtered down from the seventh floor that the name should be changed. Barrett told Cox that

Busby wanted less direct presidential identification with the project at that time, so Cox substituted the word "Executive" for "Presidential," and the effort thereafter was known as EROP. There were to be difficulties in distinguishing between CCPS and EROP; some assumed that the existence of a new name meant that an entirely new system had been devised, whereas in fact the new name described a one-time project in which CCPS was to be employed as a means.

The Bunker Committee never reconvened. The emergence of EROP may have been a minor reason, but the major cause was the appointment of Bunker as President Johnson's trouble-shooter in the Dominican crisis. Crockett and Barrett were sorry to see the Bunker Committee dissolve, but their efforts to achieve a programming system were now necessarily directed to EROP.

CONCURRENT CHANGE EFFORTS

EROP presented a formidable challenge that would severely strain the thin staff that Crockett and Barrett had assembled. The programming system was only one of many innovative projects Crockett had initiated. The EROP exercise should be seen in the context of his overall change strategy, which was reasonably coherent and tremendously ambitious. This vigorous, almost evangelistic thrust toward a variety of improvements explains how Crockett and Barrett could attract a band of loyal followers and concurrently alienate many other officials.

Crockett was personally committed to the expressed or implicit objectives of the Kennedy administration, the Johnson administration, the Secretary of State, and the Herter Committee, in regard to the management of foreign affairs—that the Department of State should "take charge." It was clear that there would be no reorganization of agencies to bring the others under the canopy of the Department of State along the lines of the Department of Defense and the Department of Health, Education, and Welfare. Therefore, the assumption of effective leadership would depend upon the introduction of conditions, machinery, and procedures conducive to interagency cooperation and coordination. The programming system was one, but not the only, device Crockett directed to this broader purpose. Secondly, if the Department of State were to assume a more affirmative role, changes had to be made within the Department to strengthen its capacity and its will to handle such a responsibility. Some of Crockett's other major change efforts directed to these related purposes are summarized as follows.

1. *A Single Foreign Affairs Personnel System:* All the primary foreign affairs agencies were using two personnel systems, the Civil Service and the Foreign Service. Moreover, only State was privileged to use the career FSO category of the Foreign Service system; the other agencies could use only the category for temporary employees (Foreign Service Reserve) and the lower-status category (Foreign Service Staff). For two years Crockett devoted much of his time and energy to two measures designed to bring together the systems of employment of the major foreign affairs agencies and to equalize their status and conditions of employment. First was the integration of the overseas officers of the United States Information Agency into the career Foreign Service Officer corps. Second was a bill to amend the Foreign Service Act of 1946 (still the governing legislation for the Foreign Service) to provide a new category of Foreign Affairs Officers into which Civil Service officials of the various foreign affairs agencies could be transferred. Both proposals were intended to cut away barriers between the agencies and to encourage flexibility and interchange in the use of personnel. The second became known as the Hays bill for its sponsor, Representative Wayne Hays of Ohio.[1]

1. Both proposals ultimately failed. The Hays bill passed the House, and both it and the USIA integration plan were considered at the same time by a special subcommittee of the Senate Foreign Relations Committee. The subcommittee reported both measures out favorably, but they were tabled by the full committee so that by the fall of 1966 the two measures were dead.

2. *A Manpower Utilization System* (*MUST*) : MUST was designed as a device to improve the assignment and development of individual personnel, and at the same time to assess, predict, and plan for future personnel needs. The system would provide guides for recruitment, assignments, and training programs, linked with long-range anticipations of personnel needs. Through the computerization of personnel data, information concerning individuals and their immediate assignments could be related immediately to the overall short- and long-range needs of the service. The system, like most of the others emanating from the Barrett staff, came to be known by an acronym, in this case MUST, for Manpower Utilization System and Techniques. (The acronym was later adopted by the U.S. Civil Service Commission for another project.) Work on MUST began in March 1965, the month of Johnson's initiating of EROP. Two CCPS men just returned from the Bonn outpost, Harr and James F. Ragan, a junior officer, were diverted to work on MUST at that time.

3. *Research and Development:* The Department of State has long had a sizable Bureau of Intelligence and Research, primarily for the purpose of accumulating and analyzing data relevant to current foreign policy questions. It had done nothing at all in systems analysis and management science as applied to the foreign affairs community. To remedy this deficiency, Crockett, in early 1965, created the Center for International Systems Research (CISR) with the hope that it would flower into a genuine "R & D" capability in foreign affairs. It was located organizationally in the Foreign Service Institute but worked physically and socially "back-to-back" with the rest of the Barrett staff. Howard Ball, a career civil servant with a vigorous interest in social science research, was appointed director. His deputy was John Golden, experienced in systems development in IBM and the Department of Defense.

4. *Organizational Development:* Crockett, Barrett, and some of their associates for some time had been interested in

socio-psychological approaches to organization, especially to organizational change. No doubt their zeal was heightened by the resistances many of their change efforts were meeting in the State Department and other agencies. By 1965 they were enthusiastic converts to the ideas of such writers as Chris Argyris, Warren Bennis, Rensis Likert, and the late Douglas McGregor. These ideas cannot be treated fully here. In general, they have to do with improving interpersonal communications and sensitivity, greater employee participation in decision making, and development of organizational forms and processes that encourage rather than inhibit creativity and commitment on the part of individual employees.

The first major manifestation of this interest was a reorganization undertaken by Crockett in his own administrative area in June 1965. Moving from a pyramidal structure to a flat one, a number of semi-autonomous programs were created. A dialogue on program objectives between Crockett and the program managers was to substitute for several layers of hierarchy that were stripped away. This effort, known as MOP (Management by Objectives and Programs), was based on the "Theory Y" ideas of McGregor.[2]

At about the same time, Crockett and Barrett began the use of the training method known as "T-grouping" or sensitivity training, employing eminent social scientists as trainers for small groups of high-ranked FSO's. This was done on contract with the National Training Laboratories. By early 1966 these and other ideas had coalesced into an imaginative program of organizational development that attracted a good deal of favorable attention from other government agencies and business firms. Its acronym was ACORD (Action for Organizational Development).

PREPARATION FOR EROP

Although Crockett accorded CCPS a high priority among his many initiatives, the others were draining manpower and

2. From McGregor's book, *The Human Side of Enterprise* (New York: McGraw-Hill, 1960).

energy at the time EROP was announced. He and Barrett sought help from outside Barrett's own staff. First, thinking that someone of ambassadorial status should direct the EROP undertaking from Washington, they sought the detailing to Washington for this purpose of the Ambassador to Guatemala, John O. Bell. As noted earlier, Bell had used CCPS effectively in Guatemala and was a supporter of it. A strong executive, Bell had had operational experience in the aid program and had been one of the principal planners of the 1961 Kennedy AID reorganization. He agreed to the temporary assignment, and it was quickly arranged. Second, Barrett negotiated the transfer of James Frey from the Latin American bureau to serve as Bell's chief of staff. Third, he asked the Bureau of the Budget to assign as many people to the project as it could. EROP had come as a complete surprise to many in the Bureau, and its staff did not greet it with enthusiasm. It took some hard negotiating by Barrett and Frey to persuade the Bureau's International Division to designate four staff members to work part-time on EROP for several months. Finally, seeking to elicit participation by substantive offices of the Department, Barrett asked the geographic bureaus to contribute manpower. Ultimately, each designated a liaison officer, and some of them participated in the later field trips.

In these arrangements, the State Department group assumed the initiative and leadership of EROP, even though the President's directive assigned co-equal responsibility to the Bureau of the Budget. From the outset, the Barrett group assumed that EROP would utilize CCPS and focus on countries that already had CCPS experience. Some in the Bureau of the Budget questioned this assumption; they preferred a more customary management-analysis kind of budget review to one in which primary responsibility would be lodged in line officers (first in the ambassadors in the field and later in the line bureaus of the State Department, according to the Barrett group's plan). But the Bureau had no ready and feasible alternative plan. Henceforth, the basic design and documents of the EROP operation were initiated by the State group, negotiated and cleared with the Bureau of the Budget and the geographic bureaus, and then transmitted. Some decisions, like the selection of posts, were discussed and cleared also with representatives of other foreign affairs agencies; and copies of all documents were furnished the other agencies. But the initiative and direction of EROP rested basically with Crockett, Barrett, and their colleagues. Their plan was that total country programs would be developed at the field posts with the help and support of visiting teams from Washington. Initial decisions would be made by the ambassadors, and the programs would then be sent to Washington for review by the Department of State and the Bureau of the Budget. Recommendations approved in this review would be transmitted to the appropriate agencies to be given effect. This procedure would reverse the customary way of doing business. Instead of appeals by State to other agencies for program changes, the agencies would now be in the position of appellants, State and the Bureau in that of arbiters. This is precisely what Barrett had in mind in the third of the four uses of CCPS as he had described it to the Bunker Committee.

The plan involved the following steps:

1. Selection of 10 to 15 missions, each having a CCPS data base.

2. Bringing the CCPS data up to date as a basis for conducting field reviews.

3. Sending guidelines to the selected missions for constructing their FY 1967 total country programs.

4. Creation of the total country package in the field, based on the work of each individual section of the mission and ambassadorial reviews of that work.

5. Receipt of the country packages in Washington, including CCPS figures showing the FY 1967 program changes and a covering ambassadorial summary of recommendations.

6. Joint reviews in Washington by State and the Bureau in order to make decisions on all field recommendations.

7. Transmittal of approved recommendations to appropriate agencies for inclusion in or amendment to their FY 1967 budget submissions.

The time schedule was tight. It was already April 1965, and the whole operation would have to be finished by early fall so that program changes could be reflected in the FY 1967 budget. This meant that the country packages would have to start coming in by early July to allow time for a staggered schedule of Washington review sessions.

The first step was taken care of quickly with the selection of the following 13 countries for EROP.

*Latin America—*Colombia, Guatemala, Mexico, Venezuela
*Europe—*Federal Republic of Germany, Italy, United
       Kingdom
*Far East—*Japan, the Philippines, Taiwan
*Africa—*Ethiopia
*Near East-South Asia—*Greece, United Arab Republic

A major disappointment was the exclusion of India, regarded by the CCPS group as the prize package among all the CCPS installations. AID vigorously opposed the inclusion of India because it was planning to conduct an intensive review of its India program during the same time period. Nevertheless, there was satisfaction that the 13 choices represented a wide range of Mission size in all five regions, and included both developed and developing countries.

To expedite the operation, the executive assistants of ten of the selected Missions were brought to Washington for a week of consultation. (Three Missions—in Japan, the Philippines, and Italy—lacked executive assistants, since the CCPS work had occurred so recently.) The executive assistants were briefed on the plan, timetables were set, arrangements were made for those Missions needing staff help from Washington, and measures were taken to speed the updating of the CCPS data.

A tentative schedule was drawn up of trips by Washington staff members to almost all of the 13 EROP Missions. These field trips were regarded as necessary to provide technical assistance to the Missions and to provide involvement by the major sponsoring groups. Thus, the "ideal" Washington team would consist of one person from State's CCPS staff, one person from the Bureau of the Budget, and the appropriate country desk officer of State. This pattern held for nearly half of the EROP missions. Several received no visitors. Three of Barrett's young FSO's—James Carney, Richard Pogue, and James Ragan—were assigned temporarily to the three Missions that lacked an executive assistant.

Early in April Crockett, Barrett, and Frey met with Secretary Rusk to report on EROP planning. On his own volition, the Secretary proposed sending a letter to the 13 ambassadors involved in EROP, urging their full cooperation. He was particularly concerned that the ambassadors be sure to take a hard look at activities that were extensions of domestic agency programs as well as those of a more direct foreign affairs nature. Most ambassadors regarded the former as minor irritants and paid little attention to them. Frey took almost verbatim notes as Rusk talked, and drafted the letter immediately on returning to his office. It went through channels, was signed, and was sent to the field only a few days later.

Later, when one of Barrett's young FSO's appeared at an EROP Mission, he was greeted by a half-jocular, half-sarcastic remark by the Ambassador. Referring to the Rusk letter, the Ambassador said: "We received your letter. When you're through here, you can go draft yourself a reply." The young FSO could not convince the Ambassador that the letter really had been Rusk's personal idea.

Bell arrived from Guatemala in time to work with Frey in producing the first and basic guidelines paper, a nine-page document that went to the field as an airgram in mid-May. It described the concept of EROP as follows:

The Review is experimental. It is designed to test a hypothesis that, if the Chiefs of Mission were free to allocate all of the resources employed by the United States Government in the countries to which they are accredited so as to support the essential roles and missions of the United States Mission in the manner which they judge most effective, they would be able to achieve more effective use and more efficient management of those resources. While each Chief of Mission now has available to him, and presumably advantages himself of opportunity to review and comment upon, the individual programs and activities of the various elements which make up the Mission, heretofore he has lacked a framework for comparative evaluation and reason to consider and recommend alternative uses of resources of various agencies in several appropriation accounts. Even if he had felt that a more effective approach to a particular goal might be obtained by an expansion of one program rather than using the resources of another, this has not appeared a practicable step.

The present Review, it should be noted, does *not* assure the Chief of Mission of approval or automatic acceptance of his recommendations, now or later. Nevertheless, his recommendations are to be based on the assumption that they will be most seriously considered and may be approved and become binding on the agencies which control the funding of various activities.

The paper also stressed consideration of policies and priorities:

Chiefs of Mission should understand that the President anticipates their most serious consideration not only of the pattern of resource use in terms of efficiency and economy, but also their thoughtful consideration of the validity and effectiveness of present strategy and tactics in achieving foreign policy objectives.

Chiefs of Mission were told that much of their existing program might seem to be "immutable" and might indeed prove to be so, but it was to be examined critically nonetheless:

It is of particular importance that all presuppositions, dogmas, articles of faith, and other fixed ideas be critically reexamined.

As to form of the submission, the message called for "a recommended program for FY 1967 set forth in the terminology and format of the CCPS," covered by "a narrative report which provides the substantive information and commentary necessary to understanding the program proposed and the basic reasoning underlying it." It was pointed out to Chiefs of Mission that CCPS "offers a ready basis for specifically identifying duplication or overlapping of efforts" and "also permits ease of comparison with prior years and assures common terminology for all programs under review."

The airgram also dealt with a troublesome problem: because EROP was to occur in a shorter time span than the conventional process of preparing for the budget, ambassadors would already have seen and reviewed agency program or budgetary submissions for FY 1967. Even if EROP had started earlier, a perfect synchronization with the budget process would not have been possible. EROP called for simultaneous review of program plans of *all* agencies operating in a given country; in the conventional process, each agency operated on its own time cycle so that program plans would pass by the ambassador for review at different times throughout the winter and spring. This last, of course, was one of the dysfunctions that comprehensive programming was designed to overcome, but for a time the two methods would have to coexist, with the conventional processes adjusting to the comprehensive approach once the latter became formally operational.

The airgram sought to convince the ambassadors that any judgments they had made on the earlier submissions of individual agency budgets should not constrain their judgments in the EROP exercise. Several grounds were suggested for this point of view: in the normal process, agency programs

would not have been placed in competition, so resource
trade-offs could not be considered; previous endorsements
might have been made on "assumptions of inevitability"
about agency programs; the belief might have obtained that
"no one in Washington would take serious interest in reviewing the validity of concepts established as habits" in foreign
affairs.

In drafting the guidelines, Bell and Frey sought to force
hard thinking about alternatives on the part of Mission staffs,
yet allow room for creativity. For CCPS Categories I, IV, and
V (Management, Standard Services, and Administration) all
13 Missions were instructed to see that their fiscal 1967 program package did not exceed 1965 CCPS dollar levels. This,
it was felt, would force a five to ten percent cut, given the
rises in costs and salaries over the two-year period. Missions
were also instructed to cut ten percent *below* 1965 levels, on
a hypothetical basis, to see what choices they would make
under this more severe constraint. For most Missions, the instructions were the same in Category II (International Relations). Missions having large programs of bilateral assistance
were given no ceiling figure in Category III (Internal Development), and Missions having small aid programs or no
aid programs were given a zero figure for 1967. To provide
an escape valve should these restrictions be too severe in the
ambassador's judgment, Missions were told to make any
recommendations for decreases or increases they wished and
to make as strong a case as they wished independently of the
exercise of conforming to the guidelines.

Soon after the airgram had gone to the field, an outburst
of guerrilla activity in Guatemala compelled Ambassador Bell
to abandon the EROP assignment and return to his post.
Only a few weeks later, Frey was offered, and accepted the
job of Deputy Chief of the International Division in the
Bureau of the Budget. This was one of several moves made
at that time in the Bureau, another being the naming of
James Clark, an experienced examiner of about Barrett's age,

as Chief of the International Division. Clark had previously served in the Bureau's National Security Division.

Although initially upset by Frey's announcement, Crockett and Barrett appreciated that the offer provided an excellent opportunity for Frey and that it would be helpful to have a good friend in that strategic post in the Bureau.[3] But the problem of staffing EROP again became urgent. Forest Horton was loaned to Crockett for the MOP reorganization, and John Abernethy was already enmeshed in the job of supervising all of the data-processing and production aspects of EROP. Because the basic design of MUST was almost finished, Barrett reassigned Harr and Ragan to EROP, with Harr to fill in temporarily as chief of staff. James Wine, a noncareer ambassador between assignments, briefly filled in for Bell. Though favorable to EROP, Wine was not experienced in the system and was soon diverted to other tasks.

During June supplementary guidances were sent to the field, including one on how to conduct field review sessions. Several models were proposed, including one that involved group sessions of key Mission officers related to specific categories of CCPS. Thus, in considering his Mission's recommended 1967 program in Internal Development, the ambassador would convene representatives from AID, the Peace Corps, the military assistance group, and the Agricultural Attache's office. But the ambassadors were free to choose whatever review methods they wished. Barrett and his staff

3. The basic organization of the Bureau at that time comprised: a Director and Deputy Director (both presidential appointees); three Assistant Directors; a group of offices which had government-wide jurisdiction on specific subjects (e.g., Legislative Reference, Statistical Standards); and a group of Divisions, each having to do with the budgets, programs, organization, and management in broad areas of federal activity (e.g., National Security, Natural Resources). Those most immediately involved in this case were one Assistant Director, Henry S. Rowen, who was soon to be given responsibility for promoting and superintending PPBS across the government, and the International Division. The latter, which included about twenty-five professional persons, had jurisdiction over the programs and budgets of the State Department, AID, USIA, CIA, and some others.

were anxious to avoid the implication that EROP was another incursion by administrative "types" into "substance." One means of doing this was to involve the substantive officers in the field (as well as in Washington) in basic decisions.

This was a source of some friction between the State Department group and the group from the Bureau of the Budget. In the field trips that took place in May, June, and July, Barrett intended that the visitors from Washington play a supportive role, much as the executive assistants were playing, and not do the job for the Mission. But some of the participants from the Bureau tended to behave more as budget examiners and to involve themselves in substantive decisions. Yet, on the whole, cooperation between the two staffs was good in the earlier stages of EROP, even though individual opinions of the Bureau people ranged from active support of the EROP approach to skepticism. As the program wore on, and particularly once the field trips were over, they participated less and less.

In June Crockett's Management by Objectives and Programs (MOP) reorganization of the administrative area occurred, and it had several effects on the programming effort. As a part of the reorganization, a new office was created, called the Program Analysis Staff (PAS). Crockett and Barrett were looking ahead to the fourth use of CCPS—that of high-level systems analysis for the top decision-makers of the State Department on the seventh floor. They decided that the time had come to create an analysis unit so such a staff could be recruited. Later, when the appropriate moment came, it would be moved to the substantive side of State's hierarchy. Barrett recruited Robert Bonham of AID to the new staff. A senior government servant with experience in the Pentagon, Bonham was to join State in September and thereafter would play an increasingly important role in the programming effort.

Another feature of the reorganization was a substantial change in the nature of Barrett's responsibilities. Formerly, his Management Planning Staff (MPS) consisted of not more than 15 persons working mainly on CCPS and also on creating and implementing new ideas and concepts for Crockett, such as MUST. As large offices in Crockett's area were broken into semiautonomous programs, their planning staffs were pulled together under Barrett, along with a few special units that had no home. Barrett's staff ballooned to more than 60 persons, became known as the Office of Management Planning (OMP), and acquired a number of additional functions. From leading a small band of disciples, Barrett suddenly became responsible for a much wider range of activities, just when EROP was demanding a major share of his time. His temporary solution was to make Harr acting director of OMP while he personally took full charge of EROP, an action which indicated the overriding importance of EROP in his mind.

The PPBS Announcement

During July and August the EROP field submissions arrived in Washington. While they were being studied and plans were being made for setting up the Washington review sessions, President Johnson made his startling announcement that a system of planning-programming-budgeting (PPBS), modeled on the McNamara-Hitch Defense Department system, would be installed on nearly a government-wide basis. From that date, August 25, 1965, the gathering momentum of the PPBS effort would have an increasing influence on EROP and all other efforts at foreign affairs programming.

The ideas and motivation that culminated in the President's instruction that most civilian agencies of government develop a PPBS had actually originated in the minds of a small number of the top leaders of the Bureau of the Budget. During 1964, Director Kermit Gordon and his two assistant directors, then Charles L. Schultze and William M. Capron, had been increasingly distressed by the inadequacy of the information submitted by agencies in support of budget requests. They were forced to make decisions about individual programs on the strength of alleged needs (dollar costs), but with little evidence as to anticipated benefits or accomplishments (products and benefits) and little indication that the agencies had considered other means of achieving these ends. Under such conditions, they felt that their decisions, as well as those of the requesting agencies, could hardly fail to be arbitrary and relatively uneducated. During 1964 and on into 1965, they began working with a few agencies—selected on the basis of the importance of their programs in key fields of presidential interest and on the likelihood that their resource demands would grow—in an effort to have them develop more data and systematically analyze it. At the same time, they sought to strengthen the Bureau's own analytic capabilities by hiring a small number of trained analysts to study and evaluate programs. Schultze resigned as assistant director in January 1965 and was succeeded a few months later by Henry S. Rowen. The choice of Rowen was a further reflection of the direction in which the Bureau's leaders desired to move. He had been involved in systems analysis in the Department of Defense under McNamara following extensive experience as an employee of the RAND Corporation. He was to become the principal leader of the Bureau's PPBS program and supervisor of its program evaluation staff.

The beginnings of PPBS in the Bureau thus had been modest, gradual, and selective. In fact, until the summer of 1965 the term PPBS, which had been invented in the Department of Defense, was not applied in the Bureau's effort. The decision to use it and to make PPBS both sweeping and immediate apparently emanated from the White House. In June 1965 Gordon resigned as Budget Director to go to the Brookings Institution. He was replaced by Schultze, who returned to the Bureau from a professorship at the University of Maryland. Soon thereafter Schultze addressed a memorandum to the President, advising him of the efforts of the Bureau to improve budgetary submissions and analysis on a selective and gradual basis. The President may have consulted Secretary of Defense McNamara. At any rate, the President's order came quickly, so suddenly that it was a surprise to many high officials in the government and even some in the Budget Bureau. In it he specifically used the Defense Department terminology of PPBS and referred to Defense as a model. The undertaking was to go into effect immediately and apply to almost the entire executive branch. The Director of the Budget was given responsibility to direct and supervise the new system.

One other factor conditioned the birth and reception of PPBS. During the preceding year the President had given great emphasis to his program of cost reduction. The PPBS announcement was made at a large meeting of the extended Cabinet that included not only the major agency heads but their deputies and assistants who had been primarily involved in the cost reduction effort. Like EROP, PPBS thus came to be related to cost reduction in the minds of many both inside and outside of government, an association that may well have dampened enthusiasm in some places and may also have clouded understandings as to its true content and import.

In his statement to the extended Cabinet, the President said that the new system "will enable us to":

1. Identify our national goals with precision and on a continuing basis.

2. Choose among these goals the ones that are most urgent.

3. Search for alternative means of reaching those goals most effectively at the least cost.

4. Inform ourselves not merely on next year's costs, but on the second, and third, and subsequent year's costs of our programs.

5. Measure the performance of our programs to insure a dollar's worth of service for each dollar spent.

The President said that the PPBS studies and reviews should operate on a year-round basis and not be squeezed into the budget cycle. For this purpose, "each of you will need a central staff for program and policy planning accountable directly to you. . . . I intend to have the 1968 budget and later-year programs presented in this new form by next spring."

Following the President's announcement, the Bureau of the Budget, under the primary leadership of Assistant Director Rowen, went to work to give PPBS operational meaning. There were speeches, seminars, training courses. Most important of all was the preparation of specific instructions to the agencies. (The basic one, published on October 12, 1965, as Bureau of the Budget Bulletin No. 66-3, is discussed below.) Thereafter, Bureau staff worked closely with individual agencies to help them develop their systems. In order that PPBS might go into effect at once, the Bureau required a very tight schedule, culminating in the submission to the Bureau of the necessary PPBS documents by May 1, 1966 (applicable to FY 1968). A most pressing early problem was the shortage of qualified staffs in the agencies and even the Bureau itself. Working with the Civil Service Commission, the Bureau arranged a series of short courses in analysis and subsequently, through the National Institute of Public Affairs, year-long training programs in systematic analysis at selected universities. In fact, this program was to become the most ambitious non-Defense university training undertaking in federal history. In 1966-67, its first year, 80 officials participated for the full academic year; in 1967-68, 93 took part.

The need for so ambitious a training program was further reflection of the view of the leaders that PPBS was fundamentally different—in content, in skills and knowledge required, and in orientation—from traditional budgeting and traditional "program-budgeting." PPBS called for systems analysis, cost-benefit analysis, operations research, and related techniques. These were not weapons in the armory of the traditional budgeteer of 1965, who had typically been a product of general administrative training and experience, sometimes supplemented by work in accounting. The new orientation was basically that of economics, and PPBS was in part a culmination of a swing toward economics that had begun with the Kennedy administration in Defense and, from the top down, in the Bureau of the Budget. No Director of the Bureau prior to 1961 had been a professional economist; none since then has *not* been one. The four Bureau leaders primarily responsible for the launching of PPBS— Gordon, Schultze, Capron, and Rowen—were all economists, and two of them, Capron and Rowen, had many years of experience in the RAND Corporation.

COMPARISON OF PPBS AND CCPS

It is not feasible here to recount all the provisions of Bulletin 66-3, the basic charter for PPBS, which is itself a condensed and tightly written document. It is necessary, however, to highlight those features most germane to this story, with emphasis upon their differences from the CCPS-EROP models as they had developed up to that point in foreign affairs.

The Agency Base. With a few exceptions, every federal department and major operating agency was directed to install a PPB system for itself—i.e., comprehending all the operations carried on within its jurisdiction. This meant that international and overseas operations would be programmed and budgeted *by individual departments and bureaus.* Each of the overseas agencies—State, AID, CIA, the Peace Corps, and USIA—was specifically directed to prepare its own PPBS. Its submissions were to be made directly to the Bureau of the Budget. With regard to overseas activities, there was no suggestion of participation by ambassadors nor of any review or other role of the Department of State. Subsequently, the Bureau encouraged some of the foreign affairs agencies to prepare some of their basic documents on individual countries, but these were not brought together by country or region.

In contrast, CCPS was specifically designed to involve ambassadors and State's regional bureaus in Washington in the decision-making process, at an earlier point in time than under existing procedures, by creating *total country packages embracing the programs of all agencies operating in each country*. The starting point for gathering CCPS data was the individual agency program in a given country, and the data would always be reported on an individual agency basis; but in emphasizing the total country packages CCPS unquestionably was geographically based rather than agency based.

Emphasis on Analysis. As indicated earlier, the projected PPB system laid heavy stress upon analysis in depth to develop concrete statements of objectives and programs (including in both cases analyses of alternatives). The projections and analyses were to be on a multi-year basis, although Bulletin 66-3 left to agency discretion the number of forward years to be covered. In contrast, CCPS laid stress upon building a comprehensive data base, an information system, as a precondition to effective analysis across agency boundaries.

Orientation to Output. This was equated with orientation to objectives as distinguished from inputs or costs. Programs and their achievements were to be measured, insofar as feasible, in *quantitative* terms. These same characteristics were also intended in CCPS, which relied largely on comprehensive planning documents (the NPP's) for statements of output, of effects to be achieved.

Program Structure.[4] Three levels of classification were specified for the accumulation of PPB program and cost data. At the top were *program categories*, or "groupings of agency programs which serve the same broad objective." Second were *program subcategories*, likewise clustering programs contributing to more narrowly defined objectives. Last were

4. The program structures subsequently developed by some foreign affairs agencies, as well as that of CCPS, are presented in Appendix V.

program elements, considered as integrated activities, against each of which costs should be allocated and whose outputs should comprise the specific products of the program. This third level was probably the most difficult and the most crucial in social (as distinguished from goods-production) activities, as in many of the programs in foreign affairs. The classification problem was basically similar to that encountered at various stages in the CCPS-EROP development. But there was one significant difference. The foreign affairs group had attempted from the start to develop classes that were more or less standard for all agencies and all countries, in order to assure comparability and the possibilities of aggregation on country, regional, and worldwide bases. The Bureau of the Budget did not require such standardization; in fact, some of the foreign affairs agencies—notably AID—permitted staffs in individual countries to develop their own classes. This of course made aggregation between, as well as within, agencies difficult—if not impossible.

The Vehicles. The basic PPB document was to be a multi-year *Program and Financial Plan,* annually reappraised and updated. Following review and approval, it would be the basis for the agency's annual budget. The plan would be supported by *Analyses* of objectives and accomplishments and *Special Studies* prepared in response to questions raised by the Bureau of the Budget and within the agency. A *Program Memorandum* would be prepared annually to summarize and justify the plan for each program category.

Relation to the Budget. The Program Memoranda and the Special Studies, prepared each spring, would become the basis for the Bureau's Budget Previews in May and June. Changes made at that time would be incorporated in budget submissions prepared during the summer and reviewed during the fall. It may be noted that the system was to be "on top of" and prior to the regular budget process, and did not require any changes in the form and classifications of budget estimates and appropriations. It was required, however, that there be a "crosswalk" between the program structure and the budget structure. CCPS was also "on top of" the regular budget process and also required a "crosswalk" to the budget (always referred to in the Barrett staff as a "torque converter"), so that the only real differences between the two systems in this regard were (1) timing, and (2) the CCPS crosswalk to a number of agency budgets simultaneously in contrast to the PPBS discrete agency approach. Bulletin 66-3 envisioned crosswalking PPBS material into the regular budget during the first year of operation, whereas this had been seen as future business during the first two years of CCPS experimentation. However, as Bulletin 66-3 was issued, the State Department and its CCPS were already confronting the crosswalk problem in a major way in the EROP exercise, as will be seen below.

The attempt to install PPB systems in most of the civil agencies of government in the course of a few months was a gigantic undertaking. Few if any of them enjoyed the advantages of the Defense Department, cited in the introduction to this book: the background of study and experiment; the trained and sophisticated staff; the existing data base; the tremendous appropriation items; and the vigorous executive, already attuned to the techniques. On the other hand, the agency base of PPBS provided organizational and budgetary anchors that were not available to the inventors of CCPS. In this respect, at least, PPBS enjoyed a major, perhaps crucial, advantage.

In this thumbnail comparison, we have deliberately emphasized the differences between the Budget Bureau's definition of PPBS and the system developing in the State Department for foreign affairs programming. Yet some felt— and some still feel—that the Defense system, the Bureau's PPBS, and CCPS were basically compatible. They rested on the same intellectual foundations and had like objectives— greater rationality in government decision making and management. The differences to them seemed basically tactical, not fundamental. (This question is discussed in Chapter VII.) In fact, the President's PPBS announcement of August 25, 1965, though a complete surprise to the programming group in the State Department, was received by them with enthusiasm. The approach taken by the President seemed to them in August exactly what they, for more than two years, had been working to bring about in the foreign affairs sector of government—their system, as the Barrett group members saw it, was a long stride toward PPBS. Now, they felt, they had even stronger presidential backing for their system than that implied in the EROP message. They took pride in the knowledge that, due to their efforts, the State Department was now well ahead of every other agency in town (except, of course, the Defense Department). They anticipated full backing by the Bureau of the Budget.

In this hopeful assessment they would later be disenchanted. There had been some friction with the Bureau during the early stages of the EROP exercise, and there was no marked improvement after the President's PPBS announcement. But the Barrett staff was jolted when the Bureau's Bulletin 66-3 in October made it clear that almost every agency that was operating overseas, including the Department of State itself, must create its own PPBS without any reference to the comprehensive system that had been under development for two years. The staff did not oppose the strengthening of systems capabilities in the various agencies. In fact, Barrett had repeatedly averred that CCPS was not intended to supplant systems in other agencies; rather, it would dovetail with them and integrate them in an overarching foreign affairs system. The disturbing element of Bulletin 66-3 to the Barrett men was its omission of any mention of CCPS and EROP. They did not expect exemption of the foreign affairs community from PPBS, but they did expect some form of recognition that would support their drive toward a comprehensive country system while at the same time encouraging the development of PPBS by individual agencies.

However, the press of work on EROP so absorbed the energies of the Barrett group during the fall of 1965 that the Bureau's bulletin became very nearly subliminal for them. They were confident that in due course a viable working relationship with the Bureau could be achieved, and no one seriously pushed the idea of making an official State Department counterproposal that would permit in foreign affairs some degree of accommodation of PPBS with the CCPS approach. It would be several months before the full significance of the presidential announcement of August 1965 would be clear to the State Department group.

THE EROP SUBMISSIONS

The State programming group had its hands full with EROP. There was at least temporary cause for satisfaction here. As the 13 country submissions were studied during July and August of 1965, it became clear that most of the field posts had responded with worthwhile jobs. Three or four of the packages complied only with the letter of the instructions, lacking major program changes or imaginative ideas. But the quality of the others exceeded expectations, given the time pressures and newness of the vehicle. These submissions contained analyses of policy issues, program changes, new ideas for structural rearrangements within the Missions. In some there were recommendations for wholesale elimination of marginal programs and the building up of more important ones. As an example of a proposed "trade-off," one Mission recommended eliminating an AID program in rural development and substituting an increase in Peace Corps volunteers, on the grounds that this would be more effective, given the local conditions. A sample of other ideas from the 13 packages follows:[5]

A major European Mission proposed eliminating or transferring to a local university its expensive USIA library, on

5. Only a widely scattered "sanitized" list can be presented for purposes of illustration because of the security classification of the EROP packages.

the grounds that American printed material was in abundant supply in the country.

Four of the thirteen EROP packages proposed eliminating entirely the operations of the U.S. Travel Service, on the grounds that local travel restrictions prevented host nationals in any numbers from traveling to the United States.

A Far Eastern Mission proposed a drastic cut in agricultural programs, which were seen as relatively unnecessary, and substitution of a sizable increase in commercial programs, which were seen as of high priority.

One Mission proposed a reorganization that would integrate the political section and USIA.

A Latin American Mission proposed integrating the separate operations of the Agricultural Attache, the economic section, and the AID mission.

A European Mission proposed closing down entirely three separate domestic agency operations.

A Mission that had been cut off the AID list several years earlier proposed reinstituting major AID loans, based on an extensive analysis of the situation in the host country.

For the first time, Mission officers representing a variety of agencies had collaborated in producing a total country program, with program choices made in relationship to policy objectives and budgetary realities. Some of the Washington desk officers for EROP countries who had participated in field trips during the ambassadorial review sessions had become enthusiastic converts. One of them salvaged the package from a Far Eastern Mission that had been watered down after the ambassador had left for Washington on consultation. The desk officer did so by consulting the ambassador in Washington and getting the original program changes reinstated in the submission. Some of the ambassadorial memoranda stated that there had been doubts at first about the operation, but that it had turned out to be a useful exercise from their field viewpoint.

THE WASHINGTON REVIEW

The country packages were submitted in two copies, one to the regional bureau and the other to the CCPS-EROP staff. The bureaus were told that they had two to three weeks to analyze the submissions and form positions on the ambassador's recommendations for the upcoming review sessions. They were also told that where a recommendation affected the program of another agency, it was the regional bureau's responsibility to notify that agency, but not to attempt to negotiate any differences of opinion with that agency prior to the formal review sessions.

No mechanism existed for the reviews, so one had to be created. A special panel, composed of Crockett, Rostow, Rowen, and the assistant secretary for the region being considered, was envisioned, and a schedule for such region-by-region reviews was set up, to begin in late August 1965. The integrated EROP staff assisted in suggesting questions to be asked of assistant secretaries. The regional bureau staffs (led by the desk officer for the country under discussion) provided staff services to their assistant secretaries and did the checking with other agencies. The complete EROP packages were processed through the computer by the EROP staff, but the bulk of the data arrived too late to be of value to the participants.

The reviews were less than totally effective. In no one session were all the principals present; in fact, for most of the sessions, they sent surrogates. Crockett attended most often, but since the meetings were held in his conference room, he was frequently interrupted by other business. Moreover, the 13 country packages were given different amounts of attention, depending largely on which one was considered first at a given session and on how much time was available. The back-up work by the CCPS-EROP staff and the regional bureau staffs received disappointingly little consideration. Because of the erratic attendance of the principals, Barrett soon took a leading role in the review meetings, functioning as *de facto* chairman.

Whatever values were to accrue from the EROP experience were due less to the review sessions than to the quality of the work done in the field and in the regional bureaus. In general, the latter supported most of the ambassadorial recommendations, and the review panels supported most of the regional bureaus' positions. There were few controversies in the review sessions. Overall, about two-thirds of the ambassadorial recommendations were approved, about 20 percent were set aside for further study, and the remaining 15 percent were rejected.

Once approved, the favored recommendations became official State Department policy, but not necessarily Budget Bureau policy. Being sensitive to the growing chill between State and the Bureau, Barrett had not attempted to make the Bureau a party to the approvals, but merely a consulting reference point in the reviews. He rationalized this by saying that he did not want to compromise the Bureau as an appeal channel for other agencies. The expectation was that the Bureau would play the role of checking up on the other agencies to see that they actually made changes in their own budgets to reflect the approved recommendations. Barrett thought an understanding had been reached between the International Division and the CCPS group in line with President Johnson's words in the EROP press release: "I shall expect each agency to respect the levels established for each of our programs by Secretary Rusk and Mr. Gordon."

THE CROSSWALK PROBLEM

The trick now was to make sure the changes were reflected in the agency budgets. Even before the review sessions began, Barrett had made up his mind that there was only one way to do this effectively under existing circumstances. His proposal was to provoke a major controversy. The normal method for instituting a change in another agency's program (recommended by an ambassador and endorsed by the regional bureau) was for the appropriate desk officer to take the matter up with his counterpart in the other agency. He would depend on the arts of persuasion, having little power to force the issue. If rebuffed, his only recourse would be to escalate the issue up the chain of command in State. Short of the Secretary (and Under Secretary), no one in State had real authority to force an issue with another agency. Few desk officers would take this route except in the rare case in which they were dealing with a vital policy matter. In fact, the desk officer could be confident that unless the issue were urgent and had policy rather than operational connotations, it would very likely get lost in the escalation process. In short, the State Department desk officer was negotiating from a position of weakness and his counterpart in the other agency from a position of strength, and both knew it. Because of this situation, there was reluctance to raise issues at all; some that had been raised had been known to drag on for years.

Aware of this, Barrett sought an "action-forcing process." He proposed to notify the EROP ambassadors which of their recommendations had been approved and to instruct them to direct the representatives of other agencies in the Missions to submit the program changes to their agency headquarters in Washington as budget amendments. Given the authority of the ambassador in his Mission, under the Kennedy letter, the agency representatives could not refuse to do this. Whether or not they agreed with the change, they had presumably participated in the original field review and had had a chance to make their case. Barrett's proposal would put the change formally into the other agency's channels. The agency then would have three choices: (1) implement the proposed change; (2) ignore it and face the consequences of noncompliance, which presumably could be serious, given the language in the original EROP message and the nature of the Secretary of State's various authorities; or (3) appeal the change to the State Department.

The last, of course, was what Barrett was after in the whole enterprise: to put the shoe on the other foot and place the State Department officer in the position of arbiter and the other agency's representative in the position of appellant. If the other agency made a good case, State might reverse the decision. If not, the other agency's next appeal channel was to the Bureau of the Budget; following that, its last appeal was to the President.

The idea was simple and might be effective. It had never been tried. When Barrett broached it to the EROP liaison officers from the five regional bureaus, it was plain that most of them did not want to try it. Barrett wanted his proposed procedure to be undertaken on the authority of the five regional assistant secretaries, in line with the continuing practice throughout EROP to give as much action responsibility as possible to the bureaus and the ambassadors. The representative of the Bureau of European Affairs carried the burden of opposition. His principal fear was that the Barrett idea would not work and the ambassadors would be "hung out to dry." Having ordered the representatives of the other agencies to submit the changes, the ambassadors would ultimately be embarrassed if nothing happened, and their presumed authority would be undercut. He preferred to negotiate the approved changes with the other agencies in the normal fashion.

Barrett argued that the old approach had never worked in the past and there was no reason to think it would now. There was not much time for negotiating if the changes were indeed to be reflected in the FY 1967 budget. He maintained that his approach would work if everyone stuck to his guns. Moreover, he said, it was necessary to cycle the recommendations to the field again anyway in order to convert the CCPS figures to budget figures.

When it became clear that only two regional bureaus, Near East-South Asia and Far East, would go along voluntarily with his idea, Barrett decided to ask Crockett himself to direct it for all the EROP countries. In late August 1965 he explained the problem to Crockett, who agreed to take the responsibility if some safety-valve provisions were included. The reasons for the procedure would have to be explained fully, and the ambassadors should be allowed to change their minds if any particular recommendation gave them great trouble under the new circumstances. Headquarters of other agencies were to be informed of all actions immediately so that they could choose the issues they wanted to appeal and have time to make their case.

All of this was done promptly, but it met with indignation in a number of the embassies involved. As became evident later, some of the ambassadors who complained strongly against the Department's passing this buck to the field were those who had regarded EROP purely as an exercise and had expected their recommendations to disappear into the Washington morass. Some had not bothered to do much in the way of field reviews and had made the decisions and recommendations themselves without consulting the field representatives of the agencies affected. Now they were in the position of summarily ordering them to transmit important program changes. Nevertheless, most ambassadors complied, although one European mission begged out of EROP entirely, and Crockett acquiesced. Other than this, few ambassadors changed their minds. They were required to report back to Washington specifically what action they had taken.

The anguish of the ambassadors was less severe than that of some of the agency headquarters in Washington. The EROP-CCPS offices suddenly became hyperactive, responding to telephone calls and indignant visitors. Where EROP had stirred only mild curiosity in the other agencies to this point, it suddenly became a very warm issue. From the late fall of 1965 throughout the winter the State group explained and re-explained the ground rules of the new ball game, usually ending with a careful description of what the appeal channels were. The callers were told that a report on EROP was being prepared for the President and that it would include information on what had happened to each approved recommendation.

One day, the Department of Agriculture formally appealed two issues to the Secretary of State in a communication which zipped down the chain of command to Barrett's office. Although the State Department ultimately yielded on both issues, Barrett viewed the event as vindication; the precedent had been established.

Clark and Frey, however, made it clear that the Budget Bureau would not check up on the changes to see that they were actually reflected in the budget. Frey had arranged for each of the Bureau's divisions to have copies of the EROP recommendations to consider in the context of the regular fall budget review. But the Bureau pointed out that it was too late in the budget process to check on the changes effectively and that many of the changes amounted to relatively small sums that would be virtually impossible to find in multi-million-dollar appropriation categories. This meant that the only sure place to find out if changes indeed had been made would be in the Missions themselves at the beginning of the new fiscal year. If an ambassador had instructed a given unit to cut two positions and if the incumbents were still at the post on July 1, then the agency had ignored the change order. Thus it would be many months before a full and certain assessment of EROP effects could be made. Meanwhile, it was necessary to go ahead with the drafting of a report to the President to be signed by the Secretary of State and the Director of the Budget. Between mid-November 1965 and mid-February 1966, repeated attempts were made to develop a mutually acceptable draft of this report. During this period, relationships between the Barrett group in the Department of State and the Rowen-Clark group in the Bureau of the Budget deteriorated to an all-out struggle that reached its climax in March 1966.

III

Escalation and Climax
(November 1965-March 1966)

SEQUELS TO EROP AND THE PPBS DIRECTIVES

DURING THE LATE FALL and early winter of 1965-66, EROP and PPBS activities proceeded on four different fronts: the attempt to produce a report for the President on the EROP experience; the development of agency-based PPB systems in the foreign affairs agencies, including the Department of State; a fundamental revision of CCPS, which was given a new title of Foreign Affairs Programming System (FAPS); and preparation for a region-wide FAPS experiment in Latin America. These activities were concurrent but their directions were not consistent or even compatible. For clarity, each is described separately.

It should be noted in advance that most of the work during this period was being carried on at what may be labeled the "Indian" level, some echelons below the heads of the agencies concerned. In the Department of State, there is no evidence that the top echelons, the Secretary, Under Secretary, and most of the Assistant Secretaries were involved or systematically informed. Crockett and Rostow were both heavily engaged in other work and were overseas a good part of the time; they were sporadically advised and consulted. The main responsibilities rested upon Barrett and his colleagues and a few others at his level. In the Bureau of the Budget,

most of the top leadership was busy with the President's upcoming budget for 1967. Assistant Director Rowen was
pressed in leading, steering, stimulating, and advising on the
installation of PPBS across nearly the entire federal government. James Clark, who had become head of the International Division only a few months before, was likewise
involved in both the President's budget and in PPBS for the
foreign affairs agencies. Primary responsibility for much of
the activities described below therefore fell upon Frey, the Assistant Director of the International Division, and a few of that
Division's staff. Thus at this stage of the story, the two principals were Barrett and Frey, two old friends and long-time
working associates in a variety of capacities, now on opposite
sides of the fence.

THE EROP DEBATE

Early in the proceedings (November 1965), Barrett and
Frey agreed that a report to President Johnson on the EROP
exercise, to be signed by Rusk and Schultze, should consist
of two parts: (1) a complete account of all the recommendations in the thirteen country packages, and (2) a covering
letter of less than ten pages that would summarize the whole.
Ragan, assigned the massive job of assembling the back-up
material, completed his work by the end of November. Meanwhile, Barrett and Frey worked on the covering letter. It was
quickly agreed that it would cover three broad themes: what
had been accomplished, what had been learned, and what
should be done next. Barrett assumed the initiative for preparing the drafts; Frey would review and criticize them; they
would negotiate their differences; a final draft would be prepared for submission to their superiors. This was the procedure as envisaged at the outset.

The first section of Barrett's draft described the whole exercise briefly and made the claim that as an experiment it
had proved workable in a number of important respects. For
the first time, ambassadors and their country teams had fo-

cused on all their activities at one time and had produced total country programs meeting constraints laid down by Washington. Most of these had been received on time and all had been reviewed in Washington; decisions had been made; and changes had been introduced in the budgetary channels of all concerned agencies, albeit by unorthodox means. CCPS had indeed provided a framework in which issues, programs, and policies could be examined across-the-board and also be considered on an agency-by-agency basis.

The draft reported that if all the approved changes were in fact implemented by the agencies concerned, the net annual savings would be in the neighborhood of $8 million. But it stressed the positive aspects of the exercise, complimenting the quality of the work done in the field and listing examples of program cuts, program increases, proposed trade-offs, and policy reconsiderations similar to those cited in the previous chapter of this study.

After this discussion of the strengths of EROP, Barrett's draft moved to the second section, a candid discussion of the weaknesses. Four points were made:

1. *Lateness in Terms of the Budget Cycle.* Although the intention had been to comply with the President's request that program changes be reflected in the upcoming budget, the exercise had simply started too late for the Bureau of the Budget to ensure that this happened. It was assumed that most of the changes that were not appealed would in fact be implemented by the agencies, but there would be no way to know until the start of the next fiscal year. The draft reported the complaints of several agencies that they had not had sufficient time to study the proposed changes.

2. *Defects in CCPS.* These included excessively detailed data requirements that tended to make the system cumbersome; lack of flexibility for encompassing some hard-to-categorize activities; and major categories that were generally descriptive rather than output-oriented.

3. *Absence of Washington Interagency Mechanisms.* The

report pointed out that both the Washington review sessions and the method for getting changes into agency budgetary channels fell far short of the ideal because *ad hoc* procedures had to be invented for each. There was no regularly constituted Washington mechanism comparable to an ambassador's country team that could handle a programming operation of the kind envisioned in the EROP exercise.

4. *Lack of a Total Regional View.* The fact that EROP encompassed thirteen Missions scattered throughout five regions instead of *all* Missions in any *one* region was a major weakness. It helped explain why no regional bureau became thoroughly involved in the exercise, and it prevented the inclusion of Washington overhead and regional costs. It also precluded analysis of alternative policies and programs among different countries.

In the final section on what to do next, Barrett's early draft reported that work was already underway to overcome the second problem, that of deficiencies in CCPS. They recommended capitalizing on the momentum of EROP by moving ahead to the following budget year in a way that would overcome the first and fourth problems, by starting the cycle earlier and by covering one entire region. (Preparations were already underway for a region-wide application in Latin America.) The draft reports stated that a start at least would be made toward improving the Washington capability to handle a programming cycle by building an analytical staff in the Latin American bureau and by activating the Program Analysis Staff (PAS). The draft concluded with the attachment, for the President's review and signature, of a proposed National Security Action Memorandum (NSAM), a type of directive which, it will be recalled, is the authoritative vehicle for presidential instructions in the national security field, analogous to an executive order. The NSAM Barrett recommended would have reaffirmed the authority of the NPP's and would formally install a comprehensive programming system in foreign affairs under State Department directions.

It would also have set up interagency committees for program analysis and review purposes.

There was not much argument about Barrett's drafts of the first two sections of the report on the accomplishments and the limitations of EROP. But on the third section—on what should next be done—there was no agreement. Barrett would send Frey a draft and some days later it would be returned with criticisms. Barrett would make changes and send them back and again they would return with criticisms. When the two men conferred to discuss the paper, Frey would often close the meeting saying that he must study it further or consult with Clark and Rowen. This went on for weeks, and it had one product: a gradual clarification of the degree to which their positions had polarized.

On the Budget Bureau side, Rowen, who had participated in EROP as a member of an overseas visiting team and as a member of the Washington review group in a few of its sessions, was cold toward CCPS. Frey himself was in a difficult position; his change of opinion about CCPS roughly coincided with his change of jobs from State to the Bureau. This exposed him to criticism from his former colleagues that he had betrayed them and their system because of his new job. Frey later commented to the authors that such an allegation was not true. He wrote:

I long had had doubts about CCPS as a programming system, but had supported its development partly because it was the only effort of its kind under way and was badly needed in foreign affairs, partly because I hoped my concerns would be taken care of as the effort developed, and partly because of personal affection and professional respect for Barrett. However, the experience of EROP (during which I happened to transfer from State to the Budget Bureau) convinced me that CCPS was deficient as a system in a number of critical respects, that the command and control—and decision-making—structure necessary to make such a system work was lacking, and that CCPS could not be linked effectively with the budget process.

My transfer to the Bureau and the advent of PPBS gave me an opportunity and a professional obligation to express these conclusions; it was not a determining factor in reaching them.

In retrospect, it appears clear that the Bureau's position against CCPS was quite firm, even at an early stage in the negotiations, though Barrett and his colleagues did not understand this until later. But the Bureau group during this period was concerned not with CCPS but with the question of how to deal with the Barrett staff. As Frey later wrote, ". . . Rowen and particularly Clark and I agonized for many an hour over those weeks in an unsuccessful effort to find some way in which the momentum and useful pioneering work that Barrett and his staff had created, and O/MP itself, could be preserved and supported in the PPBS context."

Barrett and his associates in the early stages preferred not to take the Bureau's Bulletin 66-3 seriously as it applied to foreign affairs. In a sense, they were captives of their own fervor. They had just collaborated with the Bureau on a major project based on CCPS, and despite some friction, felt confident that the Bureau would support further development on a country basis. They doubted that Rowen had consulted the Bureau's International Division in drafting the PPBS bulletin and simply assumed support of intelligent and knowledgeable persons for their kind of program. Barrett did not mention PPBS in his various drafts about EROP, in spite of the fact that most of the foreign affairs agencies were already beginning to work energetically on their PPB submissions. During the early stages of his negotiations with Frey, he thought their differences were principally technical, having to do with the structure, the detail, and the alleged inflexibility of CCPS. Such difficulties he thought, and wrote, could be overcome in the revising of CCPS into FAPS. It was not until late in the game (January 1966) that he and his associates came to realize that the real issue was between a State Department-administered, country-based system and a

Budget Bureau-directed, agency-based PPBS. This realization led him to propose a dual strategy that would recognize and encourage PPBS development on the agency base and at the same time permit installation of the comprehensive approach.

Toward the end of January 1966 Barrett went as far as he felt he could without calling it "quits." He gave up the idea of a NSAM and proposed a three-paragraph conclusion to the report, which in essence stated:

1. PPB systems for the individual agencies should be developed energetically through close cooperation of the Bureau, the State Department, and the other foreign affairs agencies.

2. Based on these individual systems and deriving from them there should be developed under State Department leadership an overall system, thus providing both horizontal and vertical approaches to programming in foreign affairs.

3. For the next programming cycle, State should test its comprehensive approach in the entire Latin American region, utilizing PPBS information wherever it was developed; and State and the Bureau should collaborate in selected countries in other regions to test comprehensive PPBSs based on individual agency packages.

Barrett's own colleagues objected to this proposal, thinking that he had yielded too much. They endorsed the coexistence of agency and comprehensive approaches—indeed, some of them felt this had been part of their plan from the beginning. But they feared that Barrett's language could be interpreted to mean that nothing should be done until the agency PPBS's were pronounced ready. Barrett dismissed this objection, feeling that if the Bureau accepted the language, he would have a license to operate, and a viable *modus vivendi* could be worked out along with the PPBS effort.

However, attitudes had begun to coalesce in the Bureau. By the time Barrett offered his compromise, it was too late. The offer inspired no confidence in the Bureau. Its staff feared that if it were accepted the State group would proceed headlong with its Latin American plans, giving short shrift to PPBS. This could be a major diversion and impediment to the urgent efforts to develop PPB systems in the foreign affairs agencies. On the other hand, the Bureau men did not want a feud with State. They preferred that the State programming group apply its creative energy and experience to the individual agency PPBS approach.

Given the circumstances of the time, the hope for a turnaround of the Barrett staff was quite unrealistic. Clark and Frey seemed to realize this and were not surprised when their overtures were ignored. As for Barrett and his staff, their resentment deepened when the compromise was not accepted, since they felt they had conceded a great deal, and that the dual systems approach was viable and offered an appropriate role for each group. They began to suspect that Clark and Frey feared loss of influence for the Bureau's International Division if the comprehensive system were allowed to succeed in foreign affairs. They believed the explanation for Rowen's coolness was what they liked to call the "NIH factor"—"not invented here."

Although the two groups met frequently to discuss their problems, there was little real communication. By February 1966, each was committed to its own approach; they were heading for a major confrontation. Ultimately, there was no agreement on language for the EROP report. As Frey later commented, "We tried to paper over our differences, but it just wouldn't work." No report on EROP was sent to the President, and it was a dead issue by March.

THE DEVELOPMENT OF PPBS IN FOREIGN AFFAIRS AGENCIES

The PPBS directive had caused a seismic jolt in Washington. It was not to be a mere refinement of existing budgetary procedures. The President and later the Bureau of the Budget had expressly directed that agency heads involve themselves personally and that new analytic staffs be developed to assist them in their decisions. Few agencies had employees with PPBS-type credentials. Moreover, the time constraint was severe; the initial round was to be geared to the next budget cycle, that for fiscal year 1968. The pressure for quick action proved a bonanza for the Washington offices of those consulting firms with experience in this kind of work, particularly in the Defense Department, and with personnel of analytic capability. Individuals with reputations in this field were in heavy demand.

The foreign affairs agencies were vastly unequal in respect to their experience, sophistication, and staff capability in the programming fields. AID was in far the strongest position. It had experienced programming personnel both at home and abroad, the majority educated in economics. They occupied respected and prestigious positions in their organizations; indeed AID Administrator David Bell himself was an economist and previously Director of the Budget; one of his first assistants, also an economist, held the title of Assistant Administrator for Program. AID also had a large-scale programming system, based upon program documents initially developed in the countries and tied in with the budget process. PPBS added certain dimensions and changes, but it could be built upon AID's going framework. As a basis for preparing its initial Program Memoranda, AID selected the nine countries having the largest AID programs and instructed the field missions in those countries to prepare submissions by April 1966. There was no attempt to set up standard program categories. Instead, the field posts were instructed to discuss policy objectives as derived from current policy documents and then to articulate specific program goals related to those objectives. Under each goal, the contributing programs were to be listed, with budgetary projections over a five-year period. A program could be listed under more than one goal and cross-referenced. Activities of any other agencies at the post that contributed toward these goals were also to be listed and discussed.

USIA developed program categories that were very little different from its budgetary categories. They were organized in media and functional terms. USIA based its PPBS on regions instead of countries, and the work was all done in Washington.

The Peace Corps asked each of its field missions to prepare a program memorandum in response to a series of questions (major problems in the host country foreseen over the next five years, Peace Corps program goals in relationship to those problems, alternative program choices, cost effectiveness of alternatives). A table showing the numbers and kinds of volunteers needed for each program over the five-year period completed the submission. The instruction stated that the program categories "generally follow previous Peace Corps nomenclature," but were grouped so that "the activities are problem, or mission, oriented." It was pointed out that categories could be added "where necessary." Robert Cox, who had been recruited from Barrett's staff to the Budget Bureau's International Division by Frey, was now a budget examiner for AID and the Peace Corps, and he was assigned to assist the latter in its PPBS design.

The Department of State, of course, had to comply with the Bureau's PPBS instructions just like any other agency, and the decision on how to handle this unintentionally widened the gap between the State programming group and the Bureau. Crockett was given responsibility. With very little discussion, he assigned it to the Barrett staff, a natural move in view of its experience in the programming field. However, all the zeal in the programming group was directed toward its own comprehensive system; no one felt any enthusiasm to develop a PPBS for the State Department alone. Barrett recognized that the PPBS assignment would get minimal attention if left in his area, and might detract from the

current efforts to improve and extend the country programming system. He decided the assignment should be shifted
elsewhere.

In the budget office of State there was some interest in taking on the PPBS assignment, particularly in view of its continuing association with the Bureau of the Budget. The
budget office was headed by Deputy Assistant Secretary Ralph
S. Roberts, an experienced administrator formerly in the Department of Agriculture, who, like Barrett, was not a career
FSO and who served under Crockett. The three men ultimately agreed to shift the PPBS assignment to Roberts. He in
turn assigned it to a small program review unit headed by
Gerald Bushnell, a career FSO with administrative background.

Even though there was no enthusiasm for PPBS in the Barrett staff, several of the members thought this switch was a
mistake. In later comments to the authors, Frey and Bushnell
voiced the same opinion. Bushnell commented: "This decision by Barrett represented a lost opportunity to turn the
Bureau initiative to his advantage, to gain needed Departmental support for the concepts of programming and to
achieve a new status for OMP" [Barrett's Office of Management Planning].

This view is debatable since the Bureau's position against
CCPS was already firm. It is also possible that if the CCPS
men had assumed the PPBS responsibility, they would have
given it inadequate attention and would thus have worsened
relationships with the Bureau. At any rate, this possibility
was not to be tested. Barrett declared that his staff was ready
to help Bushnell in any way he desired. Bushnell did consult
several times with members of the Barrett staff, and there was
no friction between the two groups. But Bushnell and his
assistants worked by themselves on the PPBS problem, which
was rendered most difficult by the fact that not much of what
the State Department did was "programmable." State either
worked at a "high level" of negotiating, reporting, and advis-

ing on policy or at a "low level" of providing administrative support around the world to other agencies and carrying on consular functions. Almost the only exception to the lack of meaty operational activities was in the area of cultural affairs. Bushnell ultimately produced a set of descriptive program categories that resembled standard budgetary classifications. It was based on regions instead of countries. All the work was done in Washington.

The first year's PPBS effort by the foreign affairs agencies was to be less than satisfactory from the Bureau's point of view, but Clark later reported to the authors that the second year (calendar 1967) promised to be much improved. It cannot be said that PPBS was received with great enthusiasm in the headquarters of any of these agencies except for AID, but over time the Bureau's initiative clearly provided a rallying point for those concerned over the possible loss of agency autonomy that might result from State's comprehensive effort. This was particularly true in the case of AID and the Foreign Agricultural Service.

THE FOREIGN AFFAIRS PROGRAMMING SYSTEM

Despite these agency-based PPBS efforts and despite the forbidding clouds in the direction of the Bureau of the Budget, the Barrett group worked intensively in the fall and winter of 1965-66 on two related projects: the modification of CCPS, taking into account the deficiencies revealed by EROP; and the preparation for a region-wide programming installation in Latin America in time for the 1968 budget cycle. For these purposes Barrett mobilized most of his staff who were familiar with programming and added some others. The leaders included, in addition to the "regulars," Robert Bonham, recently acquired from AID; John Golden, assistant director of CISR; Forest Horton, an accomplished statistician with systems experience; and Lawrence Slaughter, a computer expert hired from the Air Force.

Barrett decided that the changes in the design of the system were so substantial as to warrant a change in its name. The Comprehensive Country Programming System (CCPS) in February 1966 became the Foreign Affairs Programming System (FAPS). Among these changes were the reduction of detail, particularly the accounting for man-hours; more output-oriented program categories at the second level of classification; and greater flexibility by providing at the third level for the incorporation of program information not specifically covered by the standard categories. This last was intended to make possible a linkage with any individual-agency PPBS. The assumption was that most of the information in any foreign affairs PPBS would be allocated to the standard program categories but that other data would be incorporated through the ingenious flexible provision designed by Horton and Slaughter.

The key change was the redesign of the second level of classification through the creation of 25 "Standard Program Categories." These related to the five first-level categories, which remained unchanged. As described earlier, versions of the system up to this point had depended largely on policy documents to express desired output objectives, while the program information in the various descriptive categories of the system related to appropriate policy objectives. The EROP exercise had confirmed earlier fears that this dependency was a weakness, since the quality and levels of generality of policy documents varied so widely. The 25 Standard Program Categories of FAPS were more output-oriented than before.[1] The intent was not to divorce program information from policy objectives as expressed in NPP's and other documents, but to make sure that the system remained viable in situations where policy documentation was inadequate or imprecise.

The selection of Standard Program Categories was based not only on the group's experience, but also on an interesting analytical job performed by Horton. Using the Key Word in

1. See Appendix V.

Context (KWIC) computer program, he factored more than 30 NPP's and 900 courses of action, producing related groups from which program categories could be derived.

In sum, the changes were intended to respond to most of the criticisms that had been directed at CCPS, both from within and without the founding and sponsoring group. More specifically, they sought to make the system: less cumbersome through the elimination of detail; more flexible; easier to provide crosswalks to and from the data bases of individual agencies (including their PPB systems) ; less dependent upon the NPP's for the provision of specific program goals; directed more to program outputs.

FAPS ON A REGIONAL BASIS

The group hoped to test the new system on a region-wide basis during the spring of 1966 (for budget year 1968) . Latin America again seemed the most inviting of the regions, especially since eight of its twenty-four Missions had earlier experience with CCPS. Further, the new Assistant Secretary for that region was Lincoln Gordon, earlier the Ambassador to Brazil, an economist by background. The proposal was discussed with Gordon and some of his staff, and they seemed disposed to cooperate. It was decided to hold a conference of executive assistants in or near Washington in early March to acquaint them with FAPS. The executive assistants from all over the world were invited, since some of them would be needed to participate in the field visits to Latin America on a temporary basis and all could experiment with the revised system at their own Missions on their return.

Slaughter finished redesigning the computer program for FAPS in time, and new forms, instructions, and data kits were developed. Optical scanning methods were tested and adopted in order to eliminate several stages of physical handling of the data from the field. This required sending special typewriters to 20 Missions. The logistics for the complex operation were under the direction of Jene Lyon, a former

AID officer recruited to the Barrett staff. Tension and excitement built up within the staff as the time approached for launching the first total regional campaign.

This optimistic planning was shaken near the end of February when a proposed telegram, announcing to the field posts the FAPS round in Latin America, was circulated by the Barrett group to the Budget Bureau and the foreign affairs agencies. Both the Bureau and AID protested. After the weeks of uneasy negotiating described earlier in this chapter, the Bureau now came out flatly in opposition to State's plans. As articulated by Frey, the Bureau's position was that State should not go forward at that time with its comprehensive system, that the PPBS's would serve the need, and that a region-wide installation at that time would be a waste of resources. In elaboration of the contention that PPBS's would serve the need, Frey told Barrett (and Clark told Crockett) that State would have full rights to see all PPBS submissions, analyze them and raise issues, set foreign policy objectives, and even call for alteration of the systems to encompass additional data. Frey and Clark envisioned a dialogue that would lead to the emergence of a comprehensive system over the next few years. With all of this possible, Frey said, the only remaining point of difference was a narrow and bureaucratic one—the Barrett staff's desire to continue going to the field to collect data.

Although, to the authors' knowledge, the Bureau's opposition was not formally communicated in writing, this rejection of Barrett's draft telegram constituted an open rupture between the two groups, climaxing the deterioration of relationships of the preceding several months. The State Department group felt that they were being told to scrap the products of nearly three years of effort, energy, and experience and to collaborate actively in their own undoing. Force was added to the blow by its timing. Preparations were virtually complete for the Latin American campaign. Executive assistants all over the world were prepared to come home for the conference in early March; many already had their temporary duty orders and their plane tickets.

NSAM 341

This chronicle about country programming in foreign affairs might conceivably have come to an end right there were it not for another development, proceeding from outside any of these agencies concerned, that was coming to a head at almost precisely the same time. This was a document, later to be issued as NSAM 341, that General Maxwell Taylor had prepared on behalf of the President. Taylor was a man of great influence in Washington, first as special adviser to President Kennedy, later as Chairman of the Joint Chiefs of Staff, and finally as Ambassador to South Vietnam. He and Attorney General Robert Kennedy were mainly responsible for the emphasis on problems of counter-insurgency in the Kennedy administration and for formation of the very high-level "Special Group for Counter-Insurgency," which Taylor chaired. When Taylor returned from Saigon in August 1965, he was asked by President Johnson to make a special review of all interdepartmental activities related to counter-insurgency.

Taylor conducted his study quietly, but it soon became clear that he was now interested in preventing insurgency as well as countering it; this led him to a concern for the problems of underdevelopment which provided the seedbed for insurgency in many countries of the world. In turn this led him to an interest in improving the coordination of U.S. activities and programs in these countries and, beyond that, to an interest in better management of all foreign affairs operations. His inquiries soon led him to the problem, so well revealed by EROP, of the lack of an effective interagency decision-making mechanism in Washington.

Taylor had set up task forces to probe four aspects of the problem: organization, resources, intelligence, and training. Crockett had had several sessions with Taylor on the question of foreign affairs leadership. Late in November 1965 Robert

Cox had arranged for Taylor to be briefed on CCPS by Barrett and Harr, who spent 90 minutes describing in detail the State Department programming efforts, highlighting the comprehensive approach, the relationship to policy objectives, the nature of the system and its goals, and the good and bad features of EROP. The General listened attentively, and his questions were pertinent. He had a good understanding of programming because of his Pentagon background, and it appeared to Barrett and Harr that his overall approach was congruent with that of the State Department programming group.

Toward the middle of January one of Barrett's staff members managed to see a copy of a draft Taylor had prepared. Since Taylor wanted action, he had decided not to write a long report to the President. Instead, he had prepared an action document for the President's signature, which took the form of a National Security Action Memorandum. Taylor's draft NSAM was tightly guarded and was to be circulated for review only at a very high level before submission to the President.

The draft started out by assigning "to the Secretary of State authority and responsibility for the overall direction, coordination and supervision of interdepartmental activities of the United States Government overseas." This was strong language. To effectuate this authority and responsibility, the draft next called for creation of a new and very high-level interagency group that was, in effect, to be successor to the "Special Group for Counter-Insurgency," but with a broader mandate. It was to be called the Senior Inter-Departmental Group (SIG).[2] The key concept intended by Taylor to make this new group a highly effective one, in contrast to

2. Regular members of the SIG were to be: the Under Secretary of State, the Deputy Secretary of Defense, the Administrator of AID, the Director of CIA, the Chairman of the Joint Chiefs of Staff, the Director of USIA, and the Special Assistant to the President for National Security Affairs. Representatives of other agencies responsible for specific matters to be considered would "attend on invitation by the Chairman."

previous interagency groups, was the creation of an "executive chairman," who would have authority to make decisions binding on the agencies represented unless overruled by appeal to the next higher authority. Since the executive chairman of SIG would be the Under Secretary of State, the next higher authority would be the Secretary of State, and beyond him, the President. Of course, Taylor expected that this decision power would not be used autocratically, but that its mere existence and occasional use would help to avoid the excessive tendency toward compromise that had weakened previous interagency committees.

SIG was to be echoed at the regional level by creation of five similarly constituted and representative Inter-Departmental Regional Groups (IRG's). The executive chairman of each would be the State Department Assistant Secretary in charge of the appropriate regional bureau. The appeal route from the IRG's was to be to the SIG. Finally, the draft mentioned the need for tools to assist these groups and made reference to a comprehensive programming system as such a tool.

It was not known then when the NSAM would be approved and announced (ultimately it was issued on March 4, 1966), but the knowledge that it was underway was a comfort to Barrett as he prepared for battle with his friends in the Bureau of the Budget. But a few days before Taylor's NSAM 341 was announced, another obstacle appeared. Barrett learned that the language calling for a programming system as a major tool of the SIG and the IRG's had been deleted. This had happened in a meeting in the office of U. Alexis Johnson, Deputy Under Secretary of State for Political Affairs, who was representing Secretary Rusk in clearance and approval of the language in the draft NSAM. Taylor and Henry Rowen of the Budget Bureau had been the other principals present. Rowen had proposed the deletion on the grounds that the mention of tools marred a document that dealt so importantly with policy and that discussion of programming was redundant anyway, since the President had already called for the establishment of PPBS's on virtually a government-wide basis. This had certainly been a plausible argument to two men who were not fully aware of the State-Bureau dispute and its implications for the very leadership role of the State Department that was the essence of NSAM 341. They agreed.

This episode illustrates how an event can have a quite different impact on different people, according to their perspective. Taylor does not recall the language change nor the meeting that produced it. For Taylor and Johnson, it was apparently a minor technical matter, having little to do with whether they were for or against programming. For Rowen, apparently, the language change was a tactical victory in the struggle with the State programming group. For Barrett and his staff, the change was a major disappointment.

Yet, the Barrett men were able to reason that the essential power of the NSAM was intact and promised to provide a much firmer base for the comprehensive system than before. However, even this seemed threatened when Frey, after discussions with Rowen, pressed an interpretation of the language change on Barrett. He maintained that the deletion occurred because of a conscious decision *not* to relate a comprehensive programming system to NSAM 341 and the SIG-IRG mechanisms. He warned that there would be "trouble" if Crockett and Barrett now tried to put their system under the umbrella of NSAM 341. Barrett took this as an ominous warning, but Frey later commented to the authors that he did not intend it that way: "I was trying to convey that there appeared to be a serious difference of interpretation of a decision which would lead to another dispute tangential to the real issues that divided us."

Some days later, Crockett was able to check with Under Secretary Johnson the view that the deletion represented a decision not to relate comprehensive programming to the NSAM. Johnson denied that this was so; some time later Taylor was to make his support of comprehensive programming very clear.

There is no doubt that at the time Rowen and Frey genuinely believed their interpretation was correct. Frey argued that it was incongruous to imagine high-level groups such as the SIG and the IRG's grappling with the intricacies of a programming system like CCPS or FAPS. Barrett agreed, saying that the high-level groups would deal only with the tough issues and alternative solutions surfaced by the system and related analyses by a systems staff. The real difference between the two men was over which approach was best suited for this purpose, the PPBS or the CCPS-FAPS.

Representatives of the Bureau also questioned the legality of the NSAM, in that it assigned sweeping powers to the Secretary of State seemingly in the face of authorities granted in numerous acts of Congress to the heads of various foreign affairs agencies. The response of those supporting the NSAM was twofold; they felt that: (1) the Secretary of State had more power in those same acts of Congress than was generally recognized, since much of the authority of other agency heads had been delegated by the Secretary to them; and (2) the main thrust was to generate administrative response to clear presidential intent, not to argue the technicalities of the laws. However, the Bureau's recommendation for a qualifying phrase was accepted and inserted in the first sentence of NSAM 341:[3]

> To assist the President in carrying out his responsibility in the conduct of Foreign Affairs, he has assigned to the Secretary of State authority and responsibility *to the full extent permitted by law* for the overall direction, coordination and supervision of interdepartmental activities of the United States Government overseas. [Emphasis added.]

Despite these modifications, NSAM 341 was to become—and remained throughout this story—the cornerstone for those

---

3. The text of NSAM 341, as it was published by the Department of State, is quoted in Appendix II.

who sought to build a comprehensive country programming and budgeting system under State Department leadership. Among other responsibilities, it directed the SIG to assure "a proper selectivity of the areas and issues to which the United States Government applies its resources." It directed that the Chairman of the SIG (the Under Secretary of State) be supported by a full-time staff, and authorized him to requisition additional staff members from the member agencies. Similar staffing arrangements were authorized for the chairmen of the IRG's (the regional Assistant Secretaries). And the IRG's were given somewhat more explicit authority with regard to plans and programs than the SIG:

> The regional Assistant Secretaries, in their capacities as Executive Chairmen of the IRGs, will ensure the adequacy of United States policy for the countries in their region and of the plans, programs, resources and performance for implementing that policy.

At Secretary Rusk's request, a reorganization of the regional bureaus of the State Department was appended to NSAM 341, although it was not mentioned in the text itself. For some years Rusk had been concerned about the need to upgrade the country desk officers. The addendum to NSAM 341 coined a new title, "Country Director," and elevated the desk officers to the rank and stature of office directors in the administrative hierarchy. Changes followed in four of the regional bureaus that in some ways resembled Crockett's reorganization of the administrative area almost a year earlier. Major changes were not necessary in the Latin American bureau since it had redesigned its structure and elevated its desk officers earlier when the State-AID merger had occurred.

In a statement to "my colleagues in the Department of State and abroad," released on the same day as NSAM 341, Secretary Rusk explained that the organizational changes were intended "to enable us to discharge our enlarged responsibilities efficiently."[4] Presumably, the Secretary could have appended to the NSAM instructions regarding a comprehensive programming approach on the same rationale. The idea had been thought of briefly in the Barrett shop, but the pace of events had moved too quickly. Momentarily disconcerted by Frey's strong views, the Barrett staff had lost the immediate opportunity to capitalize on NSAM 341.

Secretary Rusk's message to his colleagues went on to say:

> There can be no room for parochial viewpoints or petty bureaucratic "in-fighting." Each of us must recognize at all times we are, in a real sense, acting for and on behalf of the President, and through him, serving all the people of the United States.

CROCKETT AND ROSTOW PLAN A DEMARCHE

By the end of February 1966, those supporting comprehensive programming in the State Department felt that time was running out and that something had to be done to break the deadlock with the Bureau of the Budget. The convergence of three of the events described above—the failure to reach agreement on an EROP report, the Bureau's blocking of the FAPS mission in Latin America, and the modification and subsequent limiting interpretation of the NSAM that would be issued in a few days—presented a challenge they simply could not ignore. A favorable resolution would require elevating the issue to higher echelons in the State Department.

Crockett had been absent for a considerable time in his annual chore of escorting Congressman John Rooney, Chairman of the powerful appropriations subcommittee that handled the State Department, on a trip abroad. He nursed the hope that when he returned home things would be looking up, but he found them even worse than before. In Crock-

4. See Appendix III.

ett's absence, Rostow had been drawn into the fray. In a series of discussions with Rowen, Rostow had pressed hard for some sort of viable compromise to end the dispute and get on with the work. He had come out of these sessions convinced there was little hope for compromise.

All the elements of the argument were worked over again in these discussions. At no time did the Bureau leaders dispute the principle of State Department leadership, or of country level programming, or of eventual comprehensive programming. But Rostow came to feel strongly that the net effect of the Bureau's approach, in terms of tactics and timing, actually served to work against these principles. The Bureau's approach was well stated in a later comment by Clark to the authors:

In seeking first to build viable PPB systems in the agencies, we were not unaware of or antagonistic to the need to evolve a comprehensive, crosscutting system that would enhance decisions affecting the whole foreign affairs community. But such a system must come at the right time and be built upon the bedrock of operating agency systems.

The State Department people could disagree with this point of view, but could not deny that it was a reasonable and respectable one. However, a deeper problem bothered Rostow. This was his belief, developed mainly in his discussions with Rowen, that a major justification for the position of the Bureau leaders was their lack of faith that the State Department had the capacity to "take charge" and exert the kind of leadership that would be necessary.

This issue had been debated at a lower level, too. Originally skeptical themselves of State's capacity for the job, the Barrett staff had changed; it was now committed not only to its systems approach but to the State Department. Its members claimed that the performance of the young FSO's and of the field missions in the EROP exercise offered convincing evidence of ability to change and to "take charge." Further, they argued that the Bureau's approach was a self-fulfilling prophecy in that it would help guarantee that the Department and the Foreign Service would not change.

When he reached the conclusion that compromise was not possible, Rostow told Crockett that the only recourse was to escalate the deadlock to the Secretary of State. Barrett and Bonham supported this idea, since they were acutely aware of the time pressure if the Latin American plans were to be carried out. Barrett already had been forced to postpone the conference of 22 executive assistants that would launch the Latin American round. The conference had been reset to begin the morning of March 14 and to last for two and one-half days.

For a variety of reasons, Crockett would have preferred to continue to seek some sort of compromise. There could not have been a more unfortunate choice of bureaucratic opponents for him than the Bureau of the Budget. As the man ultimately responsible for the scope and character of State's budget, Crockett was supposed to solve problems with the Bureau, not raise them. Moreover, Crockett had searched for supporters of the CCPS over the previous year, and he had found very few aside from Rostow. He could imagine that Secretary Rusk might have the same experience if he were asked to intervene in the current imbroglio with the Bureau. But it was hard for Crockett to believe that the Secretary would take an active role in the matter. Crockett knew that Rusk had little time for management problems as such, and that he was particularly averse to bureaucratic squabbles. Further, Crockett was under extreme pressure on other fronts, including several very difficult and celebrated personnel cases and difficulties with some of his other major change efforts.

Although he preferred compromise for all these reasons, Crockett was not sure it could be achieved. Therefore, he did not oppose the desire of Rostow, Barrett, and Bonham to take the problem to Secretary Rusk. On the day that NSAM 341 was issued (Friday, March 4), these four agreed to press ahead with a memorandum to Rusk that would set forth the whole situation. They held a series of meetings on Saturday and Sunday, March 5 and 6, in Crockett's large office on the seventh floor of the State Department. Barrett and Bonham had prepared a basic draft, but Rostow played the leading role in shaping the final product. As the group discussed the draft, Rostow would think whole paragraphs out loud while Bonham scribbled furiously.

The final draft bore the trenchant Rostow imprint. It began by quickly reviewing the NPP and NSAM 341 background and then stated:[5]

> We have from the beginning recognized that we must examine the actual use of resources in each country and region before we can be confident that our efforts overseas are being sensitively related to established policies, objectives, and courses of action. For this reason we have been working for three years on a programming system that will display in a common language present and proposed uses of all U.S. resources in relation to official objectives and purposes.

It then pointed out that experimentation in 32 countries and the EROP exercise had led to "further simplifications and improvements which we now believe give us a workable system."

Now, the draft said, two problems confronted the Department:

> The first is the negative reaction to these continued efforts expressed to a greater or lesser extent by working levels in all the foreign affairs agencies except the Department of Defense. The second is a similar but much stronger response from the working level of the Bureau of the Budget.

5. The completed draft is reproduced in Appendix IV.

The views of the other agencies were understandable, the draft said, but the issue had been settled by NSAM 341, which "both establishes the responsibilities of the Secretary of State and provides a forum for resolving interagency issues." But, it continued, the Bureau held that the PPBS's "being installed by all agencies under Bureau of the Budget Circular 66-3 are sufficient for the President's and the Department's purposes, and that the Department of State should cease its efforts to develop a comprehensive country and regionally-based system."

The basic philosophy of the group was captured in another paragraph of the draft:

> Ironically, the Budget Bureau's views represent a movement away from the tested and successful Pentagon approach that has placed the national defense above service interests and systematically arrayed service programs against specific national defense objectives. It is the essence of modern programming that the use of resources be related to objectives and purposes, not to agency functions.

The memorandum then went on to discuss at length the specific points at issue between the Bureau and State—the former's dislike of NPP's for programming purposes, criticisms of CCPS-FAPS, belief that foreign affairs programs did not compete for resource allocations, and criticisms of EROP. The essence was then presented:

> In spite of these differences, we believe that we must maintain the closest possible cooperation with the Bureau of the Budget to insure that we achieve a maximum of reciprocal benefits and a convergence between the two systems. In fact, our system can provide each agency PPBS with such data as may be desired due to the built-in flexibility of the computer program.
>
> To summarize: we have invested a considerable effort in the development of integrated planning and programming systems

covering the entire foreign affairs spectrum, based, as a Department of State system must be, on country and regional objectives. These systems are now ready for full application. The prospect of such action is being opposed in some quarters on essentially bureaucratic grounds.

Our response is that we have learned much in the past three years. We know we don't have all the answers to an evolving and complex problem for which there is no precise precedent. We are convinced that the resolute carrying forward of the effort begun three years ago is a vital link in fulfilling your responsibilities under NSAM 341. We are equally convinced that an abandonment of these efforts now will go far toward gutting the essential purposes of that document.

The memorandum concluded by calling for the Secretary's endorsement of the comprehensive systems approach and the Latin American round: "We believe the lead time permitting a review of the FY-1968 budget cycle from the Latin American region requires your decision by March 11, 1966."

Because of the time pressure, Rostow and Crockett decided to hand-carry the memorandum to Rusk and give him a personal briefing on its contents. The draft was typed in final form on Monday, March 7, and a meeting with Rusk was set for 3:30 P.M. But at three the French Ambassador delivered President De Gaulle's ultimatum on the withdrawal of NATO headquarters from France, so the meeting was postponed until 11 the following morning. Rostow was leaving that afternoon for a conference in Panama, which, with associated visits, would keep him out of the country for ten days. When the 11 A.M. meeting was also postponed, Crockett suggested that Rostow, who had a closer personal relationship with Rusk than he, try to see the Secretary for a few minutes before leaving for the airport. Rostow did this successfully and managed to give the Secretary a brief indication of the situation. He also left a copy of the memorandum on the Secretary's desk. The original was still with Crockett, who had not yet signed it. Just before taking off on his trip, Rostow telephoned Crockett and reported that Rusk had listened with interest, but that there had not been enough time to press for any resolution. He urged Crockett to follow through vigorously.

THE BELL MEETING

That Tuesday afternoon at 5 o'clock Crockett had an appointment with David Bell, Administrator of AID, a post equivalent in rank to Under Secretary of State. Bell's office was a high-ceilinged room in the old section of the State Department Building that had formerly been the office of Under Secretaries of State.

The purpose of the meeting, which had been set up some days earlier, was to discuss Bell's objections to the draft telegram regarding the proposed Latin American round of FAPS. Crockett took Barrett and Harr with him. Also present were William O. Hall, a career FSO who was serving in the position in AID that was counterpart to Crockett's role in State; and Gustav Rainis, who was in charge of AID's PPBS effort.

Crockett had a faint hope of somehow enlisting Bell and AID to the cause of comprehensive programming in foreign affairs. He and Barrett and others had always recognized the importance of getting AID solidly involved in any comprehensive effort because of the magnitude of its resources and programs around the world. The hope was faint because a gulf between State and AID had always existed, to a greater or lesser degree, regardless of whether AID was technically a part of the State Department (as was currently the case) or entirely separate from it. The gulf was not the product of anyone's evil design, but rather stemmed in complex ways from differences in personnel groups, resource levels, perspectives, and the economic bias of AID compared to the political bias of State.

It was therefore no surprise for Crockett, although a minor disappointment, to find himself listening to Bell's cordial explanation of why the State Department comprehensive programming effort should be terminated. Bell said he would not fight Crockett on the issue of the FAPS Latin American round in the sense of going to Secretary Rusk and actively opposing it. But, he said, if Rusk asked his opinion, he would tell him what he honestly thought.

Most of Bell's views paralleled those held by the Budget Bureau staff. He felt the State Department group had not sufficiently involved people of the other foreign affairs agencies in their development work. He said EROP had not helped him in making decisions, although he confessed frankly that he had never studied CCPS nor any of the EROP submissions in any detailed way. He said that CCPS-FAPS, as a programming system, was not analytical enough, in contrast to the PPBS thrust in general and the AID-PPBS effort in particular, in which Bell obviously was taking a good deal of interest. He said he could not support a dual systems approach because it would simply mean a double work load on the field staffs, which should not be necessary. And, since the President himself had ordered PPBS, the State Department group should recognize that time had passed its efforts by and that it should support the PPBS efforts instead of devoting all its resources and energy to FAPS.

These comments brought forth something of an impassioned response from the State Department group. Among other points, they asserted that there had been a long history of efforts to involve AID in the CCPS development, that most of them had been met with a bureaucratic cold shoulder, and that instead of forgetting about analysis, the State effort was trying to lay a sound foundation for it.

Bell conceded some of the points and expressed an understanding of how the State Department group felt, having "toiled in the vineyard" for three years and being asked now to step aside. At this point, the meeting broke up as Crockett left to take a telephone call. Barrett and Harr went home, but Crockett, having seen the germ of a negotiating possi-

bility, returned to Bell's office. After saying that Bell's decla-
ration that he would not fight the comprehensive effort directly was not good enough, Crockett asked what it would
take to get Bell and AID to support the State Department's
approach. Bell gave this serious thought for a moment and
then responded with several conditions. The State Department should (1) not install FAPS in any new countries, but
instead work with countries that had already had some experience; (2) emphasize in future work the improvement of
analyses of problems and alternative solutions; (3) form an
interagency working group to make sure that the interests
of all the agencies were fully considered in the development
effort; and (4) form a high-level advisory group, drawn from
both inside and outside the government, to judge progress of
the programming development effort.

Crockett asked Bell if he would agree to serve on such a
committee, and Bell said that he would. Crockett expressed
interest in Bell's conditions, and the conversation ended on a
positive note.

Later that evening Crockett telephoned Barrett to tell him
about the later conversation with Bell. It had been clear for
some time, though never overtly, that AID, for its own reasons, had emerged as the major ally of the Budget Bureau in
opposing State's comprehensive approach. Barrett and Crockett now agreed that if AID lined up with State under the conditions proposed by Bell, the Bureau of the Budget would
have almost no choice but to discontinue its flat opposition.
An interesting thought occurred to the two men. Bell may
have had the 13 EROP countries in mind when he had set
as a condition that there be no new installations, but the way
he had expressed it left the door open for activity in all 32
countries in which CCPS had been installed.

Crockett said that the next step was to follow through
quickly with the Bureau, and he told Barrett to stand by for
a meeting there late the following morning. Crockett had
already been invited by Roger Jones to come over to the

Bureau to discuss the deadlock between the agencies. Jones had been serving as special adviser to the Director of the Budget ever since he had left the position now held by Crockett. Jones had recently been asked by Director Charles Schultze to look into the "hassle" between State and the Bureau.

"BLACK WEDNESDAY"

The next morning, Wednesday, March 9, Barrett assembled his staff and described the Bell meeting and his telephone conversation with Crockett. He pointed out that the agreement would mean abandoning the regional approach in Latin America for the present cycle at least, but that it might not be too big a price to pay if it meant that State would be free to continue developing the comprehensive system in the 32 CCPS countries.

The Barrett staff often recorded its meetings on tape. From the tape of this particular meeting it is clear that the staff was not as sanguine about the news as was Barrett. All were "charged up" for the Latin American round, and most were scheduled for one or more field trips. Passports and inoculations had been obtained, itineraries were set, tickets were purchased, wives were on notice, and the executive assistants were due in from the field in a few days for the conference that was to begin the following Monday morning. More important than these logistics, there was general agreement that the regional approach would very likely make a considerable difference in terms of the system's tangible usefulness to decision-makers, especially in view of the regional mechanisms provided by NSAM 341. Bonham expressed the doubts of the staff, adding that he "smelled a large mouse somewhere" in the current negotiations.

Barrett agreed with some of the reservations, but said that all that could be done now was to wait and see what happened. Referring to the Bell meeting, he added: "The least you can say is that Crockett came up to bat in the last half of the ninth inning with two men out and the bases loaded, and he at least hit a single."

Barrett then went to Roger Jones's office in the Budget Bureau for the 11:30 meeting. This meeting was *not* tape-recorded, an unfortunate circumstance since it was to have a powerful emotional impact.

When Barrett arrived in Jones's office, he became aware that Crockett, Jones, Clark, and Frey had already had a pre-meeting of some sort. Also in attendance at the main meeting were Hall and Rainis of AID and William Sherman, a new staff aide to Crockett.

Crockett started off by saying that he thought the group ought to keep the discussion as close as possible to points on which all could agree. He talked for a while about some higher-level goals that were not contentious—the concept of programming, the importance of both the agency and comprehensive views, the President's desires. There was some discussion of the question of how to relate NPP's to a programming system, and when it became clear that this was not an area of agreement, it was set aside. There was then discussion of several models of cooperation between State and the Bureau. One idea that was suggested was to select three countries where a fair amount of PPBS action was to occur, with the Barrett staff helping the Bureau to pull the PPBS submissions together for a near-comprehensive view. It was suggested that at the same time the Barrett staff could select three other countries in which FAPS could be tested independently of any PPB systems.

Crockett then asked Barrett to comment on the three-country model. Barrett had become increasingly uncomfortable. From the way Crockett spoke, Barrett got the impression that everything had been settled in the "pre-meeting" and that games were now being played. He feared that Crockett had decided to accept the Bell conditions and to abandon the memorandum to Secretary Rusk, without making that decision clear to him (Barrett) before the meeting. But if so,

Crockett was not negotiating with anywhere near the strength made possible by the Bell conditions. The talk of a three-country experiment struck Barrett as a ridiculous concession in contrast to the relatively free hand State would have in as many as 32 CCPS countries under a liberal interpretation of the conditions suggested by Bell.

Barrett now felt completely alone. Whatever psychological set was operative in the meeting, Barrett felt that his trusted friend and leader had deserted him at the crucial moment. He uttered none of these thoughts, but instead responded to Crockett's query in a curt and minimal way, and the tenor of the meeting became brittle. The conversation labored on with further talk about forming an interagency group, forming an advisory group, and relieving State of its PPBS requirement.

The notion that Crockett had given almost everything away was reinforced for Barrett when, after the meeting, Jones and Frey in a genuine way offered some sympathy in view of the hard work and tough fight that Barrett and his staff had put up. Barrett returned to his office in a bitter and defeated mood. The morale of his staff was fragile, to say the least, with nerves generally at the snapping point. In this milieu Barrett's mood was contagious, and in a matter of minutes it spread throughout the entire staff. Someone dubbed March 9, 1966, as "Black Wednesday," and the name stuck among the staff. Whatever the facts of the matter, most of the staff now believed that Crockett had let them down. A few disputed this view and tried to stem the growing sense of failure. The strength of this reaction was partly explained by the degree to which Barrett and his staff depended on the nearly charismatic warmth and support of Crockett. When that support suddenly seemed uncertain to them, they felt severely threatened.

For his part, Crockett was mystified by the reaction. He saw the Wednesday meeting as a logical continuation of the Bell meeting the day before, and felt that nothing had been given away as yet, that negotiations were still to be carried on. (In interviews with four other participants in the meetings, two thought that Crockett had surrendered, and two did not believe this and saw the meeting as merely another step in a pattern of negotiations.)

Certainly, part of the trouble was that Crockett and Barrett had differently interpreted the Bell meeting and their subsequent telephone conversation, and neither one realized it until it was too late. Crockett felt that the Bell conditions were acceptable, and thought that Barrett understood this. The immediate need was to make sure the Bureau of the Budget would go along; and to ensure this, he felt, one was best advised to start out with the minimal areas of agreement and build from there. The Latin American round had been given away in the Bell meeting, not in the Bureau's meeting. Barrett had viewed the latter meeting as a test, but had felt that options would be preserved and that the Latin American round and the memorandum to Rusk were not yet dead. Now he felt that the momentum was completely lost, that the State Department group had no more bargaining power. He felt the meeting had been merely a negotiation about what crumbs left on the table should be given to his team.

Barrett had not realized how far and how fast Crockett had moved for compromise. On the other hand, Crockett feared that Barrett and his staff would rather gamble for glory or total defeat, risking everything in a bureaucratic confrontation. As Crockett later commented to the authors: "I really believed we had saved ourselves for another day. . . . My whole strategy was one of compromise and accommodation so long as the basic principles of what we were striving for could be retained."

However, the State and Bureau groups were to continue to have difficulty agreeing about just what those basic principles were. This was perhaps best illustrated by the way in which the two groups attempted to communicate with each other on paper following the "Black Wednesday" meeting. First, the Bureau staff attempted to set forth its sense of what conclusions had been reached at the meeting in terms of the objectives of a foreign affairs programming system:

General Objectives

1. A single programming system in the foreign affairs area will be designed to meet the needs of the President, the Secretary of State, and agency heads within the framework of the overall Planning-Programming-Budgeting (PPB) System.

2. The purpose of the system is to improve resource allocation in the foreign affairs area. It must therefore meet the needs of the officials responsible for making such decisions, i.e., the Secretary, the regional Assistant Secretaries, agency heads, as well as the Ambassadors.

3. The Secretary of State will provide leadership in developing the system, within general PPBS instructions. Budget Bureau staff will assist and support this effort.

4. Development of the system will involve full participation of all foreign affairs agencies so that it will effectively meet agency management and resource allocation needs.

5. The development of the foreign affairs programming system will be evolutionary in character, i.e., with respect to statements of objectives, program elements, meaningful measure of input and output, etc. However, the foreign affairs programming system will be based upon program and financial data provided by evolving PPB agency systems. The Bureau's efforts to improve existing agency PPB systems will therefore continue, with appropriate participation by State staff.

6. From the point of view of the field mission, there should be only one programming system and process. Duplication of data collection and review and analysis will be avoided.

To Barrett and his men, this was more of the same. They felt that it was internally contradictory, that objectives 5 and

6 would serve to negate objective 1. They countered with a document setting forth the "minimum requirements of the Department of State for a foreign affairs programming system":

First, the system must be capable of relating resources of the mission, no matter of which agency, to national objectives expressed in National Policy Papers or equivalent authoritative policy documents.

Second, the system must be capable of expressing in a common language the available resources of all agencies operating abroad so that meaningful comparisons are possible within and among missions.

Third, the system must provide information on all activities of the mission at the same point in time each year, so that comparisons may be made, and early enough in the year, so that there will be an improved opportunity for an Ambassador's judgments on his total mission program to influence decisions made in Washington for the next fiscal year.

Fourth, in addition to relating to policy objectives, the program data of the system must be capable of conversion into budgetary terms so that the cycle will be completed.

Fifth, the program data of the system must be organized in a way that facilitates analysis of alternative program choices in terms of anticipated costs and expected benefits.

Sixth, the system must be capable of generating systematic progress information so that policy and program choices can be made in the light of maximum knowledge of previous choices and resulting progress.

Seventh, the system must be sophisticated enough to meet these requirements and yet must avoid redundancy and detail to the maximum extent possible so that benefits will outweigh the effort by a considerable margin.

To the Bureau staff, this was more of the same. They felt that it was narrow, biased toward the overseas Mission, and gave little attention to the requirements of the agencies.

AFTERMATH

Whatever one might regard as the cause, the effect of the "Black Wednesday" meeting was one of demoralization of the State Department programming team. If there was any possibility of regrouping and going forward with the memorandum to Rusk, it was lost in the confusion that followed the meeting, in the sagging morale of the staff, in the communication gap that opened up between Crockett and Barrett for some days. (The memorandum was never officially sent.) Those were crucial days, since March 11 had been set as the deadline for receiving authorization for the Latin American round. After the "Black Wednesday" meeting, the Barrett staff cancelled all the preparations and notified the Latin American bureau and the field posts that the plans had been called off.

Ironically, while the Latin American plans were being cancelled, a long telegram came in from Panama, to Crockett from Rostow, containing more ideas and words of reinforcement for Crockett in the expected demarche on Secretary Rusk. When Rostow returned to Washington a week later, he found out what had happened and expressed his disappointment. He was no longer to be a factor in support of comprehensive programming, either in the State Department or in the White House, where he was to be transferred later in the year. However, his successor, Henry D. Owen, maintained interest in the subject, as did several members of the Policy Planning Council.

There was still the problem of the conference of executive assistants, scheduled for March 14, 15, and 16. Those responsible for the agenda were near desperation, since any rationale for briefing and planning sessions was gone. All that was now scheduled was an opening address by Crockett and brief presentations on the various PPBS efforts by representatives of AID, USIA, the Peace Corps, the Budget Bureau, Defense, and the State Department (Bushnell). Some felt the meeting should be called off, but Barrett overruled this, pointing out that some executive assistants from distant posts were already on their way. In any event, he said, they should be enabled to learn what was really going on in a way that could never be communicated by impersonal written means.

Thus it was that the group met at the Tidewater Inn in Easton, Maryland, with only enough agenda to cover the first day. The Barrett staff, all the executive assistants, and the representatives of the other agencies made up a group of more than 50 persons. On the afternoon of the second day Barrett gave as thorough an account as he could of what had happened over the previous few weeks. Following this, the executive assistants themselves took over the meeting, since no agenda remained. They divided into two groups (representing the EROP and non-EROP Missions), caucused for several hours, and reported back to the total group. Fred Fischer from Bonn represented the EROP Missions, and Dean Howells from New Delhi represented the non-EROP Missions.

There was a marked and interesting difference in the viewpoints of the two groups. Despite all the troubles associated with EROP, it was clear that in the EROP Missions the executive assistants were happier and busier, and Mission personnel generally were reported to be more receptive to moving ahead with comprehensive programming. The most obvious explanation for this was that there had been a beginning, middle, and (for the field posts at least) an end to EROP, and that the EROP Missions had been heard in Washington, whereas the non-EROP Missions seemed condemned to a state of drifting and unattached experimentation.

This same reason probably explains why it was difficult for the Barrett staff, at the conference and afterwards, to generate much enthusiasm for the kinds of cooperative models that had been discussed at the "Black Wednesday" meeting—they seemed like more of the past, with no real promise for a breakthrough. For weeks after the conference, the Barrett staff was to spend much of its time on half-hearted efforts to plan an activity for the current budgetary cycle around one of the models—ranging from an intensive experience in one country with full emphasis on program analysis to the joint three-country model discussed at the "Black Wednesday" meeting. None of these was to occur.

The Easton meeting was nearly a post-mortem. EROP, however one felt about it, was history; it had died; not even an epitaph remained. The Latin American regional test, the reason for the Easton meeting, was cancelled before it had begun. NSAM 341, then only ten days old, seemed already ineffective, at least to the State programming group. The approach to Secretary Rusk had not been pressed, and there was estrangement among the leaders for programming within the Department of State. In the face of opposition from the Bureau of the Budget, AID, and others, including some within the State Department, few had risen to defend or support the program. CCPS had become FAPS, but the critics regarded it as the same old "rose."

But the "true believers" had one remaining arrow in their quiver, and they were not yet prepared to give up. That arrow came to be known as the Hitch Committee.

IV

The Hitch Committee
(March 1966-October 1966)

BEGINNINGS

IT WILL BE RECALLED that David Bell, in his meeting with Crockett and others, had suggested creation of a high-level committee of experts to study the problems of programming and budgeting in foreign affairs and to advise the Secretary of State as to a course of action. After the debacle of "Black Wednesday," the proposal was picked up quickly, and it provided a basis whereby Crockett and Barrett were able to bandage their wounds and rejoin forces.

The idea was familiar. Barrett had created an advisory committee early in the game, in the fall of 1963, but after two meetings it had been allowed to expire as the development work on the CCPS speeded up. In the later months of EROP, when the Bureau of the Budget had received its PPBS mandate and had grown cool to the State Department programming effort, several members of the Barrett staff had urged a new and higher-level advisory committee. They were confident that an independent group of experts in programming and management could not fail to come down on their side of the bureaucratic deadlock with the Bureau. Barrett had rejected the idea, believing the battle could yet be won without the six- to twelve-month delay of convening a high-level study committee. Now, of course, he felt that the battle had been lost in the "Black Wednesday" affair, and that such a committee offered the only hope of a comeback. Since the initiative had been lost for the current budget cycle, there would be six months of delay in any event, time enough for a committee to resuscitate his comprehensive approach for the next cycle.

To Crockett, the committee idea appeared the best solution to a nearly impossible situation. He felt that the limits of his own power had been reached and that he could not afford to escalate the struggle with the Budget Bureau to Secretary Rusk. If, therefore, new auspices were needed to involve the Secretary and Under Secretary in making choices about programming in foreign affairs, a new high-level advisory group might very well provide just the auspices needed.

Thus it was that Bell's proposal led to the creation of what would become known as the Hitch Committee. Clark and Frey had been responsive to the advisory committee idea during the "Black Wednesday" meeting, since they had won their major objective of calling off Barrett's Latin American plans. At the time they did not realize that State would be able to act so quickly in bringing the committee idea to life, nor that such an influential figure as Charles J. Hitch would be involved. Clark and Frey later made an unsuccessful effort to get the Hitch Committee idea dropped, proposing instead that State make use of an already existing advisory committee that Rowen had created for PPBS on a government-wide basis. But both Clark and Frey had much confidence in Hitch's judgment.

Once the idea of forming a study committee was planted, Hitch's name occurred to a number of people immediately. One reason was his preeminent reputation in the programming and systems fields. Another reason was that Hitch might be available. He had left the Pentagon the previous summer to become administrative vice-president of the University of California. In fact, John Golden, the deputy head of CISR, had already succeeded in contracting for some of the limited

148 *Programming Systems and Foreign Affairs Leadership*

time that Hitch had available for consultation. This was done by means of a contract initiated by CISR between the Department of State and the Stanford Research Institute (SRI), one of the country's largest nonprofit research organizations, located in Menlo Park, California. Golden had started developing this contractual relationship the previous fall in negotiations with Stewart Blake, head of the Management and Social Systems Group in SRI. Blake had previously made an arrangement to use some of Hitch's consulting time on SRI systems projects.

Golden had developed the outlines of a modest project in conversations with Blake and some of his assistants in SRI. The project involved preliminary studies by SRI that were supposed to lead to plans and proposals for advanced systems design in the next generation of FAPS, but a central hope behind the arrangement was that Hitch might be available for direct personal consultation with Rusk. Golden believed that a major weakness of the CCPS-FAPS effort had been inadequate involvement of the Secretary and other top executives of the Department, and the failure to find an effective channel of communication to the Secretary on the subject of programming. Golden reasoned that if anyone could be effective with the top level in State, it would be Hitch. His hope was that Hitch would come to Washington on several occasions to discuss programming with the Secretary and perhaps hold a seminar-type discussion with a group of top executives of the Department. This approach had the support of Crockett and Barrett, and this is why a small amount of funds was allocated for the SRI contract, one of the few instances in the brief existence of CISR when Ball and Golden were able to obtain any money.

The contract was concluded in February, but no work had started. Its existence was regarded as a fortuitous circumstance a month later when the idea for a high-level committee emerged. Barrett immediately decided to change and broaden the SRI arrangement with a view to making Hitch the chairman of the committee that was to be brought into existence. Shortly after the "Black Wednesday" meeting, Barrett became aware that Ball and Golden were scheduled for a trip to the West Coast, numbering among their items of business a meeting with the SRI people and Hitch on March 14, the same day that the conference of executive assistants began at Easton, Maryland. Since Hitch knew little of the background, Barrett decided to send Harr with Ball and Golden for the purpose of giving Hitch a full briefing. The three State Department men met in Berkeley with Hitch, Blake, and William Breswick (the latter two of SRI), and for two hours Harr described in detail the history of CCPS, EROP, FAPS, PPBS, NSAM 341, and the State-Budget Bureau deadlock. Hitch listened thoughtfully. A soft-spoken, reflective man, he pronounced no judgments, but it was clear that he was interested. He said he might not have done the job the same way but that the changes from CCPS to FAPS seemed on the right track, the operation had some momentum which should not be lost, and it provided a good beginning toward achieving a comprehensive data base in foreign affairs.

There was no discussion of the committee idea other than the description of its genesis. All agreed that the next step was for Hitch to come to Washington for an interview with Rusk. Several possible dates in April were discussed, and Harr returned to Washington to convey the news to Crockett and Barrett. Crockett thereupon wrote a memorandum to Rusk recommending that the Secretary consider forming a high-level committee to advise him on programming, and stating that a tentative agreement to this effect had been reached with the Budget Bureau in connection with the abandoning of State's Latin American plans. He proposed Hitch as chairman and recommended that the Secretary see Hitch during the latter's visit to Washington in April.

Hitch's two-day visit to the Department on April 4 and 5 began with a dinner given by Crockett at which Lincoln Gordon, Assistant Secretary for the Latin American bureau of

State, was present. The dinner went particularly well; Hitch and Gordon were old friends and had been at Oxford at the same time. The following morning, Hitch met with Secretary Rusk for 45 minutes, and this meeting also began in an old-school-tie atmosphere. Rusk had also attended Oxford in the early 1930's. Also at the meeting were Ambassador Llewellyn Thompson, John Golden, Stewart Blake, and a young White House fellow. Halfway through the meeting, Under Secretary Ball joined the group.

Rusk told Hitch that he felt a programming system was needed in foreign affairs, but that he wanted the best advice he could get on how to go about developing a viable design. There was some discussion of the committee idea, but no decision on the subject was reached at that meeting.

Hitch then attended a luncheon hosted by George Ball at which all the Assistant Secretaries were present. Later that afternoon, he joined Blake in addressing a meeting convened by Barrett which was in effect an enlarged version of the working-level interagency committee on programming organized by Barrett as one of the points of agreement in the "Black Wednesday" meeting. At all three appearances—the meeting with the Secretary, the luncheon, and the interagency meeting—Hitch stressed several points:

that planning, programming, and budgeting are separable but related activities and are best brought together in a comprehensive system;

that quantification could be useful in foreign affairs as in Defense, but not applicable to all kinds of decisions;

that the definition of appropriate categories for foreign affairs was a most important next step, there being no simple counterpart to Defense Department weapons systems.

Gerald Bushnell, who was responsible for the State Department PPBS, asked Hitch what sort of advice he would give for developing a PPBS for an agency like State, which had few operations of its own but which supplied policy guidance and administrative services to operational agencies. Hitch replied that if Bushnell were talking about a system for State's $400 million or so of annual budget, then that was not a very interesting question; but if he were talking about the $5 billion plus for the whole foreign affairs community, that was interesting.

Somewhat puzzled by the Budget Bureau's position, Hitch found an opportunity during his Washington visit to have a brief chat with Rowen. When Hitch returned to Berkeley, he telephoned Crockett to express the view that a committee might not be necessary. He felt that the bureaucratic deadlock between State and the Bureau was ridiculous, that it ought to be possible to work out an understanding with Rowen, and that State should press ahead with its plans. Crockett made the case for a committee, emphasizing mainly its potential value as a communications channel to the Secretary. In any case, the opportunity for action during the current programming cycle was gone, so there was no real reason not to form a committee.

Crockett received the impression that Hitch would go along with the committee idea, but that it would be up to the State Department to take the initiative in setting it up in a way that would make it possible for Hitch to participate, given his time constraints. Subsequently Hitch formally agreed to chair a committee. The SRI contract was modified to cover two main functions: (1) provision of secretarial and other services to Hitch and the Committee, including preparation of documents for the meetings, and an historical analysis of State Department efforts to date; and (2) working with the Barrett staff in preliminary design of program elements and analytical models for a Foreign Affairs Programming System. In addition to Blake and Breswick, the SRI group included Lyn Johnson, Ernest Lehman, Seymour Colman, and other members of SRI's Washington staff.

FORMATION AND MEMBERSHIP

The acceptance by Hitch of the Secretary's request that he lead an advisory group was crucial; and his participation was perhaps more significant than that of all the other members of the group together. In fact, the initial suggestions for the rest of the Hitch Committee, as it was known—the official designation was Advisory Group on Foreign Affairs Planning, Programming, and Budgeting—were made by Barrett and his group. Their recommendations were discussed with Hitch and a final list was approved by him and then forwarded to the Secretary. On June 7, 1966, in the absence of Secretary Rusk, Acting Secretary George Ball signed letters, also drafted in Barrett's office, to each prospective member inviting him to serve and setting the date of the first meeting less than a week later on June 13. All accepted.

On the same day, an airgram from the State Department to all diplomatic and consular posts abroad announced the arrangements that had been made for the study and vigorously endorsed a foreign affairs programming system. The bullish tone of the airgram was not surprising, since it had been drafted in Barrett's office. It was signed, as are all such formal communications, by the top-ranking officer of the Department then present, in this case, Under Secretary George Ball. In effect, this airgram was another round in the "war of words" that had been going on between the Barrett staff and the Bureau of the Budget ever since their unsuccessful attempt to draft a final report on the EROP exercise.

The airgram was the firmest and most affirmative statement on the subject from the top of the Department up to that time. It referred to the background of the problem—the earlier experimental efforts by the Department, NSAM 341, and the agency-based PPBS:

Accordingly, the Department intends to take further steps during this year to improve the capabilities of the foreign affairs community in this field. The other foreign affairs agencies and the Bureau of the Budget will participate fully and actively in this effort. The first step will be to define the requirements for a foreign affairs programming system and its relationship to the planning-programming-budgeting systems being developed in each agency. . . . The second step will be to develop the system and put it into operation at the earliest practicable date. To assist in these tasks, the Secretary is establishing an advisory group on foreign affairs planning-programming-budgeting.

The designation of Hitch, but not the other members, was announced, as was the relationship with the Stanford Research Institute. In addition, the message stated that Crockett would establish an interagency group to advise in the development and implementation of the system.

The airgram was emphatic and positive about the future. Following development of the system "it will be installed region-by-region. . . . We will start with Latin America and follow with Africa in view of the interest and request of Assistant Secretaries Gordon and Palmer. We hope to proceed in Latin America . . . for fiscal year 1969." The airgram closed by asking each Mission chief to discuss its contents with his staff and the local representatives of all other agencies.

At the same time, a letter to much the same effect was sent to the heads of various departments and agencies in Washington. It was titled "Overall Programming System for Foreign Affairs Operations of the U.S. Government," and announced the establishment of a high-level interagency group.

The selection of members of the Hitch Committee was guided by a number of considerations: high-level representation of the key agencies; prestige and authority within the government and particularly among those agencies most concerned with the foreign affairs problem; outsiders who would lend objectivity and academic standing; persons from a variety of fields who would look upon the problem with differing but relevant perspectives, such as those of the Foreign Service, the PPBS economists, the social psychologists interested in the problems of organizational change, and the political scientists interested in foreign affairs administration. The result was an unusually mixed array of careerists, in-and-outers, scholars, and researchers, most of whom had never met one another. Only a very few had ever had more than a passing acquaintance with problems of foreign affairs programming and budgeting. In addition to Hitch, the initial members included:

1. Chris Argyris, professor and chairman of the Department of Administrative Sciences, Yale University, and author of a number of books and studies having to do with personality and organization. Argyris had for some time been working with the Barrett group in the conduct of its T-Group program for Foreign Service and other State Department officials. He was later to write a pamphlet, published by the Department's Center for International Systems Research, on "Some Causes of Organizational Ineffectiveness within the Department of State," provocative and so critical of the "living system" of the Foreign Service as to raise a considerable stir in the Department and among its critics and defenders outside.

2. David E. Bell, then Administrator of AID, earlier the Director of the Bureau of the Budget. Bell resigned during the period the Committee was active to become vice-president of the Ford Foundation, but continued with the Committee and signed its report.

3. Stewart Blake, of the Stanford Research Institute, who was directing the Institute's activities in pursuance of its contract with the State Department on programming. The Institute provided staff assistance to the Hitch Committee throughout its existence and conducted some studies of the programming problem

which are noted later. Blake had previously been associated with the PPBS effort in the Defense Department.

4. Ellsworth Bunker, businessman and noncareer ambassador in both Republican and Democratic administrations. Bunker was then U.S. Ambassador to the Dominican Republic, and, at the time of this writing, is Ambassador to South Vietnam.

5. John Diebold, president of the Diebold Group, an expert and entrepreneur in systems development and the use of computers. Diebold subsequently published an article in *Foreign Affairs* on "Computers, Program Management and Foreign Affairs" (October 1966, pp. 125-34).

6. Alain C. Enthoven, Assistant Secretary of Defense (Systems Analysis), a long-time associate of Hitch at the RAND Corporation and in the Defense Department. (Enthoven did not actively participate in the work of the Committee.)

7. Rensis Likert, professor and director of the Institute for Social Research, University of Michigan, for a long time a principal leader in survey research and group dynamics and author of a number of works of which *New Patterns of Management* (New York: McGraw-Hill, 1961) was perhaps most relevant. Likert and members of his staff were at the time engaged in a study of organizational change and its effects in the administrative area of the State Department.

8. Livingston T. Merchant, one of a handful of career ambassadors who had recently retired, who was serving in a succession of consultative capacities. (Merchant did not participate actively in the Committee and did not sign its report.)

9. Frederick C. Mosher, professor of Political Science, University of California, Berkeley.

10. Henry Rowen, Assistant Director of the Bureau of the Budget and at that time the principal spokesman and leader of the PPBS effort in Washington. Rowen had previously been associated with Hitch in the RAND Corporation and in the Defense Department. Before the close of this case he resigned to become president of the RAND Corporation.

The Committee thus initially numbered eleven members, two of whom (Enthoven and Merchant), were inactive. However, between the Committee's first and second meetings Hitch initiated an invitation to General Maxwell Taylor to join the group.[1] Hitch was motivated by what he regarded as a clear connection between NSAM 341, of which General Taylor had been principal author, and the problem of the Committee. The General agreed to serve, and he contributed forcefully in the second meeting of the Committee. In addition, Dr. Gustav Rainis, Assistant Administrator of AID for Program, participated in the first meeting in place of AID Administrator Bell. And Fisher Howe, a high-ranking Foreign Service Officer, substituted for Ambassadors Bunker and Merchant in the second and last meeting of the Committee and contributed significantly to its thinking.

The omissions were as important as the selections. The State Department itself was conspicuously under-represented. Although the roster included two ambassadors, only one participated at all, and he attended only one meeting. No one was there from the seventh floor; no one from the policy-planning side; no one from the administrative side; no one who had much significant contact with the earlier experience with program systems; and only one (Howe, a substitute in the second meeting) who was currently in the career Foreign Service. To Barrett it was essential that the Committee be, as

1. The invitation was actually proffered by Lyn Johnson, who had become the head of SRI's Washington office and was increasingly active in the Hitch Committee activities during the summer of 1966.

well as appear, disinterested and objective; therefore, neither he nor Crockett should be members. Further, Barrett was confident that a committee of intelligent, impartial people could not fail to support his position. However warranted this confidence, it resulted in a serious imbalance. Defense Department PPBS experience was represented by no fewer than four members (Hitch, Blake, Enthoven, and Rowen); and Budget Bureau experience by two (Bell and Rowen). After the Committee's first meeting, the divorce between the Committee and those most concerned with its subject matter in the Department became a source of considerable difficulty, as will be described later. Whether Barrett's hope for the appearance of objectivity was ever realized is doubtful. A year later, a Budget Bureau official described the Committee to the authors as a "captive" committee, set up and "owned" by the Crockett group.

THE COMMITTEE AT WORK

A few days before the first meeting of the Hitch Committee, Director of the Budget Charles L. Schultze addressed a letter to Secretary Rusk in which he noted the Department's intention to establish an advisory committee on foreign affairs programming and called attention to several major issues, to which, he hoped "you will give careful attention." The principal issue, he wrote, was:

> the relationship between the Secretary of State's needs and those of other agency heads in carrying out their respective responsibilities for management and program decisions. For this reason, I am sure that the views of the other agency heads as well as the advice of the advisory committee and the contractor will be valuable in reaching conclusions. . . .

The major issues were appended as a list of ten questions, most of which were expanded by a number of subsidiary questions. The first seven questions had actually been drafted by Frey of the Budget Bureau staff. Before they were sent to the Secretary, they were discussed with Crockett, who had added the last three. The letter and questions were transmitted to Hitch and subsequently to the rest of his Committee. They became the basic framework for the Committee's work.

1. What should be the relationship between a foreign affairs programming system and agency programming systems?

2. In terms of program structure, can a single set of program elements be developed which will permit programs of the agencies to be expressed in common terms that will be meaningful and usable by both the Secretary of State and agency heads?

3. In terms of programming processes and time cycles, what should be the relationship between an overall foreign affairs system, existing agency processes and cycles, and the government-wide programming and budgeting cycle, taking into account special requirements of various agencies and programs?

4. In terms of relative roles of the field and Washington, what is the appropriate and realistic role and weight of the Ambassador and field missions in resource allocation decisions?

5. How comprehensive should a foreign affairs programming system be?

6. How should non-U.S. Government resources be handled in the programming system?

7. Within the community of foreign affairs programs, are the major "trade-offs" and the program choices primarily among agencies or within agencies?

8. How can a foreign affairs programming system and agency systems best relate resources to foreign policy objectives stated in National Policy Papers or similar documents?

9. How should the effectiveness of our programs be measured?

10. What staff capability does the Department of State need both for program analysis and for operating the programming system?

In addition to the questions, each member of the Committee was presented, at the beginning of the first meeting, with a set of briefing documents drawn together by Barrett's staff. They included an outline history of foreign affairs programming to date, the latest FAPS grid, the standard outline of National Policy Papers, a listing of 466 different foreign affairs activities (produced by a special computer program), the Budget Bureau's PPBS Bulletin 66-3, the field guidances on PPBS from AID and Peace Corps, and the NSAM 341 announcement. Soon after the meeting opened, Barrett, speaking from the "galleries," gave the group an extended briefing. Rowen then briefed the group on the development of PPBS with particular reference to the foreign affairs agencies. After luncheon, Golden, then assistant director of CISR, discussed the problems of foreign affairs programming as he saw them. The balance of the afternoon was taken up with a discussion within the Committee itself of the ten Budget Bureau questions. Surprisingly there seemed to be general agreement among the group about most of them. Everyone agreed about the desirability of programming and relating it to budgeting; no one dissented that there should be a foreign affairs system, comprehending the major agencies and headed by the Secretary of State; all recognized that this must operate side-by-side with agency systems. Hitch was able, after the meeting, to draft a "shorthand summary of tentative answers" to the ten questions that reflected the sense of the meeting and that he transmitted within a few days to all members of the Committee as well as to Secretary Rusk. In summary of his summary, the Committee felt that:

an integrated foreign affairs programming system (IFAPS) is desirable and must be consistent with more detailed agency systems; one of its dimensions must be geographic;

the timing of the program budget cycle depends on whether State wishes to take initiative and leadership or wants simply to review, react, and resolve differences;

IFAPS should concentrate on agencies with large budgets;

non-U.S. Government resources should not be included in IFAPS but should be considered in the analyses;

"trade-offs" are important both within and between agencies;

there is a need for policy guidances on objectives by country, but the Committee members are not sufficiently familiar with the National Policy Papers to know whether they are adequate for this purpose;

much more can and should be done in developing quantitative measures of effectiveness of programs;

there is a need for a sizable analytic staff reporting at a very high level.

The first meeting was surprisingly bland. There were a few sharp remarks: Rowen's criticism of the "miserable" analytic quality of most of the program memoranda received by the Bureau of the Budget from foreign affairs agencies; Argyris' challenge to the allegedly authoritarian fashion in which PPBS was being thrust on the agencies; a derogatory reference to the EROP exercise. Argyris and Likert stressed the importance of considering the human dimension in introducing so great a change, and Likert spoke forcefully for more attention to the measurement of results in foreign countries and the wide applicability of quantitative measures. There was a very brief debate between Mosher and Rowen on the probable effects of installing and perfecting PPB systems in individual agencies. Mosher suggested that this would strengthen agency fragmentation and make more difficult an integrated foreign affairs system in the future. Rowen saw no reason why this should be the result.

There was little argument at the first meeting or later on, that the PPB efforts should be removed from the administration side of the Department and attached to the "substantive" offices—specifically the Under Secretary and, to a lesser degree, the regional Assistant Secretaries. This idea was not in conflict with the long-range objectives of either Crockett or Barrett. Yet, it had the effect of lessening their participation in, and influence upon, the Committee and the treatment of its report.

For the most part, the real issues remained beneath the surface. This was perhaps due to its being the first meeting among persons who did not know each other well; to the lack of familiarity with the subject matter of several members; to the lack of sharpness of many of the agenda questions. Hitch closed the meeting with the statement that the next and final meeting would be held in September and that meanwhile he and the contractor, SRI, would put together a draft report. He urged each member to write him any views or suggestions he had. A few of the members, notably Argyris, Diebold, Likert, and Mosher, meeting informally later in the day, were distressed that the Committee hadn't discussed the underlying questions and feared that they would be called upon to sign a report framed by others. However, each of the four made substantial contributions to the preparation of the report later in the summer. In response to Hitch's "shorthand summary" of the first meeting several wrote him in some detail. Argyris directed his attention to an eleventh question, not included in the original ten of the Bureau of the Budget:

> how the programming system can be truly integrated within the State Department. To put this another way, my present concern is that we are advising the Secretary of State on the substantive issues of programming but have not included any advice on how to introduce programming effectively within the State Department. Nor have we suggested how to design organizational arrangements that will help make it as effective as possible.

Pursuant to this question, Argyris raised a number of others: how to help the top echelon of the Department to realize a programming system reflects a new philosophy of management; how the concept can be "internalized" by the top officers; how to make the top echelon aware of the need for all relevant information in decision making; how to introduce the system while minimizing internal resistances. Argyris' memorandum became the basis of one of the Committee's recommendations.

Likert wrote Hitch on two themes: first, the need and desirability of quantitative measurement of consequences of foreign affairs programs and the feasibility of making such assessments, primarily through the techniques of survey research; and second, the desirability if not the necessity of introducing and carrying out a PPB system through a participative style of management rather than a "benevolent authoritative" system as widely practiced in the federal government. In this latter regard, he referred to a number of studies on organizational performance and particularly his own book, previously cited.

Diebold addressed two memoranda to Hitch. His central theme was that the accumulation and presentation of data for a PPB system should be augmented to serve other foreign affairs purposes, not just budgeting. Thus he viewed data collection as a vehicle toward "a new way of looking at foreign affairs opportunities and problems" in general. An integrated programming system "could assist us in crossing a threshold in the conduct of foreign policy."

Mosher spent several days in Washington in July, interviewing officials of various agencies concerned in foreign affairs, and then addressed a long memorandum to Hitch summarizing his findings and opinions. He stressed the desirability of an integrated approach, the necessity of strong leadership and support from the top of the State Department, the importance of a program of orientation and training for line as well as staff personnel on the programming system, and the danger that the system might be oversold.

Perhaps the most interesting of all the member responses

to Hitch was that of Assistant Budget Director Rowen. Although Rowen, like most of the others, expressed general agreement with Hitch's "shorthand summary" of answers to the ten questions, his reading of them differed from that of the other members. While endorsing an integrated system, he expressed the hope that, "for at least the next several years [it] would be based on agency systems so that agency data can be handled in the central system without the need for radical transformation from the way it is handled in the separate agency systems." Later in his memo he suggested that Hitch make a specific assignment for designing "an IFAPS structure based on existing agency structure with little or no change." Question three on procedures and timing he regarded as the crucial question. He took no position on the issue, but contributed this analysis of the alternatives:

> However, I think it may be necessary to clarify the role of the Secretary of State with regard to chains of "command." One runs directly to the Ambassadors in their role as "field commanders" responsible to the President through the Secretary of State; the other runs to the foreign affairs agency heads and thence to their component people in the field (who in turn report to the Ambassadors). There is potential for strong leadership here (notwithstanding the traditions against it). At one extreme possibility we have the present situation with SecState playing a relatively passive and piecemeal role; at the other extreme one can imagine (barely) SecState giving guidance directly to the field for the preparation of submissions to the various agencies. In between might be a process in which SecState gives general guidance to the Washington agencies and lets them handle their field relationships pretty much without interference.

Interestingly, he did not mention a fourth possibility, which was subsequently tried:[2] dual channels of Ambassador to State for the country as a whole and of agency representative

2. In the CASP experiment, described in Chapter VI.

to agency on agency program budgets. Nor did he mention the possible utilization of the NSAM machinery and the country team.

Rowen expressed doubt that, with an IFAPS system, "Ambassadors will have, in general 'a greatly expanded role,' partly because in many countries their main job is diplomacy, not resource allocation, and partly because we don't typically choose for ambassadors people with managerial aptitudes and skills."

All the memoranda of Committee members were reproduced and sent to all the other members. In addition, Bell, while emphatically affirmative in his support of the IFAPS principle, raised directly with Hitch the question of the limitations of quantitative data and analyses in attacking many of the more difficult issues in foreign affairs, and there ensued a good deal of discussion within the SRI about the handling of qualitative information and judgments in a foreign affairs PPBS. It cannot be said that this central question had been satisfactorily dealt with in any previous studies, nor was it really treated in the Hitch report.

During the summer of 1966 a number of other relevant activities were being carried on. The Stanford Research Institute, pursuant to its State Department contract, conducted an extensive program of interviewing in Washington. It prepared and distributed to the Committee a report on "The Programming System for U.S. Foreign Affairs Activities." It also prepared a memorandum addressed to Barrett suggesting a new and different classification of objectives[3] of foreign affairs and criteria for the definition of program elements in foreign affairs (but not for the elements themselves). In addition, it prepared a set of documents specifically designed for the Committee's use at its second meeting. These in-

3. SRI proposed a division of foreign affairs objectives of six classes: (1) international law and order; (2) international cooperation; (3) international development; (4) national security; (5) U.S. presence and representation; and (6) management and support.

cluded a recapitulation of Committee members' and of other agencies' responses to the ten questions; a listing of suggested criteria for a program structure and the definition of program elements in foreign affairs; a tabular presentation of the PPB structures of six agencies: AID, CIA, Defense, Peace Corps, State Department, and USIA; and a historical review, analysis and evaluation of CCPS.

Of these documents, most interesting for present purposes was the last mentioned, the critique of CCPS, which had been prepared by SRI staff members Seymour I. Colman and Ernest E. Lehman. Although not unsympathetic with the efforts which had gone before, they criticized several aspects of CCPS:

> the "apparent basic imbalance" in the program categories whereby the bulk of inputs falls within one class, "Internal Development";
>
> the excessive emphasis upon manpower inputs, especially in view of the lack of correlation between dollars and man-hours;
>
> the emphasis upon inputs and relative neglect of outputs;
>
> the absence of a firm organizational base and support from top levels in Washington;
>
> time constraints and weaknesses of staff;
>
> failure to use CCPS in basic decision processes;
>
> lack of widespread acceptance.

The critique did not, however, undertake an evaluation of the later version, FAPS, since it was "a modified continuation of previous CCPS efforts and concepts," and since it had "never been tested in the field." Members of the Barrett group later expressed resentment about this, since they felt that most of the conceptual and structural defects of CCPS had already been corrected in the redesign of the system as FAPS.

Finally, and most important, the SRI prepared several drafts of a report of the Committee, including answers to the ten questions. The documents went through a number of reviews and discussions, involving Hitch and members of the SRI staff. The product was reproduced and ready in time for Committee consideration at its second meeting. It reflected the written responses of the Committee members as well as the findings of the SRI staff during the summer; but its preparation was an independent operation. No one on the Committee itself actively participated, other than Hitch, nor did anyone from the governmental agencies concerned.

Meanwhile (before the first meeting of the Committee) Crockett, as indicated in the Ball airgram, invited senior officials—his counterparts—of other foreign affairs agencies to form an Interagency Principals' Group to discuss and resolve basic issues that would arise out of an integrated system. This group was backed by a working group, which consisted of the alternates of the principals at the working level of program development. It was intended to direct itself to technical questions in the same area. The Principals' group met once but adjourned *"sine die"* when Solis Horwitz, Crockett's counterpart in the Department of Defense, said, in effect, there was no value in further meetings until the Hitch report was completed. The second-level group met on a number of occasions, but produced no report or recommendations. During the same period, Barrett's staff made an analysis of the program structures of the various agencies in an effort to find means to reconcile them. But for the most part, those concerned with programming and budgeting "sat on their hands." Little could be done until the Hitch Committee made its report, but of course work was proceeding in the various agencies on their individual PPB systems.

On September 19, the Committee held its second and last meeting. The participants included Hitch; Argyris; Bell; Blake; Likert; Mosher; Rowen; the new member, Taylor; and Fisher Howe, substituting for ambassadors Bunker and Merchant. The Committee again reviewed and, more warmly than before, debated the ten questions and the answers to them. Taylor spoke emphatically about the need for executive leadership in the State Department and for an integrated programming system, and he related the system to his objectives in the drafting of NSAM 341. At midday, Crockett hosted a large luncheon in the State Department dining room, attended by a substantial number of top State Department officials as well as the members of the Committee. In the afternoon, three State Department "witnesses" were invited to present their views: Crockett, who spoke about the programming idea in general and about the role of country directors; Alexis Johnson, then Deputy Under Secretary for Political Affairs and a principal author of the country director idea, who also addressed himself to their role; and Henry D. Owen, Chairman of the Policy Planning Council, who discussed the National Policy Papers and their potential use in a programming system. (Owen subsequently suggested to Hitch that the Policy Planning Council might serve as a "spawning ground" for the analysis staff that the Committee would propose.)

Later in the afternoon, the basic recommendations of the Committee were discussed and, for the most part, agreed. There was somewhat less clarity about the answers to the ten questions, and there remained semantic difficulties as to the real meaning and implications of some of the expressions. Thus, while there was unanimity on the desirability of an integrated system under the Secretary of State, the relationship of such a system to existing agency systems and the respective roles of the State Department and the Bureau of the Budget remained fuzzy. The group agreed that the interest and capability of the Under Secretary of State would be vital to the effective implementation of an integrated foreign affairs programming and budgeting system. Hitch was urged to press this point upon the Secretary when he submitted the report, but this suggestion was wasted since a new Under Secretary was appointed to replace George Ball that week, well before Hitch saw the Secretary.

During the next two days, Hitch and members of the SRI group, particularly Lyn Johnson, who had played an increasingly influential role, feverishly developed a second draft of a report for the Committee. The draft was sent to all the members who in turn responded with comments, suggestions, and approvals. Hitch and SRI then made appropriate amendments and editorial changes and completed the final report on October 5. There were no dissents, and all members of the Committee signed it except Merchant, who had not participated.

THE REPORT

The Committee's report had two parts: a 2½ page letter to the Secretary, signed by the Committee members; and a 13-page attachment consisting of the Budget Bureau's ten questions with discussions and recommendations on each. The flavors of the two were quite different: the letter was emphatic and specific; the responses to the questions were more discursive and equivocal. One Budget Bureau official thought the answers to the questions were very good, but he could not go along with the letter. One member of the Committee conditioned his signature to the letter on his assumption that the treatment of the questions was an addendum "to which the individual members of the committee are not necessarily committed in detail."

THE LETTER

The letter rested upon, and reinforced, NSAM 341:

> We believe that a well designed programming system, including the necessary program planning and analysis, can provide you with a major tool for carrying out your responsibility for the direction, coordination, and supervision of the foreign affairs activities of the U.S. Government. . . . In addition, we should like to offer a general recommendation that the State Department exercise the role in the U.S. foreign affairs com-

munity envisioned in NSAM 341 by assuming leadership in the early establishment of an integrated foreign affairs programming system.

The letter described as the "key initial step" the "selection of a qualified Director to develop the kind of professional analytic capability required and to guide the early evolution of the system. He should be placed at the head of a State Department staff of analysts and programmers in the immediate office of the Under Secretary of State, who also serves as the executive chairman of the Senior Interdepartmental Group." The other recommendations included:

the solicitation of inputs to the system from other foreign affairs agencies;

the installation of a pilot installation for fiscal year 1969 in at least one region, with Latin America or Africa suggested; in this connection, the letter stressed "the desirability of sustaining the present momentum";

development of an integrated foreign affairs program structure;

a study of the problems and means to install the system in the foreign affairs environment, with the proposal that Argyris head a special subcommittee to work on the subject.

The Committee volunteered to continue "in an advisory capacity if you so desire."

The recommendations on the ten questions were less clear cut. With regard to the relationship between an integrated system and agency systems, the addendum proposed that "work proceed" in developing a comprehensive structure that should "build on [agency systems] and be complementary with them." On the question of procedures and timing, it recommended simply that "work proceed under the above guidelines to develop a timetable incorporating an annual program review." On ambassadorial role and leadership, the addendum recommended: "The resource allocation functions of the Ambassador can be determined only after his role in the overall management process is more fully defined." With regard to the comprehensiveness of the programming system, the addendum recommended "an interagency project to identify those activities of the federal government whose primary function is the support of foreign affairs," with emphasis upon agencies whose activities account for the major resource inputs to foreign affairs. On the question about the usefulness to programming of National Policy Papers, the addendum responded about the need for a system which would develop objectives, relate resources to them and provide a cyclical response of programs to environment. There was no mention of the National Policy Papers. The attachment reinforced the recommendation of the letter that a high-level analytic staff be engaged at the level of the Under Secretary and at subordinate levels for purposes of program analysis and measurement of effectiveness.

The Hitch Committee report was a good deal less than a blueprint for a foreign affairs programming-budgeting system. But it was a strong, affirmative thrust toward the development of such a system, and it keynoted the first steps in such a development: the hiring of a high-level director to be attached to the Under Secretary and the engagement of an analytic staff. It offered no assessment of the earlier efforts of the Barrett group in the Department and no guidance as to whether or how the FAPS data, system, and staff should be utilized. Nor did it really come to grips with the agency PPBS efforts and the question of how they should be related to an integrated foreign affairs system. Yet it provided the Secretary a rationale and guidance for positive action.

In view of the time constraints on the Committee and its individual members and of the wide diversity of viewpoints which they represented, the Hitch Committee report was something of an achievement, as was the unanimity of signatures. Some may have wished that the report would go further in terms of the broader ramifications of foreign affairs management—as was suggested in Schultze's original "principal issue" and in some of the memoranda cited above (e.g., those by Diebold, Likert, and Mosher). The deliberations and report of the Committee were focused and narrowed to some extent by the nature of its marching orders and of the ten Bureau of the Budget questions; to some extent by the qualifications and interests of its members, few of whom could claim expertise in foreign affairs or experience in the intricate interplay of agencies, individuals, and nations in the foreign affairs arena. Yet it is probable that most of the members came away from the work with appreciation that they were dealing with problems a good deal broader than quantitative programs and budgets. As Fisher Howe wrote, in criticism of the tentative answers to the ten questions and before the final meeting:

> The name of the game is "foreign affairs." It is not "systems analysis" or "interagency coordination." Especially, it is not "budget." If the Committee is going to be helpful to the Secretary and other government leaders, it must address the question of what you can do to make the government's effort in foreign affairs more effective. Only as a corollary to that question will matters of "systems" and "programs" and "budgets" arise.[4]

4. In a memorandum to Barrett of September 7, 1966.

V

Denouement
(October 1966-August 1967)

ALMOST IMMEDIATELY after the second meeting of the Hitch Committee in September 1966 and before its report was completed, the President announced the designation of Nicholas de B. Katzenbach, then Attorney General, to replace George Ball as Under Secretary of State. Katzenbach was best known as a brilliant lawyer and teacher of law who, as Attorney General, had contributed effectively in the field of civil rights. He had had little public association with foreign affairs,[1] and there was limited knowledge about his interests or capabilities as administrator of large and complex organizations.

Thus the report arrived at a time that was particularly inopportune from the standpoints of transition both in the job most crucial for the development of a programming system and in the appointment of a new executive who was relatively little known and (in the State Department) quite unfamiliar with the kinds of problems with which the Committee had been dealing.[2]

Hitch presented the report of his committee personally to Secretary Rusk on October 13. The Secretary said that he

1. Although as a law professor at the University of Chicago he had shown keen interest in foreign affairs and had taught international law.

2. Although Katzenbach had presided over the Department of Justice when it undertook to introduce a PPBS.

would contact Hitch later after discussing the matter with the new Under Secretary, and Hitch so advised the members of the Committee. But delay in departmental action was necessitated by the difficulty of communication among its top officers. When Hitch delivered the report, Under Secretary Katzenbach, who would have responsibility for action on it, was overseas. Upon Katzenbach's return, Rusk left the country. It is significant, too, that from early October through December Crockett was almost continuously out of the country on trips for and with the President and Congressman Rooney. The 20 copies of the report that had been given to Rusk were transmitted to Katzenbach, but it was apparently some weeks before it was brought to his attention. On November 9 Hitch received a letter from the Secretary that stated: "I have asked the Department's senior administrators to take a long look at your initial report and I hope to have an opportunity to discuss it with you in the near future." Some days later Hitch was invited to visit Washington to discuss the report with Under Secretary Katzenbach.

The meeting took place on December 2, seven weeks after submission of the Committee's report. In the conversation, it was evident that the Under Secretary intended to move ahead and was giving top priority to the choice of a suitable appointee to head the staff of analysts the Committee had recommended. There was discussion also about which region should be chosen for the pilot installation and some evident reluctance on the part of the Under Secretary to use the Latin American region for this purpose. Finally, the Under Secretary indicated that he saw no need for the Hitch Committee to operate as a group in the immediate future.

A week later Hitch wrote Katzenbach, enclosing the draft of a letter he might wish to send to the members of his committee. This apparently provided the basis for the letter sent to all members of the Hitch Committee by Katzenbach on December 20, which thanked them for "services both past and future":

The next task is ours. I want to appoint the most highly qualified person available to head the planning and analysis staff which you have recommended. And then we expect to proceed immediately with the task. Mr. Hitch has generously offered to help us oversee the budding stages of this work and when they begin to come to a focus I look forward to accepting also the offer of continuing assistance from the entire committee—to review what we have accomplished and the directions in which we are going.

In the meantime, activity on the programming front in the Department remained on dead center for the most part. Unwilling to announce their intentions about the Hitch recommendations until a director could be named for the new system, neither the Secretary nor the Under Secretary made any mention of the report. In fact, it was never officially released, despite the considerable fanfare attending the initiation and the work of the Committee. The content and language of the report were well known in other governmental agencies, especially in the Bureau of the Budget, since representatives of those agencies had been members of the Committee. Through "unnamed" informal channels Crockett and the Barrett staff saw excerpts of the report, but no official copy was ever furnished them.

The interagency groups continued inactive, pending a signal from the top of the State Department. The Executive Assistants who had been sent to the field to assist ambassadors in the programming effort were gradually absorbed by other work or reassigned; some resigned. Barrett's own staff began to seek other assignments and in some cases other employers. The SIG, which had been fitfully convened during its first several months of existence, was not convened by Katzenbach at all during this period. It, too, became moribund. In fact, Katzenbach's time was then heavily occupied in non-State Department tasks, first by the President's Crime Commission (of which he was Chairman) and second by an investigating commission on the CIA during the spring of 1967.

THE COMMUNICATIONS VOID

After Katzenbach assumed office and it became known that Secretary Rusk had assigned to him action responsibility for the Hitch report, the Barrett men took an initiative. They were hopeful that some sort of transition would be worked out for staff and resources and that there would be a resumption of action toward an integrated PPB system. On November 7 Bonham prepared a memorandum to Katzenbach for Crockett's signature. Among other things, he recommended:

1. installation of the system in at least one region to meet the FY 1969 budget cycle;
2. choice of the appropriate region by the Under Secretary on the basis of an analysis of responses to the Hitch report of the different regional bureaus;
3. outright transfer of the existing Barrett programming staff of 11 officers "as you may see fit" during the design and development phase;
4. for additional personnel, a levy on other foreign affairs agencies under the authority of NSAM 341;
5. continuation of the Hitch Committee, as the Committee itself had suggested, for continuing advice and review.

This memorandum was sent forward, but there was no response. Crockett was overseas most of this period and could not discuss the matter with Katzenbach.

Barrett and Bonham had several meetings with Jack Rosenthal, a senior assistant whom Katzenbach had brought with him from the Department of Justice. In these meetings during the winter and spring of 1966-67, they pressed for an opportunity to brief Katzenbach on the programming system and urged that at least some of the existing staff be picked up in a new unit to carry on the work pending the selection of a new leader in this area. Rosenthal was friendly, but neither suggestion was taken up. It became clear that Katzenbach and Rosenthal wanted no action until the new leader for programming and analysis was fully on board and could pick his own staff and design his own approach. This position nearly extended to a veto of the proposed new initiative in the Latin American area in which Bonham and his people were cooperating.

There were two additional reasons why this hands-off posture was understandable. One was that Katzenbach had little basis from the Hitch report or any other source upon which to judge whether the past efforts in programming had been good, bad, or indifferent. Not a technical expert himself, he needed an independent judgment by someone in whom he had confidence. Obviously Crockett, Barrett, and their staff, so long and openly committed to their own approach, could not be viewed as objective and unbiased observers.

Secondly, it could not be ignored that the programming effort, like other Crockett initiatives, was controversial and in fact vigorously opposed by many influential officials inside and outside the State Department. As the months wore on, the Barrett group came more and more to be viewed as a troublesome legacy from the past. For example, as EROP receded toward the horizon of history, it was increasingly viewed as a failure—especially by the Mission chiefs and staffs who had worked hard on it and the officers in the regional bureaus who had been involved. CCPS and EROP were now naughty words in the Department and both were connected with Crockett and Barrett. This criticism certainly reached the Under Secretary and his aides. They consequently sought to divorce the new programming effort (and its director) from the tainted past. Barrett and Crockett hoped that these negative feelings were focused on them, not their staffs, so that the talents developed would not be wasted. As will be discussed later, Crockett resigned from the Department in January 1967. Later in the spring, when Rosenthal asked Barrett about his own plans, he responded that he had definitely decided to leave the Department but would delay his departure as long as he might assist in the transition to a new programming system.

Nonetheless, Barrett's programming men continued their developmental work in expectation that they would be called upon to participate in the inauguration of a new system. They worked over and modified the proposed structure of FAPS, made an intensive study of data that had been submitted from one foreign country, and from it developed a model country program memorandum. They sponsored visits to American Missions in a number of Latin American countries by Mosher and John J. Adams, a special consultant to Crockett, to assess the problems of an integrated system from the viewpoint of the field. (The best guess at the time still was that Latin America would be the first pilot region.) Both Mosher and Adams submitted reports with recommendations, and these received considerable circulation within the Department and in other foreign affairs agencies. During this period, too, under the existing contract with the National Training Laboratories, the group sponsored a series of studies of the interpersonal and institutional problems of installing a comprehensive system, both in the field and at home.

THE QUEST FOR A BUDGET

A State Department budget request for new money for programming purposes had been put together before Katzenbach took office. It included a proposed increase for analysts and consultants attached to the Under Secretary. This was done not on the initiative of Crockett or Barrett, but by the State Department budget staff under the leadership of Ralph Roberts, following consultation with the high-ranking officials in the Department with whom Hitch had discussed his proposed report to the Secretary.

At the opening of the hearings of the House Appropriations Committee's Rooney Subcommittee on the State Department budget, Secretary Rusk's statement gave prominent support to the programming request:

One of the smaller, but nonetheless important, requests is to strengthen the Department's capability to carry out effectively the authority and responsibility the President gave me last March for direction and coordination of U.S. Government operations overseas. We moved immediately to establish an organizational structure through which to discharge this responsibility. However, a great deal of work remains to be done to achieve fully the objectives the President had in mind. I have asked Under Secretary Katzenbach to take the leadership in marshaling and putting into action the resources and other means necessary for accomplishment of the job which must be done. I understand he intends to discuss this matter with you. I want you to know I am wholeheartedly behind this effort, and consider it of great importance to the Department of State, and to the Government as a whole in improving the management of resources that go into the conduct of U.S. Government activities abroad.

Katzenbach's own formal statements expanded a good deal on NSAM 341 and emphasized the need for highly competent staff to review and influence program and budget proposals: "As an initial step, the Under Secretary of State, in cooperation with the other agencies involved, is making plans for a professional staff of the most competent political analysts and programming experts from the Department, other agencies of Government, and private life." The amount requested consisted principally of salaries for 17 permanent positions and $250,000 for consultants. Neither the request nor the testimony mentioned explicitly either PPBS or economists.

Rooney and his colleagues were obviously skeptical. After some initial sparring between Rooney and Katzenbach (Rooney queried about $24,000 for equipment: "What is the rule of thumb for this particular kind of Gooneybird?"), Rooney asked:

How important is this thing? The thought just flashed through my mind that a capable ambassador at any post, however large, would know more about this subject than anybody that you could put on his payroll. . . . I am wondering, what would be the consequence of our forgetting all about this for the next year.

MR. KATZENBACH: Things would be no worse than they have been. I think we would have lost an opportunity to make them better.

MR. ROONEY: When was this put in the budget?

MR. KATZENBACH: I think it was put in the budget last fall, probably before I came to the Department of State.

MR. ROBERTS (Deputy Assistant Secretary of State for Budget): Yes, sir, it was first submitted late in September.

Rooney's critical questioning was augmented by two other committee members, Representatives Elford A. Cederberg (Rep., Mich.) and Neal Smith (Dem., Iowa). They doubted or did not understand the need, questioned whether the new staff would not simply be a new and additional level of coordinators, feared there would be substantial increases in future years, and suggested that there already was a Foreign Service Inspection Corps. In the end, the entire request was disallowed in the committee's report to the House.

THE QUEST FOR A LEADER

An initial question in the recruitment of a head for the projected integrated PPBS was that of finding a position and title for the job. In the first place, it had to be of adequate rank and stature to attract the "best available person." Second, once attracted, the leader should command enough influence within the Department and among the other foreign affairs agencies to do the work effectively. There was one vacant post of Assistant Secretary—that for Administration, which Crockett had "abolished" in his 1965 streamlining of the administrative area, but which still existed as a statutory position. Such a rank, equaled by some ten other Assistant Secretaries, including the heads of all the regional bureaus and several levels removed from the top of the Department, seemed less than adequate for the job. Crockett's departure created another opportunity. His rank of Deputy Under Secretary, a notch above the Assistant Secretaries, might be used with some appropriate descriptive title, such as "for Foreign Affairs Programming." The title of Assistant Secretary for Administration might then be reactivated for Crockett's replacement, in the somewhat narrower responsibilities of presiding over only the administrative activities of the Department of State. This was proposed initially by Hitch, and it was reported that Under Secretary Katzenbach favored it. However, it also ran afoul of Representative Rooney. His response to the suggestion allegedly was the cryptic Rooney-ism, "If you want to increase the herd, you don't castrate the bull." Rooney's "herd" was obviously a general administrative "herd," not a programming "herd." Crockett's replacement was appointed as Deputy Under Secretary for Administration, and this possibility was foreclosed. Subsequently, other suggestions for elevating the rank of the new job above Assistant Secretary were considered, but nothing came of these discussions. The incoming program-budget leader would be an Assistant Secretary.

The search for the new director began during the late fall of 1966 and continued until the following March. The number one nominee from the start was Hitch himself, but his desirability was more than matched by his reluctance. Hitch proposed other men to Katzenbach, and first on his list was Thomas Schelling of Harvard. Reportedly among the others under consideration at one time or another were Alain Enthoven (Defense), Richard Barrett (State), Stewart Blake and Lyn Johnson (both SRI), Ralph Dungan (then Ambassador to Chile), Fisher Howe (then in INR, State), and William Niskanen (formerly with Enthoven in Defense).

Hitch's first choice, Thomas C. Schelling, was professor of economics and Associate of the Center for International Affairs at Harvard University. One of America's leading scholars in the area of international conflict and strategy, Schelling had written *National Income Behavior: International Economics;*[3] *Strategy and Arms Control*[4] (with Morton H. Halperin) and *The Strategy of Conflict*.[5] Schelling and Katzenbach had been acquainted for nearly a decade, though not intimately; in fact, Schelling had participated in inviting Katzenbach to a seminar at Harvard in the fall of 1966, soon after the latter's designation as Under Secretary of State.

In mid-December 1966, Katzenbach telephoned Schelling to ask that he accept a high-level job in State to implement the Hitch report and NSAM 341. Schelling was at first uninterested but agreed to come to Washington to discuss the matter. Between Christmas and New Year's Day he met with Katzenbach and Rosenthal. Schelling indicated a lack of interest in program budgeting *per se* and little desire to move to Washington. Katzenbach stated his intention to broaden the job well beyond budgeting and to use it to transform the State Department into a true executive agent of the President in foreign affairs, a concept that appealed more to Schelling's own idea of what was needed.

A week later Schelling and Katzenbach met again. Schelling said he felt the Hitch report did not have all the answers. A problem more fundamental than the absence of a system, in his view, was the unevenness and lack of vitality in decision making in State and the foreign affairs community. He saw as the basic need a decision-making structure that would involve the Under Secretary at its heart and would create a market for ideas and issues, a need for data and qualitative analyses that would then begin to flow through the structure. Then a system would be invaluable. On this theme, he and Katzenbach seemed to be in agreement.

At a third meeting later in January, Schelling agreed to take the job (preferably, but not necessarily, at the level of

3. Boston: Allyn and Bacon, 1958.
4. London and Toronto: Macmillan, Twentieth Century Fund, 1961.
5. Cambridge: Harvard University Press, 1960.

Deputy Under Secretary). He planned to visit Washington during the spring for one day a week to familiarize himself with the situation. He would move to Washington at the end of the academic year in June and would stay for one year, with the possibility of a second year if all went well.

It took Katzenbach about five weeks to obtain necessary executive clearances on the Schelling appointment. By March and April Schelling was visiting Washington about one day every week. His designation was not yet official and was not publicized. Nonetheless, the "Periscope" column of *Newsweek* on April 24 carried a brief note under the heading "The Games State Will Play":

> The State Department is about to get a new administrator with powers to overhaul Foggy Bottom's tradition-encrusted ways of making decisions. He is Thomas Schelling, Harvard professor, author (*Strategy and Arms Control*), a one-time "think-tank" executive at the RAND Corporation and a protege of Under Secretary Nicholas Katzenbach. Among the innovations Schelling will introduce at State in his post as Deputy Under Secretary for Administration: a "games-theory" approach to foreign policy in which players use computers to produce expected reaction of foreign leaders to American moves.

The *Newsweek* commentator was probably doing a bit of game-guessing of his own. More likely Schelling saw his role as developing SIG as a vital decision-making center for foreign affairs, utilizing the machinery of PPBS as a tool, selectively applied. There would be country "program packages" (particularly for the major countries), a push in the direction of a total foreign affairs budget to be presented to Congress by Secretary Rusk, and an effort to improve communications in the upper echelons in the State Department. In all of this, the deepening involvement of the Under Secretary in programmatic decision making would be essential, from Schelling's point of view.

During his visits to Washington, Schelling had discussions

with many officials in the State Department, the Bureau of the Budget, and the various foreign affairs agencies. The results of these conversations were apparently disillusioning. Though well received, Schelling sensed a widespread discouragement about the prospects for any early strengthening of State Department leadership in foreign affairs. He perceived a lack of clear-cut organization, to the extent that it seemed only a slight exaggeration to say that many of the top officials were not sure for whom they were working. The SIG was in such a state of disuse that it might not be possible to revive it. Also, as the spring weeks passed, it appeared that Katzenbach and Schelling came to view the job in different ways. For Katzenbach, it would make possible the delegation to an able and reliable person of responsibilities in which he (Katzenbach) had less than primary interest, so that he could deal with more important things. For Schelling, success in his prospective role would require a very close relationship with the Under Secretary and progressively greater involvement of Katzenbach in interagency decision making, using SIG and the products of systems analysis.

Early in May Schelling realized that the situation offered little prospect of success within the year he had agreed to give the job. He decided to withdraw and so notified Katzenbach just before the latter left on an extensive tour of Africa. On May 29 *Newsweek*'s "Periscope" provided the epitaph under the heading, "Foggy Bottom Claims a Victim":

> Harvard Professor Thomas Schelling, an expert on modernizing administrative operations, recently agreed to join the State Department and overhaul its time-honored ways of doing business. He made a thorough survey—and then a quick decision. In his letter of resignation to Secretary Dean Rusk, Schelling explained that the job would be too much for him.

The decision was an agonizing one for Schelling, who had already leased his home in Cambridge and was preparing to move his family to Washington within a few weeks. When

Schelling weighed the magnitude of the problems he had diagnosed against the amount of time (one year) he could commit to the task, the two just did not balance, and he feared the effort might even be counterproductive. His probable departure in mid-1968 would leave an embarrassing gap before the presidential election and would be unfair to any staff men that he could assemble. Schelling felt he could not ask them for a longer commitment than he could give himself.

Schelling's departure before he had really arrived was a blow to hopes for implementing the Hitch report, and to the hopes of Barrett and Bonham for some kind of orderly transition. Schelling's action would hardly encourage any other potential candidate. In fact, no one else was approached for the job.

FADEOUT

By the summer of 1967 the Schelling episode seemed very nearly the deathblow to the integrated programming effort and the other innovative initiatives associated with the names of Crockett and Barrett. In historical perspective, it now appears that the road downhill had begun more than a year earlier.

Already by the summer of 1966 it seemed clear that Crockett would be leaving soon, a disheartening realization for Barrett and his crew. Crockett had spent more than three expensive and exhausting years in his job, and he had come to the conclusion that what he could do, he had done. He felt that he could no longer be of more than marginal help to the programming effort. The Hays bill to extend a foreign service personnel system and the integration of USIA officers into the Foreign Service were in trouble, and by the fall of 1966 they had been tabled by the Senate Foreign Relations Committee. Crockett concluded that it was time for him to move on, but the only option open to him in the State Department was going out as ambassador, probably to a nonsensitive country because of the administrative label he wore. There was no prospect of his moving up in the State Department hierarchy, again because of the administrative label and because of the ferment he had stirred up.

At the age of 52, Crockett felt that if he were to move to the private sector, he could wait no longer. In the fall he had the thoroughly exhausting experience of managing all of the logistics for President Johnson's Far Eastern trip. When Crockett returned to Washington, it was an open secret that he was negotiating for a job in the private sector. Shortly after New Year's Day it was announced that he would leave the State Department on January 31, 1967, to become Director of Executive Resources for the IBM World Trade Corporation in New York City.

Crockett helped choose his replacement—Idar Rimestad, who was serving as Counselor for Administration at the U.S. Embassy in Paris. Rimestad had served in various administrative capacities in foreign affairs for many years. He was equipped by experience to lead the administrative activities as they were traditionally defined. This meant a return to administrative business as usual, pre-Crockett, and the appointment probably brought sighs of relief to those FSO's who were apprehensive about, or downright opposed to, Crockett's many innovations and no less to those administrative personnel who were more comfortable with administrative business as usual.

Rimestad saw as his mission the "battening down of the hatches." He soon began reversing the Crockett reorganization of the administrative area. In mid-1967 he eliminated the CISR staff, and by early 1968 the ACORD program vanished. MUST, which had been transferred by Crockett to a conventional personnel unit, was largely routinized under Rimestad and then died out. Rimestad took few initiatives in the personnel and programming areas that had been so important to Crockett, and even before Schelling resigned, he gave termination notices to the four remaining staff men still working on programming in May 1967.

One by one, over the winter and spring of 1966-1967, the Barrett men departed for other—and usually higher-paid—jobs. By the fall of 1967 only one, Robert Bonham, remained, and he had been transferred to the staff of Under Secretary Katzenbach. Bonham resigned in May 1968. Shortly after Schelling departed, Barrett submitted his resignation. Subsequently he returned to the Bureau of the Budget as Acting Director of its new Management Systems Staff. In fact, a total of eight of the Barrett staff transferred one by one into the Bureau of the Budget. The Executive Assistants, originally trained and assigned to install and manage programming systems in the field, were reassigned, absorbed into other work, or resigned, although a few in Latin America contributed to the exercise described in the next chapter.

Charles Hitch, by then president of the University of California, played no further part in the foreign affairs programming problem after recommending the appointment of Schelling. Nor did his committee. The Stanford Research Institute withdrew from the picture at the end of 1966 and subsequently hired John Golden from the CISR staff to become director of its Washington office. Most of the other officials who had been significant figures moved during 1966 and early 1967. Rostow went back to the White House from the State Department. David Bell left AID in the summer of 1966 to go to the Ford Foundation. Henry Rowen resigned at the beginning of 1967 to become president of the RAND Corporation. He was replaced at the Bureau a few months later by Fred Hoffman, also a former RAND economist who had been serving in the Department of Defense. Frey moved from the Bureau's International Division to become Deputy Director of its Office of Legislative Reference. The slate was almost clean.

During this period, when the backers and some of the opponents of the integrated program-budgeting system were scattering in various directions, work continued in the several foreign affairs agencies to develop and improve their PPB systems. During 1967 the Bureau of the Budget developed a series of pointed questions directed to substantive issues involving resource allocations, including many focused on the country level. Bureau officials considered that the submissions of several of the agencies were considerably improved. The Department of State was excused by the Bureau from the PPBS directive, except in two areas: cultural exchange and foreign building operations. For most of the rest, the budget process continued as before, unchanged.

VI

Epilogue

(Written in October 1969)

By SUMMERTIME 1967, CCPS was dead. Its proposed successor, FAPS, like the Hitch Committee's IFAPS, had never achieved life. The Committee itself never reconvened, and the proposed Argyris subcommittee on implementation was never organized. Most of the authors, sponsors, and articulate opponents of worldwide country programming had left the scene. More than most case studies of ongoing administration, this story came to a definite end. But the problems were—and are—still there, and some of the ideas growing out of the experience were reflected in subsequent developments. This Epilogue undertakes to summarize briefly the most significant of those subsequent developments that occurred between 1967 and the fall of 1969.

THE CASP SYSTEM

Even before the collapse of FAPS a new initiative toward country programming was begun in one region, Latin America. During the fall and winter of 1966-67, Lincoln Gordon, then Assistant Secretary of Inter-American Affairs, and his deputy, Robert Sayre, directed the installation of a comprehensive country-based system for planning and programming in all 24 countries in Latin America. It came to be known as

CASP, an abbreviation for *Country Analysis and Strategy Paper.*

Gordon had a long-standing reputation as an economist, administrator, and practitioner in foreign affairs. He had been Ambassador to Brazil, the largest and most complicated country in Latin America, the object of nearly half of all U.S. expenditures in the region. He was determined to make NSAM 341 effective in his region, and already the Latin American IRG was one of the more active ones. In this thrust, he was ably served by Sayre, an experienced career FSO. The two men proceeded on the CASP undertaking on their own authority. They had no official support from the Under Secretary, (indeed, at one point, he considered vetoing it) , the Bureau of the Budget, or the administrative leadership in the Department. Gordon and Sayre were willing to tap what remained of Barrett's programming staff for assistance, despite its controversial reputation in the Department. On request, Bonham and a few others contributed to the designing of CASP and reviewed and analyzed the conduct and problems of its first cycle. They worked strictly in an advisory capacity and refrained from participating in substantive decisions.

CASP was an interesting blend of some of the features of the PPBS and CCPS-FAPS approaches. The PPBS emphasis on program memoranda was reflected in the CASP requirement for: (1) a brief statement of rationale and strategy; (2) assessment of current situation and near-term prospects, meaning up to the next five years; and (3) a discussion of program options. From the CCPS-FAPS approach, CASP took: (1) the country base and initial preparation in the field; (2) the comprehensive approach covering most of the larger agencies operative in each country; and (3) an insistence on broad standard program categories so that data could be analyzed and aggregated on agency, country, and regional levels. The seven major program categories were the same as those that had been developed in the latest refinement of

FAPS during the summer of 1966.[1] Also included, but for optional use, were the subcategories of the major program packages.

A CASP submission, then, consisted mostly of the program data organized by these categories. It led off with a statement of general and specific U.S. objectives, followed by the related cost estimates of the programs to achieve them (over each of six years—the current year, the budget year, and four years into the future). The most troublesome feature of CCPS, accounting for man-hours, was dropped. Only dollar estimates (including the cost of manpower) were to be included. The CASP cycle (for the FY 1969 budget) was, in major respects, quite analogous to the EROP cycle, though it began earlier.

When the first cycle was nearing completion in mid-1967, it was possible to array some of the strengths and weaknesses of the CASP system and make some preliminary judgments about its current situation and prospects for the future.[2] The strengths included:

1. building on past experience in the programming area;

2. genuine initiative from the line leadership of a regional bureau, rather than from the administrative side;

3. selection of the most practicable features of the PPBS approach and CCPS-FAPS experience;

4. the total regional approach;

5. the framework for Washington leadership and program review provided by NSAM 341 and the Country Director reorganization;

1. The reader may compare these revised FAPS categories with the earlier (immediately post-EROP) version, as shown in Appendix V. The revised categories were: (1) Political, Internal; (2) Political, International; (3) Economic/Social, Internal; (4) Economic/Social, International; (5) Security, Internal; (6) Security, International; and (7) Cultural/Psychological.

2. The authors are of course responsible for the following critique, but they relied in considerable part upon studies conducted by Bonham and others of the first CASP cycle.

6. the fact that the Latin American IRG had gotten off to a running start largely because it had a predecessor in the Latin American Policy Committee (LAPC) ;

7. the existence of comprehensive policy papers for all Latin American countries, which had been developed and worked on repeatedly by LAPC and IRG;

8. the fact that State and AID personnel were merged in the Latin American bureau.

Some of the defects of the CASP effort became evident in the first year of operation. Many of them were predictable and expected, the kinds of problems associated with the first try at a complicated effort of this kind. Some were mechanical and correctable; others could be improved only over time with cumulative experience:

1. The quality of submissions varied widely.

2. Most statements of objectives were weak.

3. The data generally lacked rigor and consistency.

4. There was insufficient analysis, both in the field and in Washington.

5. The Washington review sessions were spotty.

6. Full advantage of the regional approach was not realized.

7. CASP and PPBS were not effectively coordinated.

8. No effective link was forged with the budget process.

9. There was no help from outside the Latin American Bureau.

Despite all the drawbacks of the first trial, the CASP effort had potential significance. For the first time, all of the Missions in a region had studied their activities and submitted their recommendations to headquarters in an organized way. Even though the Washington reviews were not as effective as hoped, the Latin American IRG met week in and week out in reasonably systematic fashion to concentrate on country programs. Decisions were made, and a great deal was learned from the experience.

During the fall of 1967, Gordon's successor as Assistant Secretary of Inter-American Affairs decided to renew the CASP cycle in 1967-68, and later it was operated in 1968-69. In each succeeding year, the cycle has been reported to be more effective. A sizable staff of analysts was formed in the Latin American Bureau to superintend it; the role of the various country directors in resource allocation was enlarged; and the Bureau of the Budget participated increasingly. Consideration has been given to extending the CASP system to one or more other regions of the world, but none has yet embarked upon it. Meanwhile, of course, most foreign affairs agencies continue to prepare their PPB submissions on an agency basis. Except for its cultural affairs exchange program, the Department of State does not make PPB submissions.

FERMENT IN THE RANKS

In 1966 an organization of young FSO's known as the Junior Foreign Service Officer's Club (JFSOC), created nearly a decade earlier as a social group, began to address itself to problems of the Foreign Service. It started with financial grievances: the wage scale, the promotion rate, and the plight of low-salaried FSO's assigned to Washington, where they drew no allowances. Over time its interests broadened and deepened, with concern about more fundamental problems— dissatisfaction over the nature of the career the young officers saw ahead of them; an interest in a more vigorous managerial role for the Department of State; a desire to participate in a restatement of the profession of diplomacy.

Barrett's ACORD staff arranged several workshops in which the "young Turks" met with selected older FSO's. Out of these workshops emerged a trenchant statement of complaints and ideas of the young officers. JFSOC was expanded, and work committees were formed to study the major problems.

About the same time, a group of "middle-aged Turks" (six mid-career officers) issued a manifesto that echoed many of the concerns of the younger officers and was couched in even stronger language. It was published in the November 1966 issue of the *Foreign Service Journal* under the title, "1966: Are We Obsolete?"

In 1967 these two groups joined forces, expanded their number, and staged a remarkable coup by taking over control of the American Foreign Service Association (AFSA). Typically, the Board of Directors and officers of AFSA had been named by an inner-circle cadre. The activists in effect formed a political party and sent ballots around the world to all Foreign Service posts. Their slate won by a thumping majority.

There were indications that many of the elders of the Service were beginning to listen to the activists. Even before the coup, the voice of the activists had been heard within a bulwark of traditionalism, the Career Principles Committee of AFSA. As chairman and vice-chairman of the committee, respectively, Ambassadors William Leonhart and Outerbridge Horsey took pains to assure that the activists were well represented on the committee.

The result was that the committee produced a progressive, almost radical, report. Many of the major ideas of the activists were similar to those espoused by the protagonists of country programming in this case, as demonstrated by a few excerpts from the interim report of the Career Principles Committee:

> The Department of State has primary responsibility for direction and coordination of the overseas activities of the U.S. Government.
>
> The Committee believes that some form of program budgeting (which is not simply administrative gimcrackery) is essential to the rational conduct of foreign affairs and indispensable to

the discharge of the Department of State's responsibilities under NSAM 341.

Information-handling is a much-neglected area. Better coordination of policies requires as a minimum a common data base among participating agencies.

The report cited the case for a "programming system for foreign affairs" and described the key roles as follows: *Assistant Secretaries*: "pivotal offices for the integration of policy, programs, and resources." *Chiefs of Mission*: should "provide a strong link between policy planning and budget execution."

In the fall of 1968, the Association published a summary report, *Toward a Modern Diplomacy*, which repeated some of these recommendations.[3] Soon after the inauguration of the Nixon administration in 1969, the Association presented its views to Under Secretary Elliott Richardson who indicated receptivity and, in fact, soon acted on some of them (including reestablishment of the Board of the Foreign Service with the Under Secretary as Chairman, and initiation of a broad survey of foreign affairs personnel by the Director General under the aegis of the Board). The Association's recent activities have emphasized reforms in personnel administration and it has sought increasingly a role of bargaining agent in pressing upon the Department its demands in behalf of the Foreign Service. Embedded in these efforts are: (1) a recognition of a broader managerial role of the Foreign Service, (2) the aspiration for State Department leadership in decision making in all foreign affairs activities, and (3) a hospitality to modern systems and techniques that may make that leadership effective.

It is too early to predict what impact this push from within the Service may have. At least it suggests that the next wave of programming missionaries may find more "natives" who are friendly; indeed, the "natives" may become missionaries.

3. Published by the Association in paperback form and also available as Part Two of the November 1968 issue of the *Foreign Service Journal*.

THE JACKSON SUBCOMMITTEE INVESTIGATES

During the summer of 1967 the Senate's Subcommittee on National Security and International Operations, chaired by Senator Henry M. Jackson (Dem., Wash.), undertook studies and hearings on Planning-Programming-Budgeting in the national security area—how it had worked in Defense, how it was working or might work in other agencies in the international arena.[4] Among the early documents growing out of this inquiry were a recapitulation of official documents about PPBS and a collection of eight articles (reprints) concerning the "key features of PPB." Four of the eight articles had been written by members of the Hitch Committee (Enthoven, Hitch, Mosher, and Rowen). The next issuance, on August 11, 1967, was a brief "Initial Memorandum," intended to raise the principal issues involved in PPB in the national security area and indicating a good deal of skepticism on the part of the subcommittee (and/or its staff) toward the subject.

More significant was the testimony before the subcommittee of Director of the Budget Charles L. Schultze on August 23, 1967. Schultze's argument was in no significant way different from the Bureau's position of the preceding years. He listed first among criticisms of foreign affairs management that "Each foreign [affairs] agency conducts its own planning without any systematic means of *comparing its programs with those of the other agencies* designed to fulfill related missions. . . ."

Schultze pointed to the usefulness of the individual countries as categories under which to analyze an agency's foreign affairs objectives and noted approvingly that four agencies had developed procedures for country-level programming

---

4. In all, 13 reports on the subject of PPBS were issued by the subcommittee as of this writing. They are listed on the back inside cover of the most recent report, entitled "Planning-Programming-Budgeting: Interim Observations," dated December 2, 1968.

(AID, USIA, Peace Corps, and Educational and Cultural Exchange in the Department of State) :

> Although progress has been uneven within the foreign affairs agencies, we anticipate a steady improvement in the contribution of PPB to *agency decision making.* [Emphasis added.]
> Perhaps the most significant opportunity to improve our decision process in foreign affairs operations lies *in the use of agency PPB materials to establish an overall foreign affairs programming system, and to provide the Secretary of State and the Regional Assistant Secretaries with a procedure to coordinate resource management in U.S. foreign affairs.*

The Budget Director expressed confidence that the regional and country PPBS's of individual agencies "can fruitfully be used to form the base of an *overall* foreign affairs programming system." As a beginning in that direction, the Bureau would, in its fall budgetary reviews, invite the State Department's regional assistant secretaries to advise on interagency program issues—based upon the *agency* program memoranda. *"Second,"* he said, "we hope to develop jointly with the State Department several overall country Program Memoranda, as models (perhaps one country in each major region will be selected) ." This resembled the experimental approach described to the authors by Clark of the Bureau in June 1967.

Schultze made passing reference to the possibility of strengthening the Secretary's leadership over foreign affairs activities through the development of foreign affairs programming, but discounted the use of the NSAM SIG-IRG machinery as being effective only for the handling of specific issues—not for forward planning. He did not discuss or even refer to the developments described in this case—CCPS, EROP, the Hitch Committee, CASP, *et al.*

A later document of the subcommittee (January 5, 1968) was a memorandum written by Thomas C. Schelling at its request. Schelling supported PPBS, stressed its use for managerial control and decision making as well as evaluation, and drew a compelling picture of the much greater difficulty of achieving success in foreign affairs than in Defense. This last theme and much of his memorandum were summarized in one sentence that surely grew out of his brief, unhappy experience in the Department of State: "PPBS can be a splendid tool to help top management make decisions; but there has to be a top management that wants to make decisions."

In Schelling's opinion, if Hitch had come into the State Department instead of the Defense Department, he might have been able to achieve something, "by a heroic exercise of both intellect and authority, and with the full cooperation of the Budget Bureau"; but, "This would have been a different task, and in many ways a harder one, than the budgetary task that he actually took on—and that one itself was a task that an ordinary mortal would have shrunk from."

There was some salve for Crockett and Barrett in Schelling's repeated endorsement of the country as the basic program package in foreign affairs and for the comprehensive approach:

> Individual countries are the basic "program packages" for foreign affairs budgeting. . . .
>
> The basic package is not the program—Peace Corps, intelligence, AID, agricultural surpluses, technical assistance, Ex-Im bank credits—but the country. . . .
>
> The point is that the basic program package is not Peace Corps, financial aid, military aid, agricultural surpluses, propaganda, or diplomatic representation; the basic package is the country.

On December 2, 1968, the Jackson Subcommittee issued the latest, and possibly the last, in its series of hearings and reports on PPBS. Entitled "Interim Observations," it was brief and somewhat inconclusive. It was critical of the fact that PPBS implementation had been attempted in all major agencies at once instead of in a step-by-step manner, commenting that the "exaggerated hopes" thus stimulated "have died away." The report also stressed that a PPB must be tailored to the special circumstances of each agency, and noted with satisfaction that "adaptation, experimentation, and selectivity were now on the PPB menu." Identified as a major piece of unfinished business was "how best to generate more coherence" in foreign affairs planning and operations:

> Would the installation of an interagency foreign affairs programming system be a promising way to extend and strengthen the authority of the Secretary of State over the conduct of foreign affairs? Is this what a President and his Secretary of State want? And is this what Congress wants? Would the expected advantages of central direction and control justify the move away from the real, or fancied, advantages of the decentralized initiative and responsibility of agencies like USIA, AID, the Peace Corps, the Department of the Treasury, and others?

THE NIXON ADMINISTRATION

During his Presidential campaign, Richard M. Nixon promised a major shake-up in the Department of State, but the first half-year of the new administration brought few startling changes within the Department. More significant was the enlargement and strengthening of the staff and apparently also the influence of the new Assistant to the President on National Security Affairs, Henry A. Kissinger. Kissinger recruited a substantial number of brilliant young officials from the Foreign Service, the Defense Department, and elsewhere.[6] On February 6, 1969, the President issued a directive that, in effect, rescinded NSAM 341 and appeared to shift primary initiative and leadership in international policy questions from the Secretary of State to the White House and more specifically to Kissinger. The IRG's were replaced

6. On these points, see *New York Times* reports of January 19 and February 5, 1969.

by Interdepartmental Groups (IG's), organized on a regional basis and likewise chaired by Assistant Secretaries of State; and the SIG became the NSC Under Secretaries Committee, to be chaired by the Under Secretary of State. But between these bodies and the gate-keeper for all problems and papers destined for consideration in the National Security Council itself was established an NSC Review Group, chaired by Kissinger and possessing authority to "assign action" to the Interdepartmental Groups as well as to other groups that might be established to deal with particular problems. These various groups differed in membership from those provided by NSAM 341 in their exclusion of representatives of AID and USIA, except on call when particular questions required their participation.[7]

On paper at least, this new directive seemed to transfer decisive influence on pressing policy questions from the Secretary and Under Secretary of State to the President's Assistant on National Security Affairs. It also seemed to shift emphasis from a broader foreign affairs perspective to one focused upon military and security matters. Accounts of a number of journalists and commentators during the spring and summer of 1969 tended to confirm that such a shift of influence had actually occurred. It may be noted, too, that part of Kissinger's staff was assigned to analytic studies, some of them organized on a country basis.

The emasculation of NSAM 341 seems to confirm General Maxwell Taylor's fears, expressed two years earlier, that if the Foreign Service and the State Department failed to meet the "tremendous challenge" of NSAM 341, "the only answer will be to review the decision and find another solution."[8] The "other solution" was clearly the development of leader-

7. Documents relevant to this reorganization appear in: Jackson Subcommittee, "The National Security Council: New Role and Structure, February 7, 1969," also in: Department of State *Newsletter*, No. 94, February 1969.

8. Jackson Subcommittee, "The Secretary of State and the Problem of Coordination: New Duties and Procedures of March 4, 1966," p. 23.

ship responsibility in the White House itself. As Joseph Kraft had written of NSAM 341 in April 1966, "if the changes are not forthcoming, then the coordinating function will slip back to the White House."[9] The Kissinger staff has recently been dubbed by some newsmen the "pocket State Department."

Response to this development in the State Department has been slow and is still uncertain. During the summer of 1969, it abolished its policy planning staff group and established a new Planning and Coordination Staff in the office of the Secretary. This staff is purportedly intended to provide, on the one hand, coordination on current operating problems and, on the other, a longer-range analytic and planning capability. It is clearly too early to define and assess the role of this new organization.

What these recent events may signify for CASP and for the country and regional orientation, one may only speculate. As of October 1969, the new administration had made no significant announcement about PPBS.

9. *Washington Post*, April 12, 1966.

VII

Epilogue—Authors' Commentary:

Issues and Lessons

THIS HAS BEEN a case about organizational change. Unlike most published cases of this genre, this was a case of failure, at least from the standpoint of those who were seeking the change. It may well be that their efforts will flower. But as of 1969 they seemed a good deal less than successful. Apart from such entertainment value as it may have, this case, like others, will be useful to the extent that it contributes to the understanding of issues, strategies, and tactics that may help in other, future change efforts in this and in other contexts. Most of the problems on which the programming thrust foundered were not transitory and were not special to this particular situation. They remain today. A good many of the issues illustrated and dramatized in the case are ubiquitous and timeless problems of public administration, applicable in almost any complex organizational context: the kinds of problems that are summarized in the abstract with "pros" and "cons" in most textbooks on public administration.

In the paragraphs that follow, we undertake to identify those specific issues which seem to us salient and to relate them to broader and ongoing problems of foreign affairs, of American government, and of public administration generally.

In introducing this discussion, we would enter three warn-ings for the reader. First, we acknowledge that we write as Monday morning quarterbacks, with all the advantages of hindsight, and perhaps also its handicaps. Yet such a review is necessary if the strategies and mistakes of last Saturday's game are to contribute to better performance in the next one. We have no reason or intent to impugn either the motives or the intelligence of any of the participants in this case. To our knowledge, every one of them was dedicated to the public interest, sincere, and capable.

Secondly, the treatment of issues that follows is admittedly, perhaps inevitably, oversimplified. Partly this is a consequence of the discipline of brevity. Each issue might merit a book-length monograph (and several of them have). More basically, it is a by-product of the analytic process. A case study like the foregoing one is a relating of events, structured primarily according to the sequence of their occurrence in time. The discussion that follows, on the other hand, is essentially analytic; it is an effort to pull out of the course of events identifiable elements that contributed to them and to describe each in its own terms, distinctive and separate from the others. In the process, the interrelationships and interdependence of the elements are minimized if not lost altogether. The forces themselves are deliberately and artificially simplified into definable categories for the purpose of better understanding of the pieces—and hopefully later, the whole. It is interesting that the intellectual process of analysis is more synthetic (in the other sense of the term) than is that of synthesis.

The third caution to the reader concerns subjectivity and bias. The authors admit to subjectivity, as must any student who is not dwelling on Mt. Olympus. Ours may be described from two aspects. First are the kinds of perspectives and values we bring to the case from our prior education and experience. Probably no one else would identify and describe the issues in exactly the way we have (though we would hope for a good deal of consensus on several of them). Second are the particular and somewhat parochial perspectives upon the case itself deriving from our own participation in it. Both of us were associated with a rather small group of "missionaries" in the State Department, as is made clear in the case, and our initial focus was inescapably tempered by that association. Through a wide variety of interviews and discussions with others, and through the criticisms of others about earlier drafts of the case (including this chapter), we have undertaken to broaden our view. We hope we have been succesful. But the reader should realize that the commentary that follows probably would have been somewhat different with somewhat different emphases had it been written, for example, by someone in the Bureau of the Budget, AID, or the Department of Defense. Yet, it is primarily a State Department case.

1. RATIONALITY AND SYSTEMS

One Budget Bureau official described PPBS to the authors simply as "making the budget process more rational." The State Department programming group also envisioned its system as providing the basis for more rational decision making in foreign affairs—of course, including the budget process. In this general sense, the objective was similar, if not identical. The precise definition of rationality in any given context is elusive, but both the Bureau of the Budget and State Department groups would agree that, in foreign affairs, it would involve:

a clearer understanding of objectives;

the enlargement in amount and improvement in quality of information relevant to decisions, including quantitative data, where pertinent;

a longer-range view;

the projection and comparative analysis of relative costs and benefits of alternative courses of action;

the relating of forward planning with programs of action and with budgets;

the bringing together of relevant information and analyses at appropriate times and at loci of decision power and responsibility;

dispassionate and objective decision making on the basis of the evidence.

In these regards and at this level of specificity, there seems to have been little reason for argument between the two groups. They were natural allies, and they had common opponents, many of which were simply what they considered the obverse of the above—i.e., the absence of agreed and clear objectives, the paucity of information and analysis, the lack of relationship between plans and programs and budgets, a short perspective in time, etc. Both perceived a splintering of decision authority on related matters among different agencies and within each, as well as some decision areas that were simply vacuums in which no official could effectively decide. Both were aware of the absence of system in important foreign affairs fields and the consequently recurrent, almost consistent, "management by emergency"—unplanned, *ad hoc,* and rule of thumb.

These matters, about which the Bureau and the State Department group were in substantial agreement, constituted a major issue in this case. In brief, it was rationality vs. all that the reformers perceived as the enemies of rationality in going organizations—habits, discordant personal values, politics, bureaucracy. In this respect, the issue in foreign affairs was little different from that in the other areas where PPBS—or other uncongenial reforms—are seeking a foothold. The paradox of this case is that this issue was so largely obscured by the dust from the collision of the two groups of reformers, groups which, *in a truly rational world,* one would expect to work together.

At this level of generality and simplicity, few would question the desirability of rationality in foreign affairs decision making. But a good many influential line officers, particularly, would question the equating of rationality with systems analysis, with quantification, and with resource allocation.[1] They would doubt the usefulness either of a detailed data-gathering system such as CCPS or of a system grounded in cost-effectiveness analysis such as PPBS to resolve many, most, or any of the hard problems in foreign affairs. This issue was a real one—how one defined rational decision making in foreign affairs—though it seldom was brought to the surface during the course of the events themselves. There was no unanimity among those line officers who generally opposed or who were skeptical of a systems approach. A good many were only vaguely familiar with CCPS or PPBS or any other "S." while others were very knowledgeable. Some opposed it outright in any manifestation; others thought it might be useful in some places and with regard to some types of activities. Their reasons for opposition and the emphases given each reason varied a good deal. Some of the arguments that were prominent among those expressed to the authors were[2]:

Diplomacy and most (or all) foreign policy decision making are carried on in a world of enormous complexity. No system could possibly accommodate all the elements that must be considered, and systems would tend to bias the result toward those elements which are quantifiable. The *sine qua non's* of good decisions and effective diplomacy are education, experience, and good judgment, not computers.

Events beyond U.S. control are occurring so rapidly that the first requirements of our overseas operations are sensitivity, flexibility, and changeability. Long-range planning in such a

1. The remarks that follow are based primarily upon conversations of the authors, singly or together, with a wide array of officials in foreign affairs, both in Washington and abroad.

2. We attempt to summarize here only the arguments against a systems approach as such. A number of other arguments associated with organization, professional perspectives, personalities, etc., are discussed in succeeding sections of this chapter.

world is useless if not impossible; if it were made effective through a systems approach, it would tie our hands. Diplomacy must be played by ear.

The most important foreign policy decisions (many, most, or all of them) have little or nothing to do with the allocation of resources and little impact upon the budget. It would be a serious mistake (or it would serve no purpose) to tie foreign policy making with the budget process (except, some would acknowledge, in certain fields like foreign aid).

It is virtually impossible (in many or most or all) foreign affairs activities to measure outputs in terms of national objectives. Cost effectiveness analyses in these fields would be futile or even seriously misleading by directing attention only to things that might be measured and ignoring other, perhaps far more important outcomes. Some of the most important and effective decisions in foreign affairs are virtually costless in terms of dollars. Foreign affairs (all or most of it) is ultimately political in purpose; and politics can't be measured.

The Defense Department model is inappropriate for foreign affairs. Defense has an enormous budget, and a very large part of it goes into weapon systems, equipment, and research and development. The most important of the dollars spent in foreign affairs goes into salaries and even Defense has not (yet) pumped its personnel costs into PPBS.

A systems approach (PPBS or CCPS) simply adds another layer to the existing excess of reports and paperwork.

The reaching of important decisions in foreign affairs involves the bringing together and the accommodation of a great variety of interests in the administration, in the Congress, among the American public, and overseas. A system could hardly accommodate these.

Some of these arguments, particularly the last one, have entirely respectable intellectual support from a sector of the academic fraternity. Few of the officers with whom we talked had ever heard of Aaron B. Wildavsky or Charles E. Lindblom, for example, but some of the responses might have been quotations from their books.[3] To these criticisms, the missionary groups in State and the Bureau of the Budget could (and did) respond. They agreed that their systems would not be useful on *all* kinds of foreign affairs problems and might not be *conclusive* on any of them, but would argue that in a great many areas a systematic approach would produce more and better information, more knowledgeable predictions, more alternative courses of action. This would make possible not only better decisions and better management but also a better basis for the decision-maker to support and defend his decisions before (and against) other power centers and interests.

But a most unfortunate aspect of the experience described in this study is that it provided so little real empirical evidence on the merits of the matter one way or the other. Of course, the PPB systems in various agencies and the CASP system which are still being tested may provide better evidence in the future.

2. THE BASE: AGENCY OR FOREIGN COUNTRY

The American foreign affairs community provides a striking illustration of a classical problem in administrative organization: the geographic vs. the functional base. For a number of reasons, the issue is here more sharply drawn than in many fields of public activity. On the one side, the foreign country provides a natural, unavoidable, geographic unit—clearly bounded, official, unambiguous.[4] Historically, the am-

3. See, for example, Wildavsky's *The Politics of the Budgetary Process* (Boston: Little Brown, 1964) and Lindblom's *The Intelligence of Democracy: Decision Making Through Mutual Adjustment.* (New York: Macmillan, The Free Press, 1965).

4. This alleged lack of ambiguity is of course something of a cartographical and legal fiction. One can hardly consider significant problems in any state without also considering its relations with other states, its neighbors, its alliances—both official and informal—its membership in "blocs," its degree of autonomy or, conversely, dependence and subservience to other states and groups of states. In fact, these third (and more) party considerations are often primary in international affairs.

bassador has long been the nation's principal representative in a foreign land, and the pronouncements of recent Presidents have emphasized their intention that he direct all official American activities in his country. The countries are geographically related roughly on a continental basis, thus providing a second administrative level—the region. Soon after World War II, following the recommendations of the first Hoover Commission, the State Department reorganized so as to recognize the region's primacy as the *line* organization of the Department. Various other developments, culminating in NSAM 341 of 1966, clearly indicated the presidential desire that the geographic base—the country with its ambassador, the region with its Assistant Secretary—be primary in foreign affairs.

Against this concept, however, operate a number of real and potent forces favoring functional over geographic primacy. One is that functions are compartmentalized among different departments and agencies (and also within them). Geographic vs. functional here means country-region vs. agency and office. And most of the realities of history and current practice favor the agency. Each has its own powers and responsibilities, usually authorized by statute and official delegation. Each seeks its own resources—i.e., budgets—and has responsibility and accountability for their use. Each has its own subcommittees of Congress to deal with on both substantive and appropriations matters. Each hires its own personnel, controls their assignments, commands their loyalties. The policy of frequent reassignments of personnel by all the agencies—from country to country, not from agency to agency—makes it difficult to build a basic *esprit* for the *American* program in a given country. A career man will be in Country A for two to four years but in Agency X for life. Thus to the legal, congressional, budgetary forces toward compartmentalization on an agency basis are added, in pronounced form, expectable bureaucratic forces in the same direction.

Over the years, some progress has been made in the coordination of foreign policy by the White House, the National Security Council, and the Department of State, and, in individual countries, by the ambassadors. But little has been accomplished in coordinating operational (as distinguished from policy) planning, in substantive work, and in resource allocation. The programming and budgeting aspirations of the State Department group constituted a threat to agency autonomy in these regards, and defense against this threat was a source of resistance.

Curiously, though, the major confrontation was not with the agencies but with the Bureau of the Budget, supported by some of the agencies. The Bureau's agency-based interpretation of PPBS in foreign affairs was consistent with its policy elsewhere in the government. PPBS was not to be used as a device to reform executive organization—at least, not at first. The Bureau pursued its PPB efforts in what it conceived as a realistic manner; it accepted the existing agency structure as given, and its PPBS directive of October 1965 (Bulletin 66-3) was seen by the State Department group as a blow at the heart of country-based programming. Perhaps a better metaphor would be "a threat to transplant another heart in its place."

Although Bureau spokesmen on a number of occasions espoused State Department leadership in all foreign affairs activities, the effect of its PPBS directive was to perpetuate—and possibly strengthen—agency hegemony over resource allocation. In the older as well as newer budget systems, no one was in an effective position to consider U.S. needs for a foreign country as a whole, a region as a whole, or the world as a whole—short of the Bureau itself. Alternative courses of action and resource trade-offs that involved two or more agencies could hardly be effective in the budget process unless by accident and *ad hoc* negotiations.

The accompanying charts depict, in highly simplified

Conceivable Models for Foreign Affairs
Programming and Budgeting

Model I
(The Agency Base)

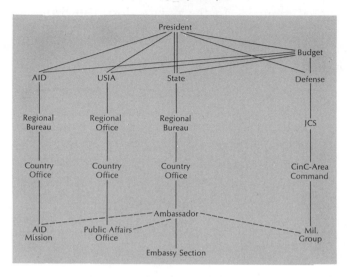

Model II
(Complete Integration, Country Base)

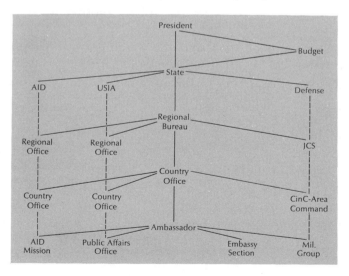

Model III
(Dual Channels)

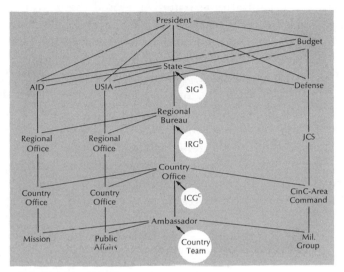

a. Senior Interdepartmental Group
b. Interdepartmental Regional Group
c. Interdepartmental Country Group

terms, three conceivable models for programming and budgeting in foreign affairs. Solid lines represent the flow downward of instructions and decisions and the flow upward of recommendations, estimates, and reports. Dotted lines represent coordination and the flow of information. Model I represents the existing pattern and the vehicle for PPBS as it was initially installed. Model II is an extreme version of complete agency integration under State Department leadership at every level. Under the time constraints of the EROP period, the State group was in effect moving toward this model. Model III, the compromise between the others, takes advantage of the NSAM 341 machinery for coordination at the higher levels. It is roughly consonant with the proposals of the Hitch Committee, the later thinking of the State programming group, and the CASP experiment.

3. CENTRALIZATION-DECENTRALIZATION

A related organizational issue concerned the locus of decision-making authority vertically—i.e., in the field (country) or Washington and, within Washington, at what level of position. The application of programming and budgeting is but a fraction of a much larger problem of communication and responsibility. Historically, ambassadors, separated from their home base by weeks of travel and mail delivery, had to operate with very substantial independence, if they operated at all. The speeding up of transportation to a matter of hours and communication to seconds has facilitated a much higher degree of centralization, and rapid communications within and among foreign countries have necessitated it. Today an American decision concerning matters internal to Brazil, Jordan, or Thailand may have immediate repercussions in Paris, Moscow, and Peking. Such external consequences can hardly be assessed fully in a country post; they almost demand centralization of responsibility in Washington. Further centralization has also been mandated by the "cold war," the "hot wars," the development of dozens of new countries, and the multilateral agencies, particularly the United Nations. It has likewise been encouraged by the vigilance and the demands of Congress.

But some developments have operated in the other direction. Increasing American involvement in a wide variety of facets of foreign societies—their education, agriculture, industry, infrastructure, health, and birthrate, to mention a few—necessitates far-ranging local contacts, familiarity with and understanding of local conditions, cultures, and trends, and opportunity for local initiative and action. The need for on-the-ground knowledge, coupled with growing specialization of overseas personnel, has contributed to growing recognition of decentralization. So have the multiplication of national states and the pace of political and social change within each.

From the standpoint of understanding of local problems, the possibility of completely centralized decision making in Washington has greatly declined.

There is thus a growing necessity both for centralization of decision making *and* for decentralization. Who should have authority to decide what kinds of things, subject to whose review and approval, if anyone's? As in the case of functional integration, discussed above, foreign affairs provides in vivid profile a classic illustration of a classic administrative problem: centralization vs. decentralization. Recent American Presidents have moved in both directions at once; they have sought to strengthen decision-making machinery in Washington and at the same time to enhance the authority and responsibility of ambassadors abroad.

It was noted earlier that budgetary reform and its most recent manifestation, PPBS, have quite consistently encouraged and implemented a higher level of decision-making authority—i.e., centralization. Yet the programming efforts of the State Department group were initiated in the field with the ambassadors. This was partly from necessity, because of the minimal interest and backing in Washington. In this regard the missionaries were running against the centralizing thrust of most budgetary reforms, although their longer-range intent, of course, was to strengthen the power of State Department officers, both in the field and in Washington. The Budget Bureau, although encouraging PPBS from a country base, clearly relied most heavily upon the existing central power centers, the headquarters of the different agencies. And interagency alternatives and trade-offs, under the Budget Bureau's system, could hardly be considered, except at the very top—i.e., the Bureau itself or the White House. In fact, its system was more likely to diminish the influence of ambassadors upon program-budget questions than to enhance them. And it would probably effect little change among the field mission chiefs of other agencies, or among intermediate officials such as assistant secretaries.

4. LEADERSHIP

There is no question that Presidents Kennedy and Johnson both intended that leadership in foreign affairs, as to both policy and operations, be centered in the State Department hierarchy. Kennedy's letter of May 1961 was explicit as to the role of ambassadors; Johnson's NSAM 341 of March 1966 was explicit as to the Secretary, the Under Secretary, and the Assistant Secretaries. Each, at his level, was to be the leader of virtually all foreign affairs activity. The programming group in State felt that an effective programming-budgeting system was a requisite to effective leadership, a sentiment that would undoubtedly be echoed in the Budget Bureau as well as among students of administration generally.

But if programming-budgeting was necessary to effective leadership, leadership at the outset was also necessary to the establishment of effective programming and budgeting. Some of the participants and observers of the events in this case attribute the failure to the absence of leadership from the top. There was not much basis for assurance among lower echelons that they would be backed up if they were in dispute with representatives of other agencies. As an ambassador later said: "When the Secretary says 'GO' loud and clear and makes everyone understand that he means to have it done, then we can fit the [program-budget] pieces together without much difficulty. But until then, why pass our time planning for something that will probably never happen?" In discussing disagreements with representatives of other agencies in his country, the ambassador said that "when it comes to an open confrontation, in most cases if I try to make an issue which will be carried upstairs, it is pretty likely that I will lose. They know it and I know it." Similar sentiments were expressed to the authors by a number of officials in the Department in Washington. Secretary Rusk urged his many assistants to assume initiative and leadership; at the same time he urged against bureaucratic conflict with other agencies. Yet such conflict was nearly inevitable if an effective foreign affairs programming system was to be established under State Department leadership.

There is little evidence that either the Secretary or the Under Secretary was much concerned about, or more than sporadically aware of, programming or PPBS until the Secretary's conversation with Charles Hitch. The letters to the field and to other agencies in June 1966 were very positive, but after that time the Hitch Committee report went into a deep freeze and has not been generally circulated in the Department. The principal high-level support for programming came from Crockett and Rostow, with an occasional helping gesture from one or two regional Assistant Secretaries and a handful of ambassadors. Indeed, there was little communication on the matter with the top echelons of the Department. This situation virtually compelled the initiation of CCPS at the country (ambassadorial) level. And the evident absence of leadership or even interest in the subject at the top of the Department may well have been an element in the Budget Bureau's decision to bypass the Department and go directly to the agencies in the introduction of PPBS. It is doubtful that any integrated foreign affairs PPBS will succeed without forceful leadership from the top. The locus for such leadership could be in either the Department of State or the Executive Office of the President.

We would emphasize that the problem of foreign affairs leadership is *not* merely a product of the mix of individual personalities, interests, and capabilities at the top. It is, in small part at least, a legal problem: the President himself lacks full legal power over all the agencies operating in foreign affairs, and the Secretary of State is in a much more limited position in dealing with other Cabinet members, such as the Secretaries of Defense and Agriculture, and with agency heads, such as the directors of CIA and AID. More important, it is a political problem, in which the Secretary of State must deal with agencies—some of which have far more clientele and congressional support than he has. It is also an institutional problem. Whatever the presidential directives have stated, the Department of State and its Secretary are not yet recognized as the directors and semifinal arbiters of foreign affairs programs in Congress or among the public at large. Further, Secretaries of State and their Under Secretaries are not chosen or appraised on the basis of their managerial competence. They are advisers to Presidents, proponents and defenders of the administration's policies before Congress and the public, negotiators with foreign powers, and fire-fighters, before they are managers. They are unlikely to be selected on the criterion of managerial talent. And if they are, they are unlikely to have the time to exercise it. Those few who have been selected with a view to managerial competence have not left particularly distinguished reputations in the Department of State. Rusk, Ball, and Katzenbach have come close to fulfilling the approved roles in the Department. But none has exhibited much sustained interest in the *management* of the foreign affairs agencies or indeed of the Department itself.

To a considerable, though not a consistent, degree, the same has been true of the second and third echelon officers in the Department of State and of the ambassadors and their deputies abroad. Relatively few have been appointed against criteria of executive management which would be very satisfying either to the Bureau of the Budget or the management missionaries in the Department. There is here a fairly clearcut disagreement in the definition of roles. All would probably agree that the top officials of the Department and its overseas missions should be leaders, but their concept of what leadership should consist of, especially with regard to activities not traditionally associated with the Department, were widely divergent. A number of the line officials in the Department and overseas complained to the authors that the management "reformers" did not understand that their central and primary mission was political policy and diplomacy, not executive management. One Budget Bureau official stated that a major reason, if not *the* major reason, that the Bureau went to the agencies with PPBS rather than through the Department was that the top people of the Department *"did not want it."* And in a comment about an earlier draft of this case, one of the leading "missionaries" in the Department wrote of the ambassadors that:

> . . . they did not really want to exercise the kind of broad managerial leadership that the President was trying to give them and we were trying to implement by CCPS and other means. Most ambassadors, both career and political, were content if their leadership was unchallenged in the political arena and if a few economic and military programs were implemented which most directly supported their own political evaluations. They really didn't want to have to decide whether or not they needed another Agricultural Attache, or that the Legal Attache was less useful to the fulfillment of U.S. policy than another Cultural Attache. They never *really,* on the whole, identified themselves with the President and his goals and his responsibilities. They continued to see themselves and be seen by other agencies as a grandiose State Department representative. . . . They didn't want to lead, didn't lead, and fought very successfully against being made to lead.

But underneath is a basic difference in role perception. At a superficial level, this reflects a semantic difference. Most State Department officers would not agree that they did not want to "lead," but for many of them leading meant, primarily or exclusively, official representation of the United States, assisting the President and Secretary of State in the determination of policy, and making sure that other American activities did not interfere with that policy. It comprehended planning of policy to be sure, but this did not mean planning, programming, and budgeting in the current Washington sense of the terms, and most certainly it did not mean CCPS.

5. BUREAUCRACIES: PURPOSES, PERSPECTIVES, AND POWER

All public organizations have some charter of purpose. And at any level of government, the purpose of any given organization is certain to differ from that of other organizations at the same level, even though there may be—and usually is—a good deal of overlap. These distinctive purposes are based upon constitutions, laws, and executive directives but are greatly modified through experience, through the changing environments in which the organizations operate, and through the impress of the people who are attracted to and employed by the organizations. When the differing views of purpose of several organizations are brought to bear upon the same problem or, as in this case, upon the same foreign country, differences are certain to arise. Such differences are normal, expectable, and ·on the whole probably desirable in a democratic and pluralistic society.

Conflicts in organizational purpose among different agencies occasionally, sometimes explosively, come to public and political attention. And whether or not they ever escalate to the President, Congress, or the public, they are there, they persist, and they may erupt on specific questions. All agencies might find agreement on a statement of American objectives overseas provided it was stated in very general and equivocal language. But each would interpret it and specify it in the frame of reference of its view of its own agency purpose. Thus, while all agencies might agree that the "development" of Country X is a desirable objective—and "development" is itself an ambiguous word—almost certainly there would be organizational differences in perspective on how it should be achieved:

AID would view it from the standpoint of long-range and primarily economic development and productivity;

the State Department would view it in the context of political relations, governmental stability, and effects on relations with other countries;

the Defense Department would view it primarily in relation to its impact upon the national security of the United States and in competition with other undertakings in the defense field;

the Department of Agriculture would consider it in relation to U.S. agricultural production, surpluses, and foreign markets;

the Department of Commerce would view it from the standpoint of trade and foreign markets for U.S. products;

the USIA would view it from the standpoint of foreign opinion and attitudes about the United States;

the Bureau of the Budget would assess it in terms of the demands of other countries and other programs, both in foreign and in domestic affairs, and the probable budgetary resources available;

et cetera.

One of the most long-standing conflicts in purpose-perspective, and one which probably had an important impact upon this case, was that between the Department of State and AID about strategies and projects in foreign assistance. AID and its predecessor agencies had become increasingly impressed that development in foreign countries was a long-term proposition requiring the best possible investments in capital and human resources, investments which might not pay off for many years to come. State, even when it agreed in principle, was concerned about the maintenance of effective diplomatic relations, the support of friendly governments, through AID if necessary, and the impact of assistance to one or another country upon the world situation. State on some occasions insisted upon assistance projects for "political" purposes which AID considered of no long-range value. And AID sometimes sponsored projects which State considered politically unwise.

This underlying difference between agency purposes and perspectives has long been a hotbed of contention between the assistance agencies and the Department of State.[5] Examples of similar endemic differences between the Department of State and other agencies in foreign affairs are plentiful, as are differences between the various agencies, other than the Department of State. In fact, they are built into the very structure of our government. Through the processes of recruitment and training and socialization, they are built into the minds and behaviors of agency officers and employees. If an agency is to be strong and viable, its basic purposes must command the support and loyalty of a substantial portion of its people. When a problem falls within the interests of two or more agencies, the distribution of authority and power between and among them to influence its resolution becomes an important and perhaps contentious issue. This is why questions which to the outsider seem merely procedural—like the timing of the budget process or the nature of its classification—so often become the source of squabbles and "infighting" between and within bureaucracies. Innovations, like those described in this case, can lead to a redistribution of decision-making power on substantive matters, threatening the lessening of influence over agency purposes of some and the strengthening of others.

Some participants and observers of the events of this case viewed them primarily as a struggle between and within bureaucracies seeking either to enlarge or to defend and main-

5. Although Bell's successor as AID Administrator stated in 1968 that it has become "much less of a problem" than it was because both sides have become more exposed and understanding "of the other fellow's business." It is interesting that he endorsed the agency-based PPBS partly on the ground that it "gives us a great deal of information that we can use to try to make this program hew to long-term development, and not get diverted—as is so often the danger—into short-term political objectives where your money is really going to be thrown away." Testimony of William S. Gaud, Administrator, Agency for International Development, in *Hearings* before the Senate Subcommittee on National Security and International Operations, July 11, 1968.

tain their influence and control over programs and purposes. In the judgment of the authors, such bureaucratic conflicts were in considerable degree manifestations and crystallizations of other and deeper issues, many of which are discussed in these pages. But bureaucratic rivalry was undoubtedly a factor, though one can only guess the extent to which it affected motivations and behavior.

We would mention three categories of bureaucratic conflict that may have conditioned this case. First was that within the State Department, between the "old line" Foreign Service and the management "missionaries" generally identified with the names of Deputy Under Secretary Crockett and Barrett, who were viewed, by some FSO's at least, as threatening to "take over" or "move in on" the historic and rightful prerogatives and scope of influence of the Service. Crockett and Barrett were seen as attacking the integrity and the image of the corps itself, not only through the programming system, but through other innovations, especially changes in the personnel system and enlargements in the membership of the Foreign Service (the unsuccessful Hays bill and the unsuccessful effort to absorb the career officers of USIA). This was a long-standing issue, going back at least to the Foreign Service Act of 1946. Crockett's aggressive activities on a wide variety of fronts once again served to bring the issue to a head. The programming effort and the people associated with it received a substantial share of the resistance of the elite corps, defending itself against what it perceived as a threat to its elitism.

Second was the sharpening conflict between the management group in the Department and the Bureau of the Budget, particularly after the President's public endorsement of PPBS, in which he directed the Bureau to supervise the establishment of the system. A vigorous, country-based program budgeting system under State Department leadership could be perceived as an aggressive thrust for power over the budgets of various agencies, a power which was then and hitherto in the province of the Bureau. It might even provide a precedent for consolidation in other Cabinet departments of authority over budgetary decision making with regard to other broad areas of federal endeavor such as education, human resources, or urban development. On the other hand, a strong agency-based PPBS would maintain and probably strengthen the Bureau's influence over foreign affairs budgets. It would have little early impact on the Department's influence, but its immediate effect would be (and was) to destroy the unit in the Department which was developing CCPS and FAPS. Representatives of both groups have denied that this kind of bureaucratic stimulus was significant in their own cases. But some did not hesitate to ascribe it to the other side.

A third set of bureaucratic rivalries arose between the programming group in State and the other foreign affairs agencies. Some of the latter, probably correctly, viewed the development of a country-based programming and budgeting system, operated by State, as a potential encroachment on the prerogatives and powers of their agency. For a variety of reasons, which can only be suggested here, the intensity of this feeling varied widely among and even within agencies. It was not very articulate in USIA, which was already closely allied with the State Department in many ways, both at home and abroad. On the other hand, AID, though technically a part of the State Department, sporadically opposed the interagency, country-based concept and at one stage allied with the Bureau of the Budget to block it. The Foreign Agriculture group, jealous of its autonomy, was opposed, as were some of the military assistance and intelligence personnel in Defense, although the central administrative level in the Pentagon was sympathetic. And the Peace Corps jealously guarded its "independence." But there were differences within agencies, too. Thus AID's Alliance for Progress personnel, already merged with their State Department counterparts in Washington and under a common head, were far more amenable than AID's central leadership, as was demonstrated in the 1967 CASP effort. Our interviews suggest, further, that the field personnel of all agencies were more likely to be in accord with a country-based system than were those in headquarters. The "country team spirit" was consistently more vigorous in the foreign country than in Washington— if it existed along the Potomac at all.

The strength of an agency's position of independence depends in part upon the degree to which its officers and employees *identify* with it and its objectives. It appeared to the authors that in most, but not all, cases, one could fairly well predict an individual's attitude about comprehensive programming on the basis of his agency and assignment. This was suggested by the transfer of a few officials who changed their positions (in both senses of the word) during the course of the case.

But one should not receive the impression that there was slavish conformism to an agency position. Wide differences of opinion and dissidents from the agency position were found in every agency—FSO's who were enthusiastic disciples of programming, Budget Bureau officials who disagreed with their colleagues; military officers and Peace Corps employees who favored a comprehensive system, and employees of the Barrett group who feared at times that their own approach was unrealistic. It is still a reasonably "open" government. The attitude of individual actors was a response to what seemed to them "best" from their perspective; it was not the product either of bureaucratic discipline or simple self-interest. But the way one sees things depends heavily upon where he sees them from, and there can be little doubt that organizational identification provides the lens. As an Army general in charge of one of the larger military groups overseas told one of the authors: "If you are asking me to choose between agency and ambassador, I am an agency man." Probably many of those in all the agencies would echo this sentiment. The Barrett group was running an uphill course.

6. CONFLICTING PROFESSIONAL PERSPECTIVES

It is a truism that one's education and experience condition his way of viewing the world and that part of the world with which he is immediately concerned. Each profession trains its members to a somewhat unique system of values and workways. And when two or three different professions are confronted with the same problem, they inevitably see it differently, define their goals differently, and project different ways of reaching these goals. All may pursue rationality, but their interpretations of the meaning of the term for any given problem may vary widely and are often in direct conflict.

This case presents examples of interprofessional conflict among three principal groups: economists, diplomats, and management specialists. Each group was reasonably well delineated and consistent in its perspectives, but there was variety within each and effort by each to co-opt or infiltrate the others.

The *economists* were relatively late comers to the foreign affairs field, except in AID, where they had exercised considerable influence for many years. The Kennedy and Johnson administrations relied increasingly upon professional economic advice. Economic organizations, like the Council of Economic Advisers,[6] and individual economists, mostly from the academic world, assumed growing stature in the government. This was exemplified by the economists' assumption of leadership in the Budget Bureau (noted earlier), the "whiz kids" in the Defense Department, and finally PPBS itself. The new leadership in federal budgeting consisted of a somewhat special breed of economists. Most of those at or near the top—only a handful in number—were equipped with experience and training in the analysis of governmental programs and their costs, gained in the RAND Corporation and/or in

6. See, for example, Walter W. Heller's *New Dimensions of Political Economy* (Cambridge: Harvard University Press, 1966), especially Chapter I.

the Department of Defense. They brought with them a faith that the modes of economic thinking and technique were or could be made useful, even essential, in decisions on resource allocation in most fields of governmental endeavor, including foreign affairs. Their approach reflected a fundamentally economic view of the world, wherein the idea of the *market* was central. In the absence of a perfect market—as in many public undertakings—the tools of market analysis were still deemed applicable. One's need was to determine objectives, set forth alternative means for reaching these objectives, price each of them, and buy the one that was cheapest (most economical). The development of both alternative objectives and alternative means, as well as the choice among them, depends heavily upon hard data, hard thinking, and sophisticated analysis. Reliable analysis must rest upon quantitative (countable) data, as to both costs (dollars) and product (translated into dollars). Many significant decisions on resource allocation in foreign affairs should thus be rational, objective, quantitative, depersonalized, debureaucratized, depoliticized. They should be reached only after careful analysis, preferably conducted by persons trained in techniques of economic analysis. It should be noted that the two leaders of the Bureau's International Division during the period when the Bureau was most actively involved in this case were Clark and Frey, neither of whom was an economist by training. On the other hand, there is no question that during that period, the basic drive for budgetary reform was PPBS, initiated, led, and pushed by economists and most notably by the Bureau's Director, Schultze, and one of its Assistant Directors, Rowen.

The world view of the *traditional diplomats* was and is almost the antithesis of that of the economists. Deriving from a long history of international diplomacy, they view themselves essentially as *representatives* of the head of state (President) before the heads of foreign states. These relationships are heavily *personal* and, in the larger sense, *political*. Until quite recently, they have had little to do with significant decisions on resource allocation, and today they are more interested in the political than in the economic implications of such decisions. They tend to draw a sharp distinction in their minds between *substance* and *administration;* the latter term, which they interpret to comprehend programming and budgeting, commands little time or respect from them; it can be delegated to technicians. Nor are they skilled in, or disposed toward, quantitative analysis. Important foreign policy decisions are the products of sensitivity, negotiation, sophistication—all developed through a broad, humanistic education and the experience of a diplomat. As one commentator wrote us: "There is much mystique in the practice of diplomacy." It is an ongoing activity aiming to maintain an effective American "presence" abroad. It is not reducible to programs and projects with specific objectives and time deadlines.

This description of the traditional view of the diplomat is, of course, overdrawn for the Foreign Service as a whole. The self-image of the service is today blurred and changing. Many FSO's, particularly the younger officers and those of all levels who are serving in, or in connection with, underdeveloped countries, assume a more aggressive, managerial role; the importance of economics in the "substance" of diplomacy has steadily risen since World War II. Yet there remains a strong feeling for the centrality of the traditional view, especially among the senior and most influential members of the service. It is interesting that the diplomats' resistance to a new programming system or PPBS was supported and matched by the majority of the permanent administrative cadre of the Department of State. Among this group, which included both Foreign Service and Civil Service personnel, there was little enthusiasm for radically new ways of doing business, and there was a tendency to see the innovative management specialists as a threat.

During the course of this story, there was actually a minimum of direct confrontation between the economists and the diplomats. The battleground between them, ultimately to become a no-man's-land, was occupied by the *management* group headed by Crockett and Barrett and identified with CCPS, EROP, and FAPS. These management specialists— like their counterparts in the Bureau of the Budget and other public agencies—were most interested in the development of a system, including planning, organization, procedures, information and communications, timing, etc., that would improve the overall management performance of the agencies concerned. In foreign affairs, programming and budgeting were viewed as tools, not only of rational decision making on individual problems, but also of the integration of power under the ambassadors, the State Department, and the President. Not economists themselves, they perceived economic analysis as a useful and even necessary part of the system, but not its heart. The heart was management. It is interesting to note that some of the leaders themselves came from the Bureau of the Budget and several later departed for the Bureau. It is also interesting that the majority of those associated with the programming effort in State were Foreign Service officers. The programming group drew from both sides.

Yet this group was attacked from both sides, too—and finally crushed between them. This was partly an expectable consequence of the three differing professional views of the world of foreign affairs, summarized above. Partly it was a product of clashes among three professional "empires," in which the management group—like Belgium in two world wars—stood between the other two. At least some of the Foreign Service officers perceived Crockett's programming effort, along with his other reform proposals, as an aggression by administrative personnel to take over the "substance." The FSO's criticized the program personnel for their lack of experience in—and therefore understanding of—the real problems of foreign affairs. On the other side, the economists from the Budget Bureau, Defense, and RAND perceived them as a "breakwater" to obstruct the rising wave of influence of economists in federal management. They criticized them as "tinkerers" who were not getting at the "guts" of the problems, as "simple-minded," and (by clear implication) as not being economists. It should be borne in mind that, during the latter part of this period, the skirmish in foreign affairs was only a sector in the battle to gain a foothold for PPBS throughout the government; some of that battle was going on within the Bureau itself.

A fourth professional group—principally *social psychologists*—contributed a somewhat different viewpoint. Brought to the State Department by the management group on a number of different projects, they influenced the later thinking and strategy of Barrett and his staff, particularly on how to bring about organizational change, with particular emphasis upon motivation and attitude change. Although it cannot be said that their influence upon the Foreign Service (particularly in the sensitivity training groups) greatly affected the outcome of the programming effort in the short run, their long-term influence may be substantial. However, they had little contact with the Budget Bureau. The major handicap to the social psychologists, and to Crockett and Barrett in using their new insights, was that their influence was not brought to bear until very late in the game, when the major controversies were already well developed. It is also possible that their influence during the course of the case was negative. They aroused suspicion among some of the permanent personnel about the Crockett-Barrett efforts in general, including the CCPS-FAPS initiatives.

7. THE PEOPLE

It is neither appropriate nor possible for the authors to dissect the individual personalities in this case, nor the specific features and problems of interpersonal relationships. From the events themselves, it is fairly clear that the two principal leaders of the missionaries, Crockett and Barrett, were able to generate intense loyalties and zeal for the enterprise among their followers, though their styles were quite different. By the same token, they aroused defensiveness, non-support, withdrawal, and, in a few instances, open hostility among many of those outside their orbit, whose behavior they sought to influence. As indicated earlier, the attitudes and reactions of most of the principal figures in this case could be fairly well predicted from their bureaucratic positions, roles, and professional perspectives. To these conditioning factors should be added brief discussions of three others that had impact upon interpersonal relations: age (or youth), the effects of personnel systems, and the duration of assignments.

The Barrett staff consisted mostly of young men in their twenties and early thirties, with few past forty years of age. A number were junior Foreign Service officers, and some came from outside. Few had very much responsible experience in foreign affairs. Yet their assignments required working with and influencing top officers of the Foreign Service, the State Department, and other agencies, far their seniors in both age and experience. They were bright, ambitious, upward-mobile, not particularly respectful of tradition and traditional thinking, sometimes impatient, and little worried about personal security in their jobs. Little wonder that they aroused criticism, defensiveness, and resentment among some of the senior officials with whom they worked. Very likely, the reactions of their seniors matched those of some of the generals, admirals, and colonels of the Defense Department toward McNamara's "whiz kids." The foreign affairs "whiz kids" lacked the backing of a McNamara. Very probably the generation gap, or at least the spread in age and foreign affairs experience, aggravated the problem of effective communication and understanding; almost certainly it provided ammunition for those who would have criticized the programming system anyway.

To the differences in age and experience were added others generated by the personnel systems and the resultant differences in norms and commitment. The proponents of integrated programming sought change as rapidly as possible, not only in techniques and operating procedures but also in attitudes and concepts about the very nature of the foreign affairs missions themselves. Here they were challenging strongly felt norms, rooted in long and honorable traditions, and supported not only by current personnel practices that governed selection, promotion, and selection-out, but also by the systems of living and working together and of mutual accommodation, embedded in the various services themselves. The agencies, and more particularly their personnel systems, would survive Crockett and Barrett as they had survived a good many Presidents and Congresses. In a perceptive recent monograph,[7] Chris Argyris described some of the behavioral consequences of the "living system" and the norms of the Foreign Service, including:

> withdrawal from interpersonal difficulties, conflict and
> aggressiveness;
> minimal interpersonal openness, leveling and trust;
> mistrust of others' aggressive behavior;
> disguise of emotional responses and feelings;
> emphasis upon the substantive, not the administrative
> activities;
> loyalties to others in the system.

As Argyris suggests, most of these attributes apply in greater or lesser degree to other established personnel systems that have had an extended past and have expectancy of an extended future. The foreign affairs personnel of AID, USIA, the Department of Defense, and others are very likely to be in a similar cast, though in varying degrees. The Crockett-Barrett group, young, ambitious, uncommitted to this kind of "living system" was quite different in almost all of the above respects. They were "open," aggressive, zealously dedicated to their mission, and, as some episodes in the case

7. *Some Causes of Organizational Ineffectiveness within the Department of State* (Washington: Department of State, The Center for International Systems Research, 1967).

suggest, emotionally responsive to the ups and downs of their progress.

Differences in the "living system" provide a hospitable environment for differences of opinion. Although the case presents few examples, and only a few more intimations, of opposition to CCPS (or PPBS) by senior officers of the Department and Foreign Service, a good many participants and observers would attest that such opposition was present, was powerful, and may have been decisive. The senior officers were polite, often passively receptive, patient, quiet, but, when the going got rough as in the spring of 1966, nonsupportive. There were few open confrontations and few written commitments one way or the other from which we might quote, except by retired officers. There was no visibly organized resistance; yet the would-be innovators both in the Budget Bureau and the State Department feel that the resistance was there and in high places. One of the latter wrote:

> The other opponent [other than the Bureau of the Budget] was the substantive areas of the Foreign Service who were no less in opposition than was the Bureau but whose opposition was never brought to open confrontation. Their opposition was exercised more subtly, but no less effectively, behind closed doors and over the diplomatic grapevine. It is my feeling that this latter opposition gave our program a mortal weakness—bastardized our product—so that we were no match for the Bureau when their confrontation came. Our product wasn't agency based or agency needed or agency supported.

One is reminded of the victory of the Foreign Service hardliners over the innovators in the State Department, other agencies, and particularly the Bureau of the Budget in the passage of the Foreign Service Act of 1946.[8] Times, themes, and strategies have not changed very much!

8. See Harold Stein's "The Foreign Service Act of 1946," in Harold Stein, ed., *Public Administration and Policy Development* (New York: Harcourt, Brace & World, 1952).

Despite the permanence of the personnel systems involved in the case—particularly the Foreign Service and the military services—and the long-range commitment they demand of their members, one cannot fail to be impressed by the short terms of involvement of individuals in specific programs and positions. Of all the key figures in this case, only one was in the same position at its beginning and end, Secretary Rusk. Most of the others moved two or more times during the period; most of the positions had three or more different occupants.

The authors, in various visits to posts in foreign countries, were impressed by the temporary nature of most key field assignments and the transitory attitude of incumbents toward their position and country of assignment. A minority of those among the several hundred interviewed expected to be at their posts for more than another eighteen months. All expected to rotate to another post or back to Washington before very long. Curiously, in those career personnel systems where the lifetime commitment is strongest—the Foreign Service and the military—the post commitment is likely to be the weakest. Under current policies of relatively frequent rotation, an officer tends, soon after he gets his feet on the ground in his current assignment, to be concerning himself about his next one.

The development of a new system, such as one for programming and budgeting, can hardly produce many demonstrable results within two or three years' time. Yet few who might undertake to install and develop such a system could anticipate being there when its fruits (hopefully) might be reaped. There was little incentive to risk an innovation whose initial costs might be substantial, when the later benefits and credits would probably accrue to someone else. It is ironic that the criticism often directed at political appointees —that the temporary nature of their appointments militates toward short-range goals and efforts—also applies to many career servants. Among all these people—the political appointees in Washington and the field and the career people in Washington and the field—the personnel systems operated against long-range commitments to programs that would not produce short-range results. To them, CCPS, FAPS, or PPBS could offer few attractions.

8. CIRCUMSTANCE AND HAPPENSTANCE

A major difficulty of case histories of this kind in conveying a sense of administrative reality arises from their very focus on individual issues and upon the developments and events over time as perceived from the perspective of those issues. The slice of administrative life which a case study reveals is likely to be a very tiny one in the total context of public organizations. Its significance may appear, even to its participants, to range from near zero to nearly one hundred per cent. CCPS and later PPBS could hardly have seemed more than minor ripples on the outside of the vortex of foreign affairs during a period which encompassed the Cuban missile crisis, the assassination of President Kennedy, the Dominican revolt, the beginning of escalation of the war in Vietnam, to mention only a few of hundreds of critical events and problems for the foreign affairs community. Some of these developments, quite external to the case itself, had important impacts upon it. Thus, the unhappy developments in Vietnam gave impetus to General Taylor's study of organization for foreign affairs generally, which ultimately resulted in NSAM 341. The Dominican uprising occasioned the President's assignment of Ambassador Bunker there, and this was at least one reason that the Bunker Committee dissolved. And President Johnson's decision in 1965 to direct PPBS on a government-wide basis apparently resulted from considerations in which foreign affairs were, at most, minor, and there is no evidence that any of the foreign affairs agencies participated in it or even anticipated it. Yet some observers came to believe that it was the real death-blow to CCPS.

It is also important that the degrees of involvement in,

and commitment to (or against), CCPS and/or PPBS varied widely among the *dramatis personae* of this case. The range in involvement and commitment extended from those who were occasionally and distantly concerned (to whom a system might seem a good thing in the abstract or, conversely, a minor and spasmodic irritant) to those immediately and totally immersed (to whom it might seem an all-consuming mission or a total evil to be resisted at all costs). In between these extremes lay a spectrum of individuals more or less involved, more or less committed. Some felt that a system was a desirable thing which should be supported, along with other things; and others considered it a considerable nuisance which should be resisted when the opportunity presented itself.

The extent of involvement and commitment depended in the first instance upon one's position and the scope of its responsibilities. And secondly it varied over time with the ebb and flow of other problems and concerns competing with CCPS or PPBS. Some of Barrett's staff and some of the Executive Assistants overseas were, for a period, totally immersed in the development of CCPS. Barrett was, too, for a while, but later, as the dimensions of his job enlarged, CCPS commanded only some 50 percent or less of his energies. For Crockett, CCPS was only one of scores of reforms he was pushing—one of the two or three most important—but still only one. Furthermore, a host of extraordinary pressures were converging upon him constantly, so that, over any given period of time, CCPS could claim only a fraction of his energy and attention. Thus it is entirely possible that a Katzenbach, a Rostow, a Crockett, a Barrett, and a Bonham could all entertain favorable views toward a programming system, yet when faced with a strategic decision about it, reach different and even opposing positions. This may explain, for example, the differences between Rostow and Crockett about going to the Secretary for support in their sharpening struggle with the Bureau of the Budget. For a time at least, Rostow was more involved in and insistent about an early and favorable decision about CCPS, even if it required open confrontation, principally because he perceived it as an essential implementing tool for the National Policy Papers. For a variety of reasons, most of which had little to do with the programming effort, Crockett favored compromise; it did not seem to him a strategic time to pitch a major battle with the Bureau of the Budget.

The case is replete with significant incidents and coincidents over which the principal actors had little or no control and which they could hardly predict. Many of these had to do with the assignments, transfers, and travels of key personnel. The early beginnings in Latin America were made possible by the interest of Edward Martin, then Assistant Secretary for that region. His replacement by Thomas C. Mann abruptly terminated that interest and prompted the transfer of the germinal staff to the administrative area under Crockett. Later, the appointment of Lincoln Gordon to the same position probably made possible the renewed interest and the CASP undertaking. The appointment of Katzenbach just as the Hitch Committee report was being finished certainly influenced the disposition of that report, as did the various travels of Rusk, Katzenbach, and Crockett during the fall of 1966. The uprising in Guatemala in the spring of 1965 forced the return of its Ambassador Bell, just as he was getting underway as director of the FROP exercise; and a few weeks later, the departure of Frey to accept an appointment in the Bureau of the Budget removed its principal engineer at a crucial time.

9. CCPS, FAPS, PPBS: STRATEGY AND TACTICS

In retrospect, it does not appear that there was much difference over the long run in the systems as they were visualized by their respective advocates. The goals of rationality and system in foreign affairs decision making were fundamentally the same, with minor differences in emphasis; this was evident in some of the statements by prominent figures quoted earlier in the case. The similarity became more evident in the modifications of CCPS to FAPS, and the later revision of FAPS to simplify, reduce detail, and target on larger issues. The later expressed intention of the Bureau of the Budget to focus on a small number of selected countries, working through the country desk officers, and in this way to develop overall PPBS country program memoranda, would likewise constitute a movement toward common objectives.

The basic issue between the FAPS and PPBS approaches, then, was how to move from *here* to *there;* that is, tactics. If there were basic agreement on the locus of *there,* there were differing perceptions of the locus of *here,* and this contributed to widely varying judgments as to tactics. The State Department group thought it was already well along the track when the Budget Bureau perceived the initiative as just starting. The former made its start with the country as its base and *in* the country, because there was no other firm base from which to start and because it believed the country was the correct base in any event. At the time, it will be recalled, there was no PPBS directive; no NSAM 341, with its SIG and IRG's; no Hitch Committee proposal. The Bureau, on the other hand, made its start on the strength of a PPBS directive that quite clearly enunciated an agency base; subsequently it chose to ignore the NSAM 341 and the Hitch Committee recommendations, except as very long-range goals. Among other things, this difference in timing probably contributed to real differences in perceptions of how to overcome the institutional and political obstacles that both groups recognized.

However, this case convincingly demonstrates the truism that differences in tactics can be extraordinarily important. It is possible (though unlikely) that either type of approach might have reached the same goal, given five or ten years. But, as summarized below, the *initial* tactics were very different:

	State Dept. Group (CCPS and FAPS)	Bureau of the Budget (PPBS)
base	geographic-country	functional-agency
organizational responsibility	State Department— Ambassadors	Bureau of Budget— agencies
emphasis	information gathering	analysis and programming
relation to budget	not immediately related	tied in with budget process
inputs and outputs	emphasis on inputs	emphasis on outputs
classification	common system for all agencies	each agency to determine its own
conceptual approach	managerial	economic
policy base	National Policy Papers (where available)	objectives to be prepared by agencies
installation:		
locus	field	agency headquarters
mode	persuasion and consent	directive
pace	experimental, gradual	immediate

It should be emphasized that most of the features and distinctions indicated above were true, or were intended to be true, only at the outset. Thus the Bureau intended ultimately to develop its system toward a comprehensive country base. And the State Department group intended ultimately that its system be tied in with the budget process. CCPS was, at the beginning, essentially an information system, not a program-budgeting system nor an analytic system, mainly because its founders felt that there was no information to analyze or on which future programs and budgets might be based. The Bureau, on the other hand, built on existing information systems within the agencies. It may be noted too that, with regard to a good many of these features, neither group had much option. After the presidential PPBS announcement, the Bureau *had to* proceed immediately, *had to* relate PPBS with next year's budget process, and *had to* be installed by directive. The State Department group, on the other hand, felt that in building a completely new system that deliberately crossed existing systems, they *had to* be experimental and gradual, *had to* proceed by consent of ambassadors, and *could not* immediately relate their system to the budget process.

As we have noted earlier (in Section 1) the clamor of the debate between the two approaches tended to muffle a more basic issue: the viability, usefulness, and limitations of any quantitative system tied in with the budget process toward more effective decision reaching and management in so volatile a field as foreign affairs. There were and still are a good many doubters, particularly in the policy echelons of the State Department and the Foreign Service. There remains a need for marrying quantitative analysis with judgment based upon qualitative considerations, but it does not appear that a romance between the two was materially encouraged by the events described in this story.

10. STRATEGY FOR INSTITUTIONAL CHANGE

If we leave aside the arguments about the objective merits of *any* quantitative system and the relative merits of the CCPS approach vs. PPBS approach, the case may shed some light upon the basic problems and conditions of effective institutional change. Assuming for the moment that CCPS represented a needed and desirable innovation, to what reasons (other than its objective demerits) can we attribute its total failure? What might have been, and might later be, the ingredients of success?

In the first place, the setting within which it was undertaken was an extraordinarily difficult one for this kind of innovation. It undertook to relate in a common system widely different organizations, some with ancient and venerated traditions, some relatively new, heady and operational. It threatened both the traditions and the headiness. Second, the organizations with which it was concerned were continually exposed and reacting to events, actions, criticisms at home and abroad which would permit only minimal and sporadic attention to the establishment of any system. In the epidemic of international crises and political crises at home, building a completely new system was a little like constructing a hospital just south of the DMZ in South Vietnam.

During part of the same period, PPBS was installed and had some, though apparently spotty, success (and it has been dropped in some areas of the foreign affairs operations, including most of the State Department itself). But why, one may ask, was PPBS partially successful and CCPS a failure? One consideration, we think, is that PPBS was substantially less radical and threatening than CCPS. The former accepted and built upon existing structures and power centers (agency headquarters) and related itself to existing processes and procedures, including the government's strongest decision-forcing process, the budget. CCPS, in contrast, threatened existing power centers, including some of those within the State Department, and it was not related to the budget process. Furthermore, PPBS had certain forces going for it which CCPS lacked: a vigorous and widely publicized presidential directive, repeatedly reinforced by presidential statements; frequent, sometimes daily, contacts between the President and the principal engineer of PPBS, the Director of the Budget, contacts which were widely known in Washington; sympathetic professionals (economists) in key positions in some of the agencies in which PPBS could be most effective (notably AID and the Defense Department); and ultimate administrative control of agency budgets in the Bureau of the Budget, itself the principal sponsor of PPBS.

Still CCPS had a chance as did its sequel, FAPS, and the successor proposed by the Hitch Committee, IFAPS. All of them failed.

Why?

There has been a good deal of soul-searching among the Barrett men on this question. Prominent among their explanations are these:

The top officers of the State Department, the Secretary, Under Secretary, and some immediately below contributed occasional but not active or consistent support, and only very seldom anything that might be termed leadership; this reflected, in part, the inadequate communications between the Crockett-Barrett group and the top echelons of the Department. As one highly placed official later wrote: "Under Secretary Ball told me on several occasions that he simply did not understand what Barrett and his boys were talking about, and Katzenbach was obviously not actively interested, except in recruiting someone else to handle the matter for him."

There was insufficient participation in designing and experimenting with the proposed system by those who would be most affected—hopefully benefited—by it, namely:

1. the substantive officers of the Department, at home and abroad;
2. the officials of the other agencies, at home and abroad;
3. the officials of the Bureau of the Budget.

This, of course, also reflected a failure of communications between the CCPS sponsors and the other groups, which in turn was a by-product of the identification of CCPS with the administrative "types" in the Department.

There was insufficient emphasis, during the development and experiment stages, on establishing a commonality of interest in those foreign affairs problems which were clearly linked with one another for two or more of the foreign affairs agencies and in demonstrating how the system might benefit all of those involved in the solution of those problems. To the others, the system looked too much like a "gimmick" of State's administrative "types." Flowing from this, there was inadequate demonstration of what the system might do in helping on sample problems.

The Crockett-Barrett group commanded too little prestige, either as experienced experts in foreign affairs or as experts in management systems among a fraternity in which prestige is important. Very probably full success would have required at least one or two prestigious figures from each of these sides.

Finally, there was insufficient (or too tardy) assistance and prodding from *outside* the foreign affairs community. Some students of organizational change have stressed that participation from outside the organization itself is an essential ingredient. Such external impetus may take three forms, all of which were illustrated in this case. One is through exhortations and directives from above, herein illustrated by the presidential directives about EROP and NSAM 341. A second is the provision of outside, prestigious expertise on the objective problem, herein illustrated by the Hitch Committee and the Stanford Research Institute. A third is the engaging of experts in organizational development whose instruments are the breaking down of communications barriers, and creation of a climate whereby insiders can identify their own problems and find their own solutions. It was illustrated by the engagement of the National Training Laboratories, the sensitivity training sessions, and other devices. The President's EROP directive was pretty much negated by his PPBS announcement and later the Budget Bureau's directive on the subject. NSAM 341 foundered in the Department's irresolution about making the SIG and the IRG's effective. The report of the Hitch Committee and the work of the Stanford Research Institute dwindled to zero because of the travels of the principals and the ultimately unsuccessful negotiations with Thomas Schelling. And the sensitivity training, a slow process at best, came too little and too late to have much impact upon the outcome of the CCPS (FAPS) effort.

It is impossible to say which of these factors was decisive or whether it was a *gestalt* of all or several of them. But cumulatively they do suggest that, for important organizational change, one should seek:

a leader who will be continuously supportive;

a prestigious person, under the top leader, who will devote most of his energies to the effort;

a basis for commonality of interest among diverse officials on problems of concern to all of them;

participation of those officials who will be affected in the change effort;

experimentation in those problem areas where a significantly useful progress can be demonstrated—and advertisement of that progress;

enlistment, from outside the organizations concerned, of involvement and assistance of all the three kinds enumerated above;

a few participants in the change effort who command prestige among the groups of officials whose support is mandatory.

Of course, if all these elements are present, the situation is ideal. It is perhaps where some of the elements are significantly lacking, as in the State Department in the present story, that the energies and drive of the aspiring innovator are most needed. Then the innovator must decide whether it is worth it to make the try in the face of all the obstacles and odds.

Perhaps the least that can be said in this case study about Crockett and Barrett is that they had a good idea of what they were up against and still they made the try. The words of a commentator in the *New York Times* might have been written about them:

> The administrator, politician or planner who holds convictions enough to battle for solutions—and solutions are always partial, imperfect, debatable and without guarantees—must be an extraordinary combination of gutter tough and intellectual visionary. He does it, surprisingly in an age of cynicism, because he cares.[3]

Finally, to quote a famous musical comedy song, any innovator of important organizational change needs at least "a little bit of luck."

On that we are confident that the proponents of both CCPS and PPBS would agree.

3. Ada Louise Huxtable, "World of the Absurd," *New York Times,* January 14, 1968, p. D25.

Appendixes

Appendix I.

Organization of the Department

of State, November 1966

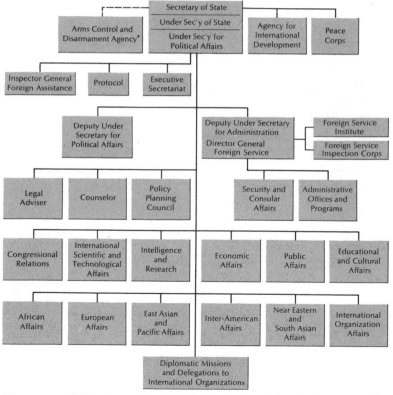

*A separate agency with the Director reporting directly to the Secretary and serving as principal adviser to the Secretary and the President on arms control and disarmament.

Appendix II.

Foreign Affairs Manual Circular No. 385, Based Upon NSAM 341, and also Announcing the New Positions of Country Director, March 4, 1966

1. AUTHORITY AND RESPONSIBILITY OF THE SECRETARY OF STATE

To assist the President in carrying out his responsibilities for the conduct of foreign affairs, he has assigned to the Secretary of State authority and responsibility to the full extent permitted by law for the overall direction, coordination and supervision of interdepartmental activities of the United States Government overseas.

2. ACTIVITIES NOT INCLUDED

Such activities do not include those of United States military forces operating in the field where such forces are under the command of a United States area military commander and such other military activities as the President elects to conduct through military channels.

3. DEFINITION OF "INTERDEPARTMENTAL" ACTIVITIES

Activities which are internal to the execution and administration of the approved programs of a single department or agency and which are not of such a nature as to affect significantly the overall U.S. overseas program in a country or region are not considered to be interdepartmental matters. If disagreement arises at any echelon over whether a matter is interdepartmental or not in the meaning of this circular the dissenting department or agency may appeal to the next higher authority as provided for in the following paragraph.

4. THE CONCEPT OF EXECUTIVE CHAIRMEN

The Secretary of State will discharge his authority and responsibility primarily through the Under Secretary of State and the regional Assistant Secretaries of State, who will be assisted by interdepartmental groups of which they will be executive chairmen, i.e., with full powers of decision on all matters within their purview, unless a member who does not concur requests the referral of a matter to the decision of the next higher authority.

5. THE SENIOR INTERDEPARTMENTAL GROUP (SIG)

To assist the Secretary of State in discharging his authority and responsibility for interdepartmental matters which cannot be dealt with adequately at lower levels or by present established procedures, including those of the Intelligence Community, the Senior Interdepartmental Group (SIG) is established. The SIG shall consist of the Under Secretary of State, Executive Chairman, the Deputy Secretary of Defense, the Administrator of the Agency for International Development, the Director of the Central Intelligence Agency, the Chairman of the Joint Chiefs of Staff, the Director of the United States Information Agency, and the Special Assistant to the President for National Security Affairs. Representatives of other departments and agencies with responsibility for specific matters to be considered will attend on invitation by the Chairman. Such other departments and agencies may raise matters for consideration of the SIG.

The Chairman of the Senior Interdepartmental Group (SIG) may designate the Under Secretary for Economic Affairs or the Deputy Under Secretary for Political Affairs to chair the SIG in the Chairman's absence.

The SIG will assist the Secretary of State by:

a. ensuring that important foreign policy problems requiring interdepartmental attention receive full, prompt and systematic consideration;

b. dealing promptly with interdepartmental matters referred by the Assistant Secretaries of State or raised by any of its members, or, if such matters require higher level consideration, reporting them promptly to the Secretary of State for appropriate handling;

c. assuring a proper selectivity of the areas and issues to which the United States Government applies its resources;

d. carrying out other duties and responsibilities of the Special Group (counterinsurgency), which has been abolished;

e. conducting periodic surveys and checks to verify the adequacy and effectiveness of interdepartmental overseas programs and activities.

The SIG will encourage interdepartmental action and decision making at the Assistant Secretary level to the greatest extent possible.

The SIG will meet in the Department of State regularly and specially at the call of the Chairman.

The Chairman will be supported by a full-time staff headed by a Staff Director who will also serve as the Special Deputy Executive Secretary of the Department. Staff personnel will be furnished on the Chairman's request by the departments and agencies represented on the SIG. The Chairman may request departments and agencies to designate a point of contact for the Staff Director on matters affecting their interests.

The Staff Directors of the Interdepartmental Regional Groups will assist the Staff Director of the SIG as he requires by providing staff support on regional matters of interest to the SIG.

6. THE INTERDEPARTMENTAL REGIONAL GROUP (IRG)

To assist the Assistant Secretaries, an Interdepartmental Regional Group (IRG) is established for each geographic region corresponding to the jurisdiction of the geographic bureaus in the Department of State. Each IRG shall be composed of the regional Assistant Secretary of State, Executive Chairman, and a designated representative from Defense, AID, CIA, the Organization of the Joint Chiefs of Staff, USIA and the White House or NSC staff. Representatives of other departments and agencies with responsibility for specific matters to be considered will attend on invitation by the Chairman.

The regional Assistant Secretaries, in their capacities as Executive Chairmen of the IRGs, will ensure the adequacy of United States policy for the countries in their region and of the plans, programs, resources and performance for implementing that policy. They will be particularly watchful for indications of developing crises and when such matters require higher level consideration, will recommend appropriate measures to higher authority for dealing with emergent critical situations in their regions.

A regional Assistant Secretary may designate a Deputy Assistant Secretary to chair the IRG in the Chairman's absence. IRG meeting and staff procedures will be patterned on the SIG.

7. INTERDEPARTMENTAL LEADERSHIP AND COORDINATION OF
   COUNTRY MATTERS

A new position of Country Director will be established in the regional bureaus to serve as the single focus of responsibility for leadership and coordination of departmental and interdepartmental activities concerning his country or countries of assignment. In particular he will:

a. provide continuing departmental and interdepartmental leadership in planning, coordination, and implementation of decisions;

b. raise specific matters for consideration by the IRG, and bring detailed knowledge to IRG discussions when so requested;

c. serve as the base for crisis task force operations as necessary.

The Country Director will be responsible for seeing that the Ambassador's needs are served both within the Department and government-wide. He will ensure that the mission is fully supported in the full range of its requirements: policy, operations and administration.

Each Country Director will organize and develop such contacts, channels and mechanisms as are appropriate to and necessary for full interdepartmental leadership on country matters, and for full support to the Assistant Secretary.

To assist in providing guidance and direction to the Country Director, the Assistant Secretary will have one or more Deputy Assistant Secretaries whose areas of responsibility will be defined by the Assistant Secretary.

Positions of Office Director and officer-in-charge will be abolished as the transition is made to the establishment of Country Director positions.

Appendix III.

Message of the Secretary of State "To My Colleagues in the Department of State and Abroad" on the Occasion of NSAM 341, March 4, 1966

The President has assigned to me and the Department of State additional responsibility for the over-all direction, coordination and supervision of the interdepartmental activities of the United States Government overseas. This assignment extends to the limits permitted by law and covers all operations of the United States Government abroad except U.S. military forces under area military command and such other military activities as the President may elect to conduct through military channels. The President's directive also established a systematic mechanism for considering the views of other agencies involved in our activities abroad, and for reaching decisions promptly. This responsibility will be discharged in Washington primarily through the Under Secretary and the regional Assistant Secretaries of State. They will be assisted by interdepartmental groups of which they will be executive chairmen with full powers of decision on all matters within their purview. Thus, the Department, and the regional Assistant Secretaries with respect to their geographic areas, will exercise leadership functions and responsibilities at the seat of Government similar to those delineated for Ambassadors within the countries of their assignment by the President's action of May 1961.

In accepting these expanded duties, I have assured the President that the Department will be organized and manned to perform them effectively and expeditiously. I have also assured my colleagues in the Cabinet that their interests and needs that relate to activities abroad will receive careful and sympathetic consideration.

To enable us to discharge our enlarged responsibilities efficiently, I have today directed certain organizational changes be undertaken systematically within the Department.

The Under Secretary and other designated officers of the Department will proceed immediately to strengthen our capability to meet this new challenge and to establish, through prescribed interdepartmental groups and other means, the interdepartmental working relationships essential to achievement of the President's objectives.

No organizational chart can substitute for the abilities and attitudes of people. Our job requires the exercise of exceptional qualities of leadership and demands that officers working on country and regional matters apply an overview of wisdom and judgment that transcends bureau or departmental interests, and focuses on the needs and purposes of the United States Government as a whole in its relationships with other nations. They will be dealing with difficult multiple-agency and Government-wide issues of policy, the planning and control of programs, and the distribution of resources. Their tasks will encompass not only the anticipation and management of crises but the handling of day-to-day operating problems and the orderly promotion of the objectives of our Government with such responsibilities. There can be no room for parochial viewpoints or petty bureaucratic "in fighting." Each of us must recognize that at all times we are, in a real sense, acting for and on behalf of the President, and through him, serving all the people of the United States.

I particularly hope that the new and increased responsibilities given to the geographic Assistant Secretaries and the gradual establishment of the new positions of "Country Directors" will enable us better to serve both the President and our missions abroad. I look to the Country Directors to assume full responsibility, under their Assistant Secretaries, for all activities in the country or countries assigned to them, and to be single focal points in Washington to serve our Ambassadors. In a sense, we are applying the valuable experience that has been gained in the operations of Country Teams abroad to operations here in Washington.

I wish to assure all the Assistant Secretaries that the formation of the Senior Interdepartmental Group will not reduce their access to me. Indeed, I would hope that the work of the SIG would make it possible for problems to come to me more systematically · than in the past.

I know that all of you will share with me a deep resolve to justify the confidence in the Department which the President has manifested by his directive today. Our job is to serve the interests of the United States. Our paramount concern is always the safety of our nation—in familiar words "to secure the blessings of liberty to ourselves and our posterity." We know that it is no longer possible to find security apart from the rest of the world—that we must work incessantly toward a safe environment, toward a reliable peace in which all men can enjoy a better life. In working toward that goal we serve not only our own deepest interests but those of all other peoples who want freedom, progress, and peace.

/s/ Dean Rusk

Appendix IV.

Draft of Memorandum for the Secretary of State

Prepared for Signature of Messrs. Rostow and

Crockett (Never Officially Transmitted),

March 7, 1966

Subject: The Future of Planning and Programming

Pursuant to your 1962 instructions, we have undertaken in selected countries around the world a program of National Policy Papers that analyze United States interests and provide comprehensive statements of United States strategy, objectives, and courses of action. To date we have completed NPPs for thirteen countries. Another six are in preparation. When the latter are completed we will have authoritative detailed policy documents for the countries in which 42 per cent of all U.S. expenditures (except military) are made.

You have now been assigned additional responsibilities for the over-all direction, coordination, and supervision of interdepartmental activities of our Government overseas by the March 3, 1966 NSAM.

We propose the following steps as essential to rapid and effective implementation of the President's directive in the fields of national and regional policy planning and programming:

a. An acceleration in the NPP program through revision and streamlining of the methods and procedures used in their preparation and approval.

b. The design and prompt provision of authoritative interim policy papers for those countries where a completed NPP cannot be expected within the next six to twelve months and where we intend (as in the case of the Latin American countries) to establish foreign affairs programming.

c. The installation as rapidly as possible of a foreign affairs programming system in successive regions to complement the policy planning actions.

We have from the beginning recognized that we must examine the actual use of resources in each country and region before we can be confident that our efforts overseas are being sensitively related to established policies, objectives, and courses of action. For this reason we have been working for three years on a programming system that will display in a common language present and proposed uses of all U.S. resources in relation to official objectives and purposes.

Various versions of this system have been experimentally installed in thirty-two countries throughout the world, thirteen of which used the system as the basis for last year's Executive Review of Overseas Programs. On the basis of this experience, we have prepared further simplifications and improvements which we now believe give us a workable system.

Two problems confront us.

The first is the negative reaction to these continued efforts expressed to a greater or lesser extent by working levels in all the foreign affairs agencies except the Department of Defense. The second is a similar but much stronger response from the working level of the Bureau of the Budget.

Several of the foreign affairs agencies, notably AID and FAS, view our planning and programming activities as a potential constraint on their discretionary authority and a threat to their institutional autonomy. They point out that these inferred invasions are inappropriate so long as they are being held individually accountable for their programs by the President and Congress. While we can understand and to an extent sympathize with these concerns, we believe the issue has been settled by the President's directive which both establishes the responsibilities of the Secretary of State and provides a forum for resolving interagency issues.

Although we established agreement earlier with Mr. Schultze, the working level of the Bureau of the Budget has continued to oppose the Department of State's developing a capability to examine foreign affairs programming on a country and regional level involving the resources of all U.S. agencies. They believe the Planning, Programming, and Budgeting Systems (PPBSs) being installed by all agencies under Bureau of the Budget Circular 66-3, are sufficient for the President's and the Department's purposes, and that the Department of State should cease its efforts to develop a comprehensive country and regionally-based system.

It is perfectly clear to us that the programming system we envisage is a necessary complement to the various agency PPBSs. The analysis by the Bureau of the Budget of agency budgets and programs in terms of their specific functions cannot be intimately related to country and regional policies and cannot, therefore, meet our needs and responsibilities. A foreign affairs program must be built from the ground up, from individual country and regional policy objectives, and with full knowledge in each country of the role of each agency in fulfilling national objectives under the guidance of the Ambassador.

The working levels of other foreign affairs agencies are attracted to the more traditional Bureau of the Budget approach because it avoids the assessment of their programs in the light of all pertinent national objectives. They may also see in this approach a way of diluting the Ambassador's responsibilities for the orchestration of all country programs.

Ironically, the Budget Bureau's views represent a movement away from the tested and successful Pentagon approach that has placed the national defense above service interests and systematically arrayed service programs against specific national defense objectives. It is the essence of modern programming that the use of resources be related to objectives and purposes: not to agency functions.

In working level debates with the Budget Bureau, three major arguments are advanced against the Department's planning and programming system:

a. *The NPPs are not sufficiently precise to provide a base for budget programming.* The NPPs go further than any previous national policy papers in relating policies and objectives to specific courses of action. They do not—and they should not—pretend to specify in full detail, aid, information, counter-insurgency, and other operational programs. They do, however, provide a single authoritative instrument for relating the use of resources in a country (or a region) to high priority tasks and thus help assure "a proper selectivity of the areas and issues to which the United States Government applies its resources." Put another way, the National Policy Papers were never designed to do the work of the various agencies for them, nor to do the work of the Bureau of the Budget in critically reviewing agency operations. But they do fill a gap which cannot be fulfilled by any other means known to us—a gap made vivid for us all in 1962 when we confronted a proliferation of uncoordinated national policy papers arising from the several agencies.

b. *The Department of State programming system does not meaningfully array resource data, nor do foreign affairs programs compete for resource allocations.* In part this is a reflection of the functional vs. purpose argument cited above. As we indicated there, the BOB's current approach to programming is to develop PPB systems for each major department and agency. In the foreign affairs area, this approach will result in vertical reflections of agency programs that are closely tied to the financial structure and the organizational and functional delineations of each agency. Our approach, on the other hand, has been to design a horizontal array of inter-agency programs closely tied to policy objectives and national purpose. We believe both views—the vertical and the horizontal—are desirable and will provide valuable insights into trade-off possibilities, alternative solutions to problems, and program gaps, overlaps and duplications.

The second half of the BOB contention, namely that foreign affairs resources are not competitive, in our opinion is simply not true. The authorized programs of the various agencies engaged in foreign affairs do offer alternatives and options when reviewed from the standpoint of national objectives. An unfavorable U.S. balance of payments situation with a given country may be improved more by the visit of a trade mission or a trade fair than by the work of a U.S. Travel Service office. Successful negotiations to remove travel and currency restrictions may have more impact than either. Rural development in a given country may be more effectively and economically performed by Peace Corps volunteers than by AID technicians. Educational development may be more effectively accomplished by supporting local institutions than by financing study in the U.S. All three of these examples involve program decisions that cut across existing agency lines.

The problem is not lack of competition but rather the absence of techniques and mechanisms for identifying and resolving competition. Cost benefit analysis in defense relates resources to our ability to kill people. Foreign affairs does not provide any simple mathematical equivalent. A simple quantitative approach to student exchanges or, even, to agricultural credit, or other AID operations would be illusory. To say the problem of adjusting resource use to foreign affairs objectives is difficult—and requires wisdom and intimate knowledge of each country—does not mean that we are justified in abandoning our effort to feel our way towards a matching of resource use to country and regional objectives. An effort to manage foreign affairs resources by agency budgeting in Washington, without examining carefully their use in each country, abandons the problem; it does not solve it.

c. *The absence of provable budgetary changes flowing from the experimental review of agency programs in last year's thirteen country exercise (EROP).* This assertion is only partially true. A number of program changes are being made by the various agencies themselves as a result of Ambassadorial recommendations. It is true that the Budget Bureau (largely because of time factors) did not include EROP recommendations in their consideration of agency budgets. For example, the budget for the U.S. Travel Service was increased by some $1,700,000 despite firm recommendations for reductions totaling $350,100 from Ambassadors in four of the eleven countries in which the Travel Service operates.

It is fair to say that the missing element in EROP was an institutional mechanism that could effectively implement the decisions which resulted from the analysis of data collected across agency lines. The President's action creating the SIG and IRGs in each region solves that dilemma.

In spite of these differences, we believe we must maintain the closest possible cooperation with the Bureau of the Budget to insure that we achieve a maximum of reciprocal benefits and a convergence between the two systems. In fact, our system can provide each agency PPBS with such data as they may desire due to the built-in flexibility of the computer program.

To summarize: we have invested a considerable effort in the development of integrated planning and programming systems covering the entire foreign affairs spectrum, based, as a Department of State system must be, on country and regional objectives. These systems are now ready for full application. The prospect of such action is being opposed in some quarters on essentially bureaucratic grounds.

Our response is that we have learned much in the past three years. We know we don't have all the answers to an evolving and complex problem for which there is no precise precedent. We are convinced that the resolute carrying forward of the effort begun three years ago is a vital link in fulfilling your responsibilities under NSAM 341. We are equally convinced that an abandonment of these efforts now will go far toward gutting the essential purposes of that document.

We therefore recommend that you:

1. Officially endorse these efforts in appropriate notifications to the executive departments and agencies and our Ambassadors; and,

2. Authorize us to proceed with our plans for the immediate installation of the foreign affairs planning and programming system in the Latin America region.

We respectfully urge prompt consideration of these recommendations. We believe the lead time permitting a review of the FY-1968 budget cycle from the Latin America region requires your decision by March 11, 1966.

Appendix V.

Program Structures of CCPS, FAPS, and PPBS

A. Evolution of First-Level Categories in CCPS and FAPS.

Initial, 1963	CCPS, 1964	CCPS-EROP, and FAPS* 1965-66	Final FAPS, and CASP 1966-67
Influencing	International	Management	Political, Internal
Assistance	Relations	International	Political,
Reports	Internal	Relations	International
Special Services	Development	Internal	Economic/Social,
General Support	Reports	Development	Internal
	Special Services	Standard Services	Economic/Social,
	General Support	Administration	International
			Security, Internal
			Security, International
			Cultural/ Psychological

* The primary classification in the last version of CCPS and the first version of FAPS were identical, but there were substantial differences in the second and third levels.

B. Comparison of Second-Level Categories, CCPS and FAPS, 1964-66

In many ways the development of viable categories at the second level is more difficult and critical than at the first level of the "program packages." In the State Department programming effort, changes were made at the second level more often than at the first level. Following are the second-level categories (for two of the five "program packages"—the two substantive ones) for three different versions of the system: early CCPS, late CCPS, and early FAPS.

Level I Category	Level II Categories	
CCPS-1964	CCPS-1965	FAPS-1966
International Relations	Political Economic Social/Cultural Security	Official Relations Contacts Exchanges Dissemination of Information Assistance, Bilateral Assistance, Multilateral	U.S. Influence & Presence U.S. Policies Support U.S. Exports & Tourism to U.S. Other Economics Bilateral Multilateral Organizations Special Programs
Internal Development	Political Economic Social/Cultural Security	Official Relations Contacts Exchanges Dissemination of Information Assistance, Bilateral Assistance, Multilateral	Feeding Health Population Control Internal Stability Institution Development Skills Development Infrastructure Capital Formation General Support Special Programs

Note that the second-level categories for 1964 are sectors, for 1965 they are techniques, and for 1966 they are objectives ("output-oriented"). The essentially neutral character of the categories in the CCPS explains why the same set of categories is applied to both of the program packages whereas the categories differ for each package under the FAPS.

C. Sample Program Structures of Some Foreign Affairs Agencies for PPBS, 1966

1. *State Department*—9 Programs:
   I. Direction of Foreign Policy
   II. Conduct of Bilateral and Regional Affairs—African Affairs
   III.   "   "   "   "   "   " —Inter-American Affairs
   IV.   "   "   "   "   "   " —European Affairs
   V.   "   "   "   "   "   " —Far Eastern Affairs
   VI.   "   "   "   "   "   " —Near East and South Asian Affairs
   VII. Relations with International Organizations, International Organization Affairs
   VIII. Public Services
   IX. Central Administration Services

Programs were further divided to the second and third level under the headings:

   A. Direction
   B. Political and Politico-Military Affairs
   C. Economic Affairs
   D. Consular Affairs
   E. Educational and Cultural Affairs
   F. Administrative Support
   G. International Travel
   H. General Substantive Support

2. *USIA*—7 programs by region: Far East, Africa, Near East-South Asia, Latin America, West Europe, Soviet Union-East Europe, and other

   Each program subdivided according to media: radio, motion pictures and television, press and publications, centers and English teaching, exhibits, books, exchanges, personal contacts, research general support

3. *AID*—Each of the major AID countries developed its own structure, so all were different. These classifications were referred to as goals and subgoals. The goals developed for two countries (but not their subgoals) were:

India

1. Improvement of B/P to achieve per capita growth of 4% by 1971
2. Accelerate transformation to commercial agriculture
3. Increase productivity and welfare of individuals and families
4. Improve educational system to produce trained manpower
5. Encourage fuller utilization of manpower
6. Increase the supply of electric energy
7. Expand the capacity and capability of transport facilities
8. Improve states' capacity to plan, implement and manage development

Nigeria

1. Improved planning and policy analysis
2. Unified, development-oriented, efficient education system
3. Relieve manpower bottlenecks
4. Industrial development
5. Agricultural development
6. Public sector investment

4. *Peace Corps*—Programs were submitted from each country in a standard two-level structure. The first level was as follows:
   program direction and support
   food supply (the problem of hunger)
   education (the problem of ignorance)
   health and sanitation (the problem of sickness and disease)
   public and private institutions (the problem of nation-building)

The Island of the Grass King

*"On the back of the Great Dane
rode an old woman in a green cloak."*

The Island of the Grass King

The Further Adventures of Anatole

by Nancy Willard

ILLUSTRATIONS BY DAVID MCPHAIL

Decorative letters by John O'Connor

Harcourt Brace Jovanovich

NEW YORK AND LONDON

Requests for permission to make copies of
any part of the work should be mailed to:
Permissions, Harcourt Brace Jovanovich, Inc.,
757 Third Avenue, New York, N.Y. 10017

Printed in the United States of America

Library of Congress Cataloging in Publication Data

Willard, Nancy
The island of the grass king.
SUMMARY: Anatole embarks on a fantastical
journey to the island where the wild fennel grows.
[1. Fantasy]   I. Title.
PZ7.W6553Is   [Fic]   78-20574
ISBN 0-15-239082-0

First edition

B C D E

For James, to take on his travels

The Island of the Grass King

ennel," said Grandmother, "if I only had my fennel back! It used to grow right here. I believe the winter killed it."

And breathing heavily, she sat down on the stone bench hidden among the larkspurs at the back of the garden. Anatole sat down beside her. It always alarmed him when she wheezed for breath, but he tried not to show his concern.

"Did you take your medicine, Grandma?"

Grandmother drew from her pocket a little bottle with a spout at one end and a bulb at the other. She held the spout to her mouth, pressed the bulb, and inhaled deeply. Then she held up the bottle to see how much was left.

"Nearly gone," she observed. "The doctor said I could only take it twice a day. It helps my breathing, but it can't be good for me. Now if he'd prescribed fennel tea, I could drink as much as I wanted. Fennel's an old cure for asthma."

"Can't you buy more fennel?" asked Anatole.

Grandmother brushed some dead leaves off the face of the sundial.

"No. Not like what I lost. Your grandpa got the seeds from his high school botany teacher, who got it from an island he once visited where fennel grew wild. Wild plants are best for healing. Well, nothing lasts forever, does it? How hot the sun is! I'm going indoors."

Anatole followed her to the back porch, and together they cleared the old magazines off the swing, leaving only Plumpet, Anatole's orange cat, snoozing at the foot. Grandma never allowed anyone to interrupt Plumpet's naps, and if the cat chose to curl up on Grandma's paper while she was writing a letter, she simply wrote around her, though it left a great hole in the middle of her letter, like this:

Dear Anna and Theo,

I hope you are en-
joying your stay in London.
Anatole and I are getting along
famously. Today he vacuumed
the downstairs while I made
a lemon pie. Then in the
afternoon we went to a
garage sale, and he bought a shoe box full of
baseball cards for 25¢. and guess who he
got? Babe Ruth! Love,
mother

Grandma sat down on the swing and closed her eyes. Anatole sat down beside her and did not close his, for over the back of the swing hung a map of the world, and he enjoyed finding all the places he would visit someday. First he found England, because his parents were there right now, and just yesterday he had gotten a postcard from his papa with a picture of the Queen on it.

Then he found Florida, where Grandma spoke of going for the winter, but never did. The brown-winged splotch that lay just north of Florida and south of Bermuda puzzled him, for it did not seem to be one of the real places that had names. And there were odd streaks to the west of Puerto Rico, where the rain had leaked in through the roof once and left its footprints on everything.

Far away the sky rumbled. Anatole sat up and peered through the screens to see if a storm was gathering, but the evergreens and wisteria grew so thickly around the porch that he could see nothing but leaves and the leaves' shadows which brushed like lace over the floor.

Grandmother opened her eyes.

"Listen."

"Thunder," said Anatole.

"Mother Weather-sky is moving her furniture," said Grandmother. "She's never satisfied with the present arrangements."

Suddenly a great crack of thunder shook everything, and the rain seemed to burst from the clouds. It roared like a drumroll on the eaves-trough overhead, yet the lacy shadows on the floor did not fade.

"Rain and sun together," said Grandmother. "That means a rainbow. I haven't seen one for ages."

"I've never seen a rainbow," said Anatole. "I mean, not in the sky," he added, for his mother had shown him the earth rainbows that lazed in puddles on the road after a storm, and his father had shown him the small rainbows stirred up by the lawn sprinkler and had told him they didn't come from the hose.

"Perhaps big rainbows are extinct," said Grandmother. "I used to wish on the big rainbows. Or perhaps there's one just behind those trees."

"Can we wish on it even if we can't see it?" asked Anatole.

"Of course we can. I wish that my housework would do itself tonight."

Anatole did not tell his wish, for fear it would not come true.

"And can Plumpet make a wish too?" he asked. "Only I'll have to make it for her. I suppose she would like to talk our language, so she could tell you when she's hungry."

"She does quite well already," said Grandmother. "In the meantime, while we are waiting for miracles, we have the Sears Roebuck catalogue to wish on."

Grandma kept the catalogue by the swing so that she and Anatole could consult it when they wanted to make wishes.

Now they leafed through the toy section, page by page, deciding what they would like to have most. Grandma chose for herself a lovely bride doll, which she said she had always dreamed of as a child but never owned. Anatole chose the disguise kit. Then, as a favor to Grandmother, he turned to the section on kitchenwares, but he was so long in finding the page on dishwashers that when he was ready to make his wish, he found Grandmother had fallen asleep.

He laid the catalogue on the floor and tiptoed indoors. From the dining room table rose the dark shapes of teapots, urns, and pitchers. He and Grandma had found them all this very morning after his ball rolled under the guest-room bathtub, and they'd both scrambled down on their hands and knees to fetch it. First he found a harmonica with dust in its teeth.

"That belonged to your mother," said Grandmother. "She used to play 'Yankee Doodle' on it while she stirred the cheese sauce on the days I made broccoli for supper. I didn't know it was still in the house."

"Can I have it?" asked Anatole.

Grandma nodded and put it in his pocket. Then suddenly they both spied something round and flat under the tub, and Grandma gave a shout of joy.

"So that's where I hid the silver! It's been missing for two years."

And she pulled out a platter and half a dozen forks and a short squat coffeepot. The coffeepot had feet, three of

*". . . when he was ready to make his wish, he found
Grandmother had fallen asleep."*

them, which ended rather ominously in claws. Anatole did not believe these things could be real silver—they looked so dark—but he carried them downstairs anyway. And when Grandma brought out the tin of polish and two polishing cloths, he set to work and soon saw how much lay hidden under the heavy tarnish.

But they hadn't finished, and the coffeepot had one bright side and one dark side. Anatole took up the cloth and, feeling very helpful, began to rub away at a spot on the dark side of the coffeepot. And now a curious thing happened. The more he rubbed, the more he saw. Leaves appeared here, flowers there, and a dozen animal faces behind them, till he believed he was looking into a forest in which the sun was just rising.

He was so busy that he did not hear Grandmother come up behind him.

"What a wonderful discovery! I never knew there were so many creatures on that old coffeepot."

"Can we eat off these dishes tonight?" asked Anatole.

"*You* can," said Grandmother. "They're too fancy for me."

"But you bought them!"

"No, I didn't. When your father's great-aunt died, all her things were sent to us. She bought those dishes. You can't imagine the number of curiosities we received when she died. The only one I like is the barometer. It really works."

And from the top of the china cabinet she lifted something that looked like a clock with only one hand. Its numbers were in all the wrong places, and it was set in the belly of a white pig.

"I wish I had a barometer," said Anatole, who was fond of pigs.

"When the needle moves to the left, it's a storm. To the right—"

Suddenly a clap of thunder shook everything. And Grandmother, as if it had been a bell, said, "Time for supper."

They ate peanut butter sandwiches in the kitchen on the dropleaf table that wiggled if you leaned on it too hard, and Grandmother tried in vain to pry open a jar of strawberry preserves, remarking all the while on the obstinacy of inanimate things. And then they listened to the rain turning itself on and off, till the windows grew quite dark. Anatole took out the harmonica and tried "Yankee Doodle." Grandmother listened gravely. By the time he reached the last line he was winded.

"You play almost as well as your mother did," she observed. "I could always tell how she was feeling by the music she played. She used to play 'Ruby' when she was feeling low. Do you know 'Ruby'?"

"No," said Anatole. "Is it harder than 'Yankee Doodle'?"

"It's slower but longer," said Grandmother. "It was popular once, in certain circles."

When they had cleared the table and rinsed the dishes, Grandmother helped Anatole make up the sofa in the living room. Though there were plenty of beds in the house, he liked the sofa best of all. He did not ask her to tell him a story, though she told lovely stories. His mother had warned him not to give Grandma extra trouble in any way. So he said, "Do you have any nice picture books I can read to-night?"

"What kind do you want tonight?"

"I want another book about monsters."

"I think we have found all the monster pictures in the *National Geographic*, but I have another book you might like just as well," said Grandmother, and she disappeared into the sun-room.

When she came back, she was holding a fat book bound in brown leather and tooled with gold. "Did I ever tell you why we were so poor when I was little? My father was a doctor, and if people couldn't pay him in money, he'd let them pay him in whatever way they could. He once treated a man who lived in a castle. You'd think a man who lived in a castle could pay his bills. But no, he gave my father this book about a man who goes on a long journey. When I was a child, my sisters and I mapped out the whole journey in our back-yard. And how the patients used to stare when we said, 'Look out! You're walking on the Enchanted Ground!' or 'Watch your footing, that's the Hill of Difficulty!' for there was nothing to be seen but the asparagus patch and the front steps."

And she opened the book to a picture of a dragon breathing fire and smoke on a very small man standing just at the edge of its enormous paws. Plumpet jumped on Anatole's lap, as if she wanted to look also.

"Have you any monsters in this house?" asked Anatole.

"We'll go exploring one of these days and find out," said Grandmother.

"Can I keep Plumpet with me tonight?" asked Anatole, hoping Grandmother wouldn't put her outside, for sometimes she roamed about the house at night, pouncing on moths. She never caught the moths but she always woke up Grandmother.

"Plumpet, you take care of Anatole," said Grandmother. "Make sure he brushes his teeth."

Anatole brushed his teeth, but he forgot to change from his shorts to his pajamas and to take his sneakers off, and by the time he remembered, he was too sleepy to care. He looked for a few minutes at the pictures in the book; then he stretched out his arm to the table behind him and turned out his light.

But the moon did not turn off hers. For a few minutes Anatole heard Grandma coughing upstairs. Then silence seemed to fill the house from top to bottom. Even Plumpet had stopped purring, but she warmed Anatole's feet with her stomach, and he was glad for her company. If he were home, his mother would come to him and sing his favorite song about the boy who played the harmonica so well that he was king of the world. *Every thing that heard him play* (here she would tuck him in), *even the billows of the sea* (here Plumpet would jump on the bed), *hung their heads and then lay by* (here she would turn off the hall light and he would begin to feel sleepy).

He did not feel sleepy now. He glanced into the round mirror over the fireplace and saw the dining room. The moon was shining through the French door at the far end.

Presently he heard voices. Glancing again at the mirror, he thought he saw lights moving across its pale surface. Very quietly he got up and crossed to the door that joined his room to the other and peered between the hinges. What he saw astonished him.

A teapot was rolling in the silver polish like a pig in a puddle, and the forks were scrubbing each other with their prongs, and the platter was shouting angrily to the dishes in the kitchen. Anatole crept around the door and edged out till he had a good view of the kitchen. The glasses from which he and Grandma had drunk lemonade only a few hours before were dancing in the sink, and the plates were all lined up on the drainboard singing:

> "The kettles and the dishes,
>   they rule the happy home.
>   Of all the rooms in Grandma's house,
>   the kitchen wears the crown."

"So Grandma got her wish!" exclaimed Anatole to himself.

An old skillet caught sight of him and nudged him out of his hiding place.

"He shall settle it! He shall settle it!"

And hearing that someone of importance had arrived, the cups and glasses and plates marched from the kitchen and assembled themselves around Anatole. There was something especially touching about the cups, for every one had a chipped lip or a handle broken off, and they stood as proudly as soldiers who have come through a great battle.

"Well, which of us wears the crown?" asked the skillet. "The silver dishes, spoiled things, who never do a lick of work, or the good folk of the kitchen, who really earn their keep and are thrown into the garbage at the end of their lives?"

Anatole was about to say that the silver did very well for company dinners and the kitchen dishes were awfully noble to help out the rest of the time, but before he could find words, a great light flooded the room, and all the dishes turned around to see where it came from. Beyond the French door, the moon had gotten itself tangled in Grandma's clothesline.

"Look!" said Plumpet. "There in the yard!"

It was not the moon that sent such brightness everywhere, but something enormous that shook the light off its wings like drops of rain. Anatole pulled back the latch on the door and ran outside in time to see the wings rise and fall and disappear behind Grandma's broken-down garage.

ven during the day, Anatole stayed clear of the dark passage behind Grandma's garage. The neighbors who lived in back of Grandma piled their old leaves and grass cuttings there. Nettles and Virginia creeper grew in all directions. An abandoned lilac bush had long ago shut out the sunlight, making the place a perfect garden of toadstools. The car in Grandma's garage had been driven by Grandpa before he died. Grandma did not like machines. She did not know how to drive, and she kept the car only for sentiment. Through the broken slats in the back wall, one could see old mowers, scythes, bottles. Mildew spotted everything.

At the edge of the dark yard, Anatole paused. He thought once more of the wings and the extraordinary brilliance they had shaken on the grass, the clothesline, the dining room floor. Then he crept around the corner of the garage and held his breath.

On the heap of dead leaves stood a giant horse. It was as high as the garage, and as gray as a stormy sky, and it was fanning its wings back and forth, stirring the leaves and brushing away the toadstools. With every pulse its wings scattered a burst of light, and the nettles shone—now red, now green, now blue, now silver.

"On the heap of dead leaves stood a giant horse."

"So you see," said the horse, as if resuming an old conversation, "rainbows are not extinct. My brothers and I often come here, but your Grandma never prunes her shrubs, so she never sees the rainbow anymore."

"Are you the rainbow?" asked Anatole.

"No, indeed. There is only one rainbow in the sky, and the rain lets people see it in different places, at different times. I know this, for I live at the top of it when I am not visiting the earth. Nice garden, your grandmother's. I saw you sitting with her this afternoon."

"I didn't see you," said Anatole.

"No," said the horse. "My brothers and I, we keep to ourselves."

"Then why can I see you now?"

"Because you wished that Grandma might get her fennel back, and I've come to take you to the place where it grows wild. Are you ready to leave?"

Anatole clapped his hands.

"Oh, yes! Is it far?"

"Very far," answered the horse.

He lowered his head and turned over a dead leaf with his hoof. "I don't suppose you've got a few oats in the house you could spare? It's no trouble to you, this journey. You have nothing to do but sit on my back. As for me—"

"Just a minute," said Anatole, and he ran across the wet grass into the house.

The pots and pans and plates, huddled at the French

door with their spouts and handles pressed to the glass, crowded around him.

"What did you see? What did you see?"

"I found a horse," said Anatole, making a path through them. "A rainbow horse. And he's going to show me where Grandma's fennel went, and she'll be well again. Let me by."

They followed him into the kitchen, shouting and clamoring as he climbed up on a stool and searched the cupboard for the oatmeal. Then he remembered that Grandma had used it to make granola. So he took down the jar of granola, which smelled sweetly of almonds and honey, and he was about to carry it out to the horse when a voice said, "And what will Grandma eat for her breakfast?"

Glaring at him from the top of the breadbox was a crouched Plumpet. The silver coffeepot was knocking against Anatole's shins, demanding to be heard, and the boy seized it and shouted, "Now be still, you stupid thing!" and he poured it half full of granola. Then he pushed the jar back on the shelf and hurried outside with all the pots and dishes clattering at his heels, and he held up the silver cof- feepot to the horse.

The horse dipped his nose into it, sighed with pleasure, and did not lift his head till he had eaten down to the very bottom.

"Fine oats," he murmured. "The earth always gives me such an appetite." And he bent one huge wing and swept Anatole onto his back.

"Are you ready?" asked the horse again.

"Yes," said Anatole. Something thumped down behind him.

"I'm coming to take care of you," purred Plumpet, settling herself at his back. "I promised your grandmother, you know."

With a rush of wind the horse rose straight into the air, and whether they passed through the leaves or around them, Anatole did not know. He only clung to the horse's mane and closed his eyes.

"Look down," said Plumpet. "What a fine sight."

Below them, Grandma's house and the road on which it stood were growing smaller and smaller. Now they were passing the dairy at the edge of town. The cows huddled in the yard, the milk trucks were just setting out into the dark, but from where he sat Anatole could see the sun pushing its shafts of light across the earth as if it were raking the houses and fields together.

"Why, you've brought the coffeepot!" exclaimed Plumpet.

Anatole looked down and, sure enough, nestled under his arm was the silver coffeepot, one side shiny, one side still dark, for he had never finished polishing it. He held it up to his ear, but to Anatole's relief it behaved like an ordinary pot, neither speaking nor moving. For the first time he wondered where he was going.

Leaning forward, he put his mouth to the horse's ear, which was as soft as violets and he called, "Where will I find the fennel?"

"You will find it in Mother Weather-sky's garden," answered the horse.

"Are you taking me to her?"

The horse grew stubborn and would not answer. At last he said, "When the Roadkeeper asks you your destination, just tell him you are going to see Mother Weather-sky."

"And will Mother Weather-sky be glad to see me?" asked Anatole.

Again the horse fell silent, and when he finally spoke, his voice sounded sad and far away.

"Well, I'm bound to tell you, she doesn't like visitors."

Anatole started to ask why, but the cat interrupted him.

"Look down, look down!"

Under the horse's hooves the clouds broke, and a handful of islands floated like leaves on bright water. He recognized Florida and the thin curve of Cuba, Santo Domingo to the south and Puerto Rico farther south yet, and all by itself to the north a peppering of very tiny islands. Those were the Bermudas.

The horse dipped closer to the water below, and the boy watched the waves roll, gather themselves into hills of green glass, and break into pieces. In the rising of the waves he could see what each was carrying. One hauled a glittering load of compasses, another half a dozen chairs, a third the sails of a ship. The largest looked quite empty, yet when it broke, Anatole heard the cries of drowning men, and he turned quickly away, for fear that he would see their bones in the wave that followed.

All around them, clouds swelled into monstrous creatures, dragons with spiked tails and needle-sharp whiskers,
ogres with huge mouths and a single eye or with eight eyes
and a single foot. Though Anatole had often amused himself
finding monsters in the clouds, he had never imagined
them close up. They floated by him, still and blind as statues,
terrible to look at but harmless.

"They are all asleep," said the horse, "but when they
wake up, watch out!"

"Can they hurt us?" asked Anatole.

"They can't hurt me," said the horse. "If lightning hits
me, I break apart and come together again."

Anatole thought uneasily of the voices in the wave.

"Are we close to the island?"

"Why, it's just below us!"

"I can't see anything but water below us," said Anatole.

"That's all you can see from the outside. But when I've
put you on the island, I promise you'll see it plain enough. I
can't talk any more now, for the clouds are stirring themselves."

The horse moved very slowly between the monsters, as if
the air itself weighed him down. When Anatole bumped his
elbow against a two-headed elephant, he found to his surprise that it was soft and boneless, like smoke. The beast
opened its eyes, stared at Anatole, lifted its trunks, and
trumpeted.

At once the other beasts opened their eyes and, catching
sight of the boy and the horse, rolled toward them, raising a

cold wind that blew the travelers helplessly this way and that.

"The storm has caught us," called the horse over his shoulder. "Jump off!"

"No!" shouted the cat and the child together.

"Jump off, I say! Quickly!—"

Suddenly the dragon opened its mouth and shot out a long tongue of fire, and Anatole felt the horse shatter like crockery under him, and he saw the shimmering wings sail away by themselves into the sky. The next minute he landed not on the waves but on the island, just as the horse had promised.

he storm was gone. The sky, washed clean, shone blue as a bunting's wings. Waves lapped at Anatole's feet and terns skittered along the bright lip of the water.

Plumpet was washing vigorously behind her ears.

"Salt," she said. "I am sure it was the salt in the sea that saved us. I've seen your mother toss a pinch of salt over her left shoulder when she spills it, and she won't do as much for pepper or cinnamon." Stretching herself lazily, she added, "Did you bring the map? I would like to know where we are."

"So would I," said Anatole.

Before them glittered the sand. Behind them rose a thicket of wild sea grapes, and beyond the thicket were the dark crowns of pines, as tall as steeples. Anatole shaded his eyes and looked up and down the beach. Nobody was coming or going in either direction, but off to the left, where the water met the land, stood a little telescope on a tripod that might have been gold once but now wore a heavy coat of barnacles. Kicking off his sneakers, Anatole ran down the beach and put his eye to the lens. Though he turned it this way and that, he saw nothing but darkness. When he tried to pull it up, the tripod seemed to take root in the sand. Disappointed, he walked back to Plumpet. Over his shoulder he saw the waves licking up his footprints as the telescope sank slowly into the sea.

"The tide is coming in," observed Plumpet. "Listen."

A bell sounded, so far off and mournful that Anatole shivered. It might have been a buoy or a lighthouse warning some passing ship of danger. It rang once more, this time in a high sweet voice like a chime, and as if answering a summons, a small shiny creature scuttled out of the thicket and rubbed itself joyfully against the boy's legs.

"Oh, it's Grandmother's coffeepot!" he cried. "How glad I am that I didn't lose it!"

And the coffeepot shook itself like a dog and trotted round and round on little silver paws, opening and shutting its lid for joy.

The bell sounded a third time. Grabbing his shoes, Anatole climbed the sloping beach to the thicket, for now he was sure the bell had rung from that direction. The branches parted themselves and showed him a tunnel that led straight into the thicket. The sun slipping in and out of the leaves threw emerald lights along the path, and the air was the color of Plumpet's eyes.

"It's almost as if someone were expecting us," said Anatole.

Plumpet put her nose in the tunnel and caught the scent of freshly buttered toast.

"Then we'd better not keep them waiting," she purred and darted down the green path ahead of him.

The leaves gave off a delicious fragrance, rather like

cloves, and Anatole was not surprised to hear the steady hum of bees all around him. The coffeepot, stumbling along on its short legs, could not keep up. Anatole tucked it under his arm and hurried after Plumpet. Ahead of them, at the far end of the tunnel, they saw a cave. A ring of candles hung from the ceiling and spread its warm light over a round table, covered with a blue-checkered tablecloth. On the table, someone had carefully arranged four white napkins rolled into gold napkin rings, four teacups, four gold spoons, four gold knives, and a porcelain teapot, white as a new tooth, from which steam rose. And in the middle of it all was a plate of freshly buttered toast.

"Why, we're in somebody's dining room!" exclaimed Anatole.

Around the table stood three stools and a baby's high chair with MIRANDA lettered in gold on the back. But the walls of the cave were all given over to cupboards and drawers. A low door at the back led off into darkness.

"Perhaps a monster lives here," said Anatole.

"Perhaps it doesn't," said Plumpet. "I'm famished."

"I suppose we shouldn't sit down till we're asked," said Anatole, hoping Plumpet would tell him it was all right, when you were very hungry, to eat first and be asked later. She always did the correct thing.

Suddenly footsteps on dry twigs crackled from the back of the cave. Plumpet sprang to Anatole's shoulder in alarm.

Out of the darkness stumbled a little man. He was not much taller than Anatole, yet he looked old enough to be his great-grandfather, and he was pulling his beard out of his suspenders, which shone like a pair of matched rainbows on his leather shirt, the color of dead leaves. Anatole shrank back, but the old man did not notice.

"Wonderful to see you," he greeted them, "simply wonderful. It's been ages since I've had a visitor. Usually *she* gets them before I do. I've had the table set for centuries. I *hope* the tea is still hot." He clasped the teapot in both hands. "Names! Names!" Turning to the coffeepot nestled in Anatole's arms, he shook his finger at it. "You! Potiphar!"

The pot did not budge.

"Not Potiphar? The Lord of Sheffield!"

Still the pot did not move.

"Not Sheffield, either? Quicksilver, then. Is your name Quicksilver?"

At that the coffeepot leaped into the highchair and drummed its spout on the tray.

"And you?" said the old man, in a softer voice, looking from the cat to the boy and back again.

"My name is Anatole."

"Plumpet here," said the cat. She thought the old man very clever for having guessed the name of the coffeepot, when she hadn't known it had one all the years it lived in Grandmother's house.

"We're delighted to meet you, Mr.—" She glanced at the name on the high chair—"Mr. Miranda."

The old man laughed.

"I'm not Mr. Miranda. I don't even know Miranda. Was

she a puppy? A lizard? A bird? I found all the furniture in the cave when I moved in. The tide rushed into my old cave and carried everything away. Here now, we'll have a party in honor of your arrival."

By the light of the candle, Anatole caught a glimpse of animals painted on the ceiling, mostly reindeer and buffalo. The light gliding across them made them appear to be running away.

"Where are we?" asked Plumpet. Her voice trembled a little.

"You are on the island of Sycorax," replied the old man. "Do sit down."

When they were seated at the table, he helped them all to tea and toast—even the coffeepot, who sucked the tea into its spout like an anteater and shot it high into the air like a whale. And how skillfully it opened its lid and caught every drop!

"What a pity the tea doesn't come in bags with fortunes on the tags," Anatole whispered to Plumpet. "In a place like this, I am sure all the fortunes would come true."

"It *is* a pity," said the old man, "and we have no music. Can you sing, boy?"

"No, but I can play the harmonica," said Anatole, and he took it out of his pocket and played "Yankee Doodle." The old man listened, cocking his head to one side like a bird.

"Did you get it from the sea?" he asked.

"No, from my grandmother."

"I hope everything is satisfactory?" he continued.

" 'No, but I can play the harmonica,' said Anatole, and he took it
out of his pocket and played 'Yankee Doodle.' "

Anatole helped himself to a second piece of toast.

"It's very good, thank you," he said. "Do you often have visitors here?"

The old man shook his head.

"Mostly I sleep. I might sleep a hundred years, I might sleep an hour. I sleep till I'm wanted. My telescope watches for visitors, and when I'm wanted, it rings me awake. People come, they eat my bread and drink my tea, and they go on their way."

"Doesn't anybody ever stay?" asked Anatole.

"Nobody," answered the old man. "All the folks that come to me are looking for something. So are you. And wherever you're going you'll need a road to take you there. That's my business. Roads."

"Do you sell maps?" inquired Plumpet.

"I sell roads," said the old man. "When this island was young and nameless, you could find roads everywhere. They'd be floating on every stream and hiding under every stone. Mother Weather-sky and her sisters collected them all and made me Keeper of the Roads. I don't keep them, though. I sell them."

"Won't you run out of roads someday?" asked Anatole.

"No, for they always come back to me when travelers are done with them."

"In my country," said Anatole, "the roads stay where they're put."

"A poor sort of arrangement," said the old man. "Look here."

He gestured toward the hundreds of drawers niched in the wall around them.

"Do you know what I keep in these?" he demanded.

"Buttons?" suggested Anatole. They reminded him of the drawers in the sewing store where his mother bought buttons and embroidery thread.

"Buttons, indeed! This drawer is cut from a single ruby. And the one beside it, from a single emerald." And while the Keeper of the Roads praised them, they shone so brightly that you could have read a book by their light. "They hold roads. No two drawers are alike, and no two roads lead to the same place."

"What kind of road do you keep in here?" asked Anatole, pointing to a drawer studded with opals. The fire in the stones shivered like lightning, as if the road inside were losing its temper. The Keeper of the Roads opened it and lifted out a golden chain, long and heavy and restless as a snake. It undulated nervously around his fingers, winding and unwinding.

"Nice to look at but cold to travel," he remarked. "Unfortunately it takes you to the most dangerous part of the island. Once it took travelers to and from a city of gold. Now the city is gone, but the road doesn't know that. Roads keep their old habits, you know."

And he coiled it up like a spring and popped it back into the drawer.

"What's in that diamond drawer?" asked Plumpet.

The Keeper of the Roads opened a crystal drawer and

picked up a road that shone softly, like one long tear. Plump-
pet gave an involuntary purr.

"It's very attractive, isn't it?" agreed the Keeper of the
Roads. "Oh, it takes you through some lovely places, but it
ends badly. Where did you say you wanted to go?"

"We want to find Mother Weather-sky," said Anatole.
"Have you a road that will take us to her?"

The Keeper of the Roads stopped smiling.

"I was afraid you would ask for that one. You don't look
like the sort that travels the diamond way."

"Then you've got that road?" asked Anatole eagerly.
When the old man hesitated, he added, "I don't have any
money to buy it, but maybe I could earn the road? I'm a good
weeder and raker—"

"No, no, my dear, I can't take anything for this road. It's
so full of dangers I can't possibly give it to a child. To a
soldier with a sharp sword, yes. To a strong man with a pride
of lions to defend him, yes. To a wise man with a headful of
lore and a handful of spells, yes. But to a child, no. Why do
you want to find Mother Weather-sky?"

"I want her to give me some of her fennel. It's supposed
to cure asthma."

"You don't look sick," observed the Keeper of the Roads.
"You look in the very pink of health."

"Oh, I don't want it for myself," explained Anatole. "I
want it for my grandmother."

The Keeper of the Roads sighed so heavily that the
candles flickered.

"If you were traveling for yourself, I might turn your mind another way. But when people want a thing for somebody else, they'll never give up till they've found it. The road you need is in this drawer. No, not that amethyst one, this plain wooden drawer. Be patient, please. It always sticks."

The road to the garden was dull as dust and thin as snakeskin and so snarled you couldn't tell the end from the beginning. The Keeper of the Roads laid it on his open palm and blew on it. It didn't move.

"Let me warn you about this island," he said. "It's a shifty sort of place, full of fogs and storms, but when the fogs lift and the storms pass, how beautiful it is! That's Mother Weather-sky's work, of course. Everything that comes loose in her storms she keeps in her garden—figureheads, fountains, flags—and her garden is vast. It's not a garden really— it's a grave. You won't find a single green thing growing in it."

"Then where *is* the garden?" cried Anatole.

"This whole garden was an island once," answered the old man. Once more he blew on the road, as if he were sighing over it. "Such a garden! It had the usual things, of course, garlic and roses and marigolds, but herbs that could work great magic grew here as well. The island attracted magicians the way a magnet attracts pins. Most of them came and went, and the sea washed away their runes and residences, for the sea is clean as your cat here, always licking and polishing. But long ago a magician more powerful than the rest was tossed ashore in a storm."

"Is he still here?" asked Plumpet, glancing around uneasily.

"No, that was a long time ago. He scrambled out with his black velvet suit on his back and the *Red Calfskin Book of Magic* under his arm. You've heard of that book, no doubt."

"No, I haven't," said Anatole.

"Indeed! The *Red Calfskin Book* is the most powerful book of spells ever made. The Magician—he never had another name that I know of—wrestled it at midnight from the ghost of a famous wizard, and the ghost tore away the cover and the first five pages and carried them away. In those days the island was ruled by the King of the Grass."

"Oh, I've heard of him," exclaimed Anatole. "The King of the Grass—he's the grasshopper, isn't he? My grandmother is very fond of watching grasshoppers."

"I do not think the island of Sycorax was ever ruled by a grasshopper," said the old man. "I have often been told the King wore a crown of fennel. That would be difficult for a grasshopper."

"So that's where I must look for my fennel," said Anatole in a discouraged voice. But the old man took no notice.

"The Magician didn't like regular gardens. He liked things that lasted. He wanted a garden of gold. He wanted to be king so he could order his people to make him one, but they wouldn't have him. So he turned the houses into trees and the people into stones."

"And the King too?" whispered Plumpet, appalled.

"The King and his Queen he locked up in a golden tree in Mother Weather-sky's garden. I believe he gave the key to Mother Weather-sky; I have heard she wears it at her waist, night and day. He couldn't change the King and Queen into stones, because the spell he needed for that was on the first page of the magic book. Their child escaped, but nobody knows where."

"What happened to the Magician?" asked Anatole.

"Drowned," answered the Keeper of the Roads. "Mother Weather-sky whispered a tale of sunken treasure in his ear and blew him a broken ship. He'd scarcely mended it and hoisted sail when she raised a storm that sent ship, Magician, and book to the bottom of the sea. She likes to run things herself, you know."

"So to find the fennel, I have to free the King. And to free the King, I have to get the key from Mother Weather-sky."

"Exactly. And she'll do her best to destroy you."

A low rumbling, deep under the rocks, startled them. Quicksilver jumped out of the high chair and rubbed against Anatole's ankles.

"I think I should like to go home," said Plumpet.

The Keeper of the Roads reached over and scratched her between the ears.

"Don't be afraid. The island is full of noises. Sometimes a thousand twangling instruments will hum about your ears, and sometimes voices. And if you've waked after a long sleep, they'll make you sleep again. Anatole, take off your left shoe."

Anatole kicked off one sneaker and stood on his right foot like a water bird before the old man. The Keeper of the Roads knelt down, spat on the road, and stuck it to Anatole's bare heel. At once the road faded, growing paler and paler until it disappeared entirely.

"What happened to the road?" asked Anatole.

"It's invisible," replied the Keeper of the Roads. "That's the only kind of road I keep. Whoever carries an invisible road always gets to the end of it. The only danger is losing yourself."

"How can we lose ourselves if we keep to the road?" asked Plumpet.

"Why, you might start out as a cat and end up a feather. You might start out as a boy and end up a bracelet of bright hair about a bone."

"How ghastly," exclaimed Plumpet.

"Watch out for wizards," continued the Roadkeeper. "Don't drink from strange wells. And lie low during storms."

"Watch out for wizards," repeated Anatole, "don't drink from strange wells, and lie low during storms. Is that all?"

"That's enough," said the Roadkeeper pleasantly.

"Just a minute," said Anatole. "How can we follow the road if we can't see it?"

"Oh, the island has plenty of roads of the ordinary sort,

and there are any number of footpaths that will take you, sooner or later, to Mother Weather-sky's garden. Remember to ask directions of everyone you meet. Come, I'll show you the footpath into the forest. It branches out of my dining room to the west."

CHAPTER FOUR

The footpath led straight into the forest and wound its way between pines and oaks so tall that the tops looked as if they were holding up the sky. Light breathed in and out of the canopy of branches, squirrels called to each other on their precarious journeys, birds flooded the woods with songs, blackberries gleamed in the hedges and thickets. Anatole improvised a suitable celebration on his harmonica. It was the sort of time and place that made you glad to be alive. Walking made Anatole hungry.

"Oh, Plumpet, let's pick blackberries and have a picnic!"

"Berries are not to my taste," answered the cat. "A little mole or slice of freshly killed mouse—"

The boy made a face.

"I can't eat with you if you're going to slice a mouse."

"Then I shall dine privately," said Plumpet. Like a gloved hand, she slipped into the berry thicket, and a wise choice it was, for if she had not left the path, she would never have discovered the stream, running clear and cold between banks of wild thyme and spearmint. Crouching on the mint, she discovered russet-backed crayfish swaying in the water weeds and speckled trout keeping watch over their nests. All this she studied as a hungry customer studies a menu in a restaurant.

Anatole was so busy picking blackberries that he did not notice Plumpet when she returned, picking her teeth with a claw not her own.

"Young crabs," she purred. "Haven't had 'em in years. If you want a cool drink, follow me."

Pushing through the thicket after her, Anatole gave a cry of delight. Honeysuckle filled the copse with a heavy sweetness, everything under his feet was in flower, everything in the stream glistened. The rocks made a path of stepping stones to the opposite bank. Anatole was about to jump on the first one when Plumpet leaped to his shoulder.

"Hush! Mind the adder!"

Across the water, a hedgehog scurried into the reeds. The birds fell silent. Quicksilver lifted his spout and made small snuffling sounds. Not three feet away from them, a coil of spotted gold darted from under a leaf and glided into the stream. Anatole picked up an acorn and tossed it after the snake. It missed—he was glad of that—and struck the earth like a bell.

"Buried treasure!" exclaimed Plumpet. She sprang to the spot and applied her claws. Anatole knelt beside her and pushed aside handfuls of dirt, but it was hard work and he made so little progress that he soon sat back on his heels to rest.

"What I need is a shovel," he said.

"What you need are claws," said the cat. "You're not properly equipped for a long journey. Ah, what's this? A nose?"

They both leaned forward. Poking up through the dirt was a nose about the size of Anatole's, only smooth and transparent and hard as crystal.

"Why, it's made of glass," said Anatole, astonished.

"Fancy following an acorn and finding a glass nose," said Plumpet. "Where there's a nose, there's a face, at least in most cases."

They dug more eagerly now. Quicksilver carried the dirt away as fast as they scooped it out. Next a glass cheek came into view, then two glass eyes, glass lips slightly parted, a chin of dimpled glass, a glass forehead, and a glass neck. The face that shone up at them was young, pretty, and perfect in every detail.

Anatole took a stick and pried free two shoulders. They were covered with glass hair, finely etched into straight strands that fell on both sides of the face. Plumpet uncovered two glass arms, a glass bodice and a full glass skirt, and two glass feet without shoes. The whole figure was dressed in a long-sleeved glass frock, pleated at the waist, but otherwise so plain that the dead leaves on which she lay could be clearly seen, as though through a magnifying glass. Together the boy and the cat lifted the girl out of the earth and stood her up in the sunlight.

She was not much taller than Anatole, and she was perfectly clear, like a window, except for a little gold whistle embedded on the left side of her chest, where live children have hearts. Anatole couldn't help admiring the whistle. It was shaped like a blade of snake grass, the kind that makes a rude noise if you hold it tight across your mouth and blow, and it seemed to draw light to itself so that it glittered like a tiny sun. But to get the whistle, he would have to smash the girl, a thought he put out of his head at once.

"What shall we do with her?" asked Anatole.

"Wash her," answered the cat.

Together they lifted her very carefully and laid her in the water.

"Fetch leaves and we'll scrub her," said Plumpet, for whom cleanliness was next to godliness. Every morning she scrubbed behind her ears, even outside in the coldest weather. As Anatole stooped to gather leaves, a cry went up from the stream.

"Help me!"

Spinning around, he saw the girl staggering to her feet, pulling at bunches of reeds to raise herself from the water. He ran to her and stretched out his hand, and she grasped it in her own. Her touch sent chills through him, it was so hard and cold.

"You're alive!" cried Anatole.

The girl waded ashore and glanced from the boy to the trees to the water to the cat, up to the sky and down to the wet roots shining in the mud.

"What does that mean, 'alive'?" she asked.

"Why, it means to walk and talk and eat and breathe," said Anatole. He paused. He felt he was explaining it badly.

"And where did I come from?" she continued.

"We found you in the earth," said Plumpet.

*"He ran to her and stretched out his hand,
and she grasped it in her own."*

"Where I came from didn't look a bit like where I am now. Was I alive in the earth?"

"You didn't look alive," said Anatole.

"You looked dead as a caught mouse," added Plumpet.

"Was I dead?" asked the girl.

"The question is, Were you ever alive?" said Plumpet. "You have to be alive before you can be dead."

"I think you were asleep," said Anatole.

This answer evidently pleased her, for the whistle at her heart glowed like the cold fire in Grandmother's opal ring. The girl walked up and down the banks of the stream, swinging her arms and admiring the way they caught the sunlight.

"Alive. I'm alive. So that's who I am."

"Oh, that isn't *who* you are," said Plumpet. "That's *what* you are. What we all are. You have your own name. I am Plumpet. This is Anatole."

"And that little shining one?"

"He's my coffeepot, Quicksilver."

"Such lovely names," said the girl with a sigh. "Where did you get them?"

"From Anatole," said Plumpet.

"From Mama and Papa," said Anatole.

"And Quicksilver?"

"From the Keeper of the Roads," said Anatole.

The girl looked thoughtful.

"*Anatole*," she said softly. "*Anatole*. I like your name best. Can I borrow it?"

"I don't think so," he answered, feeling perplexed. "Didn't your parents give you a name?"

Immediately he wished he had not asked. He was sure she had no parents, and now she would want to know what parents were, and even the simplest questions sounded hard when she asked them.

"Perhaps you could find your own true name, as cats do," said Plumpet. "When a kitten is given its true name, it is read to from the *Book of Names* that have done good service in the past. When the kitten sneezes, the name being read is its real name, known only among cats."

"But you don't have the *Book of Names* with you," said Anatole.

"My dear Anatole," said the cat, "I have stood god-mother to many a kitten, and I know the book by heart. Let us all sit down, and I'll begin the list."

They seated themselves on the mossy upholstery of the roots.

"Tybalt, Tomasina, Tabitha."

Plumpet paused.

"She doesn't look like a Tabitha," said Anatole. "She looks like a Susannah."

He meant to say that she looked like a photograph of his great-aunt Susannah as a young girl, which he had often admired in his mother's album.

"Minette, Minousse, Mimi."

"How long does the list go on?" asked the girl.

"Till you sneeze," answered the cat.

"Sneeze soon, won't you?" said Anatole. "We've got a long journey ahead of us."

"What *is* a sneeze?" asked the girl.

"Your nose tickles, you open your mouth, you close your eyes, and your breath just explodes. You can't do it on purpose, so it's no use trying," he added, for the girl was wrinkling her nose and opening her mouth and making the most hideous faces.

"Do the dead sneeze?" she asked.

"Only the living sneeze," said the cat.

"Then I shall manage it. Go on with the list."

"Miez, Gilbért, Tom—"

"Tom isn't right for a girl," said Anatole. "I think Susannah—"

Suddenly an acorn crashed through the trees and chimed off the girl's left shoulder.

"I sneezed!" she shouted.

"That's not a sneeze," said Plumpet.

"Why not?" demanded the girl. "Why should we all sneeze the same way?"

The cat could think of no reply.

"What name was I saying?"

"I was saying Susannah," said Anatole.

That settled it. Her name was Susannah. And now that she was somebody, she wanted to know what business they had in the woods. Then Anatole explained they were on their way to Mother Weather-sky's, to free the King of the Grass. And when he found the King of the Grass, he would ask for some of the fennel that grew in his crown, and he would take it to his grandmother, who had said nothing would heal her half so well as a cup of tea brewed from that herb.

Susannah turned to Plumpet.

"And why are you going? Do you have a grandmother, too?"

"I was sent to take care of Anatole," purred the cat. "Of course, I also wanted to come for the adventure of it all. I plan to write my memoirs some day, and I intend to fill them with the most fabulous adventures. It would be nice if a few of them were true."

"I would like to meet the King of the Grass," said Susannah.

"Then come with us," said Anatole.

Susannah gave him such a grateful smile that he decided she wouldn't mind if he asked, "Why is that whistle inside you?"

Susannah glanced down at it and shrugged. "Don't other people have whistles?"

"It's not common," said Plumpet. "Some children swallow pins or pennies, but I never knew anyone who had a whistle for a heart."

"Now you know one," said Susannah.

They returned to the footpath and set out. Anatole tried to play "Yankee Doodle" on his harmonica, but the farther they walked into the woods, the more the harmonica played its own tunes. Finally, it refused to play anything that

Anatole recognized, though he blew the right notes for the tunes he knew. Very soon the woods grew so dark that they could not see the path before them. Quicksilver took fright and darted between their legs. They walked only with great difficulty, for fear of treading on him. At last Anatole picked him up and carried him.

"It would be a terrible thing if Susannah tripped and smashed herself to smithereens," said Plumpet. "I feel sure some magic is at work. It's much too early for nightfall. Let's stop here and rest till the darkness passes."

"What if it doesn't?" inquired Anatole.

"My dear Anatole, I have known the nine kinds of darkness: the darkness of night, the darkness of evil, the darkness of sorrow—"

Her voice trailed off. The present darkness was making her sleepy. Anatole found himself yawning as well. The last words he heard before his eyes closed were Plumpet's:

"—so you see, my dear Anatole, there is no kind of darkness that sooner or later isn't followed by light."

’ve found two more!” shouted a voice.

Anatole opened his eyes. In the pale light of early morning, a dozen golden retrievers peered down at him, as if he were a fox they had just flushed out of the underbrush. Anatole was not afraid of dogs; he had often been knocked down by the golden retriever who lived next door to him at home, but he had never been at the center of a pack of dogs, and he did not like the way they showed their teeth.

“If they weren’t standing on their hind legs,” he said to himself, “they wouldn’t be any taller than I am. So perhaps they’re not as fierce as they look.”

A Great Dane pushed his way through the pack, stretched out one paw, snapped a collar around Anatole’s neck, and yanked him rudely to his feet. With his other paw he was leading Susannah by a leash. Anatole was dismayed to see that she wore a brass-studded collar exactly like his own. He glanced around for Plumpet, but she had disappeared.

The Great Dane pointed to Quicksilver, crouched in Anatole’s arms.

“What do you call that one?” he barked.

“A coffeepot,” answered Anatole.

“Collar it!” howled the Great Dane.

And two retrievers stepped forward and slipped a collar around the neck of the coffeepot.

The first rays of morning broke over the trees. Susannah glittered and the whistle at her heart glowed, now a soft yellow, now deepening like an ember to bright orange. The dogs drew back in surprise.

"Are you under enchantment?" inquired the Great Dane.

"What does 'under enchantment' mean?" asked Susannah.

"It means you have lost the face you were born with. Were you born a dog?"

Susannah shook her head.

"Or a lizard?"

"Certainly not a lizard."

"Perhaps a hedgehog?"

"I have never been a hedgehog," said Susannah.

The Great Dane shook his head at her.

"That's too bad," he said. "There's special consideration for creatures under enchantment. The Governor doesn't want to arrest anybody on false charges. He doesn't want to condemn a rabbit to thirty days in the dungeon and have him turn into a horse. Prisoners, march!"

The Great Dane pulled their leashes so hard that they were obliged to follow him. The rest of the dogs ran behind, yapping among themselves.

"But why can't you put the horse in jail?" asked Susannah.

"You can't imprison a horse when you have condemned a rabbit. Every creature in this kingdom gets a fair trial. The fourth prisoner says he's under enchantment; but if you ask me, he's just trying to help his case."

"Where is the fourth prisoner?" asked Anatole, afraid that Plumpet had not escaped after all.

"He's there in the clearing," answered the Great Dane.

Ahead of them, surrounded by bloodhounds, stood a rabbit, seven feet tall, with emerald green fur and hoops of gold that gleamed in the tips of both his ears. He wore purple silk trousers cut off at the knee, and a leather vest several sizes too small for him. His right leg was sound, but his left leg was wood, and when he spied the Great Dane pulling his prisoners, he thumped his wooden leg till the ground shook, and hazelnuts clattered down on the dogs like hail. Not a single prisoner was hit.

"Hey, friends, what are they hauling you in for?" roared the rabbit.

"I don't know," said Anatole.

The Great Dane tied the rabbit's leash to Anatole's collar, so that the new prisoner now led the rest.

"Prisoners, march!" bawled the Great Dane.

With a deep sigh, the rabbit heaved forward, pulling the others after him. Very soon a stone lodged itself in Anatole's sneaker. "How much better to be made of glass like Susannah, or silver like the coffeepot, and feel nothing," he said to himself. Violets, pansies, and daisies covered the path. The trees smelled of cinnamon and cloves. Each growing thing

"Ahead of them, surrounded by bloodhounds, stood a rabbit seven feet tall, with emerald green fur and hoops of gold . . ."

had reached its perfection; soon the blossoms on the wild cherry trees would drop, but now they hung like creamy clouds under the beeches and oaks. It was spring, it was summer, it was no season, it was the best season of all.

"A penny for your thoughts," said the rabbit, "though of course I haven't got a penny."

Anatole considered his thoughts and decided that the pain in his neck and the ache in his feet weren't worth even the promise of a penny. So instead, he said that he and his friends were going to Mother Weather-sky's garden, to rescue the King of the Grass. And he told him about the fennel that grew in the King's crown, and how he wanted to bring some to his grandmother, so that she would be well again. The rabbit looked very surprised.

"I had no idea you were on such an important expedition," he said. "I assumed you were out for a walk." Then he added, "Good luck."

"Thank you," said Anatole.

"I'll bet you're wondering why I'm here," the rabbit went on. "Go ahead, ask me."

"Why are you here?" asked Anatole.

"I'm accused of stealing the lettuce from the Governor's royal gardens, which he grows to fatten rabbits for his table."

"And did you?" asked Anatole.

"I did. Oh, I'm guilty of that and a good deal more. But I'm sorry for you poor chaps. You're innocent."

"Then why did they capture us?" asked Susannah.

"Because you were sleeping next to me," said the rabbit.

"I didn't see you next to me," said Susannah, puzzled.

"Nor I you. But there we were, only a few feet apart, you on one side of the tree, I on the other. The dark spells that come over this forest have given me some strange bedfellows. I once spent the night not two feet away from an enormous dragon."

"And did you slay him?" asked Anatole, eager for a rousing story of conquest.

"No," answered the rabbit. "I ran. Lucky for me, I woke up first."

The memory of his escape pleased him so much that he began to sing, in a fine tenor voice that rang through the woods.

"Shall Captain Lark the dragon slay?
I came, I saw, I ran away."

"Is that your name? Captain Lark?" asked Susannah.

"At your service," said the rabbit. "Won't you give me yours?"

"I am Susannah. This is my friend Anatole. That's his coffeepot, Quicksilver."

"Susannah, Susannah," sang the rabbit softly. "You are the most beautiful lady in the woods. In fact, I think you're the only lady in the woods. Look sharp, friends. When we reach the rise, you'll see the Kingdom of the Dogs."

Over the top of the hill no trees grew, and the land dipped into a green valley, as round as a bowl. Anatole felt sure the grass had been mowed that morning, for he could smell wild onions and crushed clover, just as he smelled them at home after his papa had mowed the lawn. Around a cluster of low white houses ran a white picket fence, which did not look strong enough to keep anybody out. As the little party drew nearer, Anatole saw it was built of bones, polished white and studded with precious stones.

"How beautiful!" cried Susannah. "How the wall shines!"

"You would too," said Captain Lark, "if you wore all that wealth. It's as stuffed with jewels as a plum cake with raisins. Pearls, sapphires, emeralds. They don't come out, though. I've tried to pry them loose. That ruby in the middle of the main gate would make your fortune."

The Great Dane ran forward and unlatched the gate.

"Where are we going?" asked Anatole.

"To the Governor's palace. Prisoners, march!"

"Just as if we could do anything else," whispered Susannah. "How he loves to order people about."

The Kingdom of the Dogs was not so tidy inside as it looked from a distance. The houses were shabby but well built, roofed with copper sheets that shone in the sun like a field of pennies. Some of the doorways were carved with fantastic beasts, and above the doors Anatole read the names of the families that lived behind them: *The Towsers, Old Tray, The Trot Family*. Between the houses, the grass lay trampled in curious swirls, as if some restless creature had turned itself round and round before falling asleep in it.

"Behold the garden of my undoing," said Captain Lark,

pointing to a broad field of lettuce. "That's the Governor's royal garden."

"Where is everybody?" asked Susannah.

"Out of sight. It's considered bad luck to catch the eye of a prisoner, though if the Governor condemns us to death, you can be sure of a good crowd."

"He won't condemn us to death, I hope," said Anatole.

Captain Lark shrugged.

"That depends on what kind of dog he is today."

"But isn't he always the same kind?" asked Anatole.

"He's never the same kind. He's the same dog, but never the same kind. Every morning he changes."

The Great Dane's ears twitched to show the prisoners he was listening to every word.

"But the punishment," said the Great Dane, "that doesn't change."

"What is the punishment?" asked Anatole.

"Death by the swing," said the Great Dane cheerfully. Seeing Anatole's bewildered expression, he added, "We have in our kingdom a swing that throws people into the sky. They never come down again."

Susannah turned to Captain Lark.

"Is this true?"

The rabbit nodded.

"I've heard of the swing, but I've never seen it. Only creatures condemned to death ever see the swing. The dogs who send them into the sky see it, of course. But they won't talk. Look sharp, children. Here's the Governor's palace."

It looked, thought Anatole, like his papa's toolshed, only much bigger. The front door was painted white and cut so exactly like a gravestone that he couldn't help looking for an inscription, and indeed he thought he saw a faint line of carved shapes that might have been letters when the door was new.

"I know it's a grand and fearful place," said the Great Dane, "but you must go in by yourselves. Those are the regulations."

He took off their collars and leashes and pushed the door open for them, and Anatole stumbled after Captain Lark and Susannah into darkness and heard, with a sinking heart, the door close behind them.

As his eyes grew used to the dark, he saw they were standing in an enormous room, empty save for half a dozen torches that burned in sconces on the walls and threw long shadows across the rushes strewn over the stone floor.

"Nobody's here but us," said Anatole, relieved.

"Hush," warned Captain Lark. "Look where the shadows grow thickest, at the far end of the room. He's a bulldog today. That's unlucky for us."

Suddenly Anatole saw the Governor clearly: a giant bulldog sitting on an old blanket. The instant the boy saw him, the dog spoke.

"Come forward," he said in a slow rusty voice, "and tell your story."

His words called forth a small circle of light at the edge of the blanket, just big enough for one person to occupy.

Anatole turned to Susannah, but in the darkness she was nearly invisible. The torchlight flickered and danced on Quicksilver's sides. The whole room seemed bent on doing them harm.

It was Captain Lark who stepped into the light first.

"Governor of the dogs, you see before you a poor creature under enchantment. I was born Bartholomew Gosnold Lark, of Sweet Chalybeate, Virginia."

"Virginia," growled the dog softly. "Is that under the water or above it?"

"It is above the water at all times and under the stars at night and under the sun by day. I was the Captain of the *Morning Star*, bound for Africa with a cargo of rum and gunpowder. We sailed out of Salem, Massachusetts, on June 23, 1850—"

"Why, Captain Lark," exclaimed Anatole, "that would make you over a hundred years old!"

"Enchantment," said the rabbit, "is a great preserver of youth."

"Be still!" barked the Governor. "Go on with your story."

"To put it plain, we were taken by pirates. My crew was murdered and I was given a choice: to join the pirates or be fed to the sharks. Against my will, I joined the pirates. A shipwreck landed me on this island, and a magician gave me this shape to punish me for stealing his gold."

Captain Lark wiped his forehead with the back of his paw and stepped back into the shadows. The bulldog remained silent for several minutes. Then he turned to Susannah.

"Tell me your story."

"I have no story yet," said Susannah. "I came here with this boy and a cat who is no longer among us. I have nobody else in the whole world."

Anatole did not wait for the Governor to demand his story.

"I am on my way to ask the King of the Grass—"

But he got no further, for at the words *King of the Grass,* the bulldog swelled to four times his size and rage shook his body like a storm.

"I condemn you to death! All of you! Let the swing be made ready at dawn!"

he floor gave way beneath them and dropped them straight down into darkness. They landed on bare earth, shaken but unhurt.

"Where are we?" shouted Captain Lark.

"In the dungeon," hissed the Governor. Teeth bared, he peered down at them. Before any one of them could speak, he slammed the trap door shut and left them there. By the light of a tiny window high in the earthen wall, they looked at each other. Below the window, set with bars of polished bones, was the faint outline of a door that had neither latch nor lock, and a tangle of roots sealed it shut.

"Is this the end of everything?" asked Susannah. "This dark little room?"

"Stone walls do not a prison make," sang Captain Lark, but his good cheer sounded forced. "Climb on my shoulders, Anatole, and let's rattle the bars."

Anatole climbed up, but the window stayed out of reach, and Captain Lark refused to let Susannah climb on Anatole's shoulders for fear she would fall and break.

"Then it *is* the end," wailed Susannah.

"This may be the end or it may not be," said Captain Lark. "When the swing throws us up into the sky, we may simply find ourselves somewhere else. Then you can ask the first person we meet to point out the way to Mother Weather-sky's garden. If you need someone to protect you, I offer my services."

"Thank you," said Susannah.

"We would be very pleased to have you join us, Captain," said Anatole.

"What time do you think the dogs will come for us?" asked Susannah.

"Sunrise," the rabbit answered. "It was always sunrise when we sent our prisoners to walk the plank."

"To walk the plank?" repeated Susannah.

"To die," said Anatole.

"Oh, Captain Lark, how dreadful!"

"I'm very sorry, my lady," murmured the rabbit. "I won't speak of it again."

Suddenly a muffled voice rasped, "Move the stone and let me in!"

Quicksilver scooted away in terror. The stone on which he had been sitting shifted ever so little, and when Anatole lifted it up, a large rat put its head through the hole and blinked at them.

"Don't be afraid," whispered the rat. "Your friend the cat sent me to show you a way out of the dungeon. Follow me down the tunnel."

And the rat slipped out of sight. Quicksilver followed it, and Susannah, after peering carefully into the hole, climbed after Quicksilver.

"Come on, Captain Lark," called Anatole, easing himself in after Susannah.

From the mouth of the tunnel he heard Captain Lark's voice, trembling with disappointment.

"The door is too small for me. You go forward. I'll dig it wider and meet you later."

"You can't dig alone," said Anatole. He shouted for the others to help, and they all crawled back into the dungeon. The earth around the tunnel was soft. They dug fast and soon enlarged the entrance.

"This time let Captain Lark go first," said Anatole.

The rabbit lowered himself carefully into the tunnel until only his ears showed, their golden rings twinkling. Then he stopped.

"Keep going," urged Anatole. "What's the matter?"

"I'm stuck," grunted the rabbit. "The tunnel gets narrower here."

"Can't you back out the way you came?" asked Susannah. "We'll dig it wider."

"I can't go backward or forward," groaned Captain Lark.

They all began shouting at once, till a rap on the door under the window silenced them. Captain Lark, pushing and struggling, pulled himself back into the dungeon just as the roots that bound the door snapped apart and the loose earth trickled down the wall like tears.

The door broke open, and the Great Dane bounded into the room.

"Halt, or be torn to bits!" he barked.

He threw a circle of rope around them and pulled it tight, gathering them together like sheaves.

"Surely, you aren't going to execute us now," said Captain Lark. "Sunrise is the usual hour, I believe."

"For us there is no usual hour." The Great Dane smiled. "During the day you'd give our citizens a little amusement, but the Governor is eager to be rid of you. A noisier bunch he's never heard. And when he discovers this"—he pointed to the hole in the floor—"he'll thank his stars he didn't wait."

Anatole just had time to grab Quicksilver before the Great Dane herded them into the corridor. No lights glowed at the far end, and Anatole supposed that they had a long walk ahead of them, but soon the air grew cooler, and he glanced up and saw overhead the whole shimmering fabric of the stars.

"What beautiful lights live in the sky," said Susannah. They stepped outside. A spicy fragrance nearly took Anatole's breath away. Captain Lark wiggled his nose.

"It is the night-blooming cereus," he observed. "A great bush of it grew by the house in which I was born."

He spoke so calmly that Anatole asked, "Aren't you afraid?"

"Of high places, yes. When we ride up in the swing, please hold my paw."

A dead sycamore, bone white in the moonlight, rose over the crest of the hill to meet them. Anatole gave a gasp of relief. Instead of a place of execution, he saw a deserted playground. The swing was like the one in his backyard, though its ropes were longer and would travel farther.

"Lovely view," remarked the Great Dane. He untied the rope that bound them together. "We always give our prisoners time to admire the view."

Below them, in the valley of the dogs, moonlight touched every hummock of grass. A bird cried out in its sleep from a distant forest. Captain Lark drew a deep breath and said very quietly:

> "The earth is all before me: with a heart
>   Joyous, nor scared at its own liberty,
>   I look about, and should the guide I choose
>   Be nothing better than a wandering cloud,
>   I cannot miss my way."

"Are you a poet, sir?" asked the Great Dane.

"No, no. Once the tide brought me a book—"

"Time's up," snapped the Great Dane. "Into the swing."

"I have to face front or I shall be sick," said Captain Lark. He jumped up on the seat, grasped the ropes, and stood facing the place where, in a few hours, the sun would rise, though they would not be here to watch it. Nevertheless, he took care to keep a cheerful face, just as if he were starting out on a vacation.

"Susannah, you get in next, and then you, Anatole."

"Let's be a sandwich," said Anatole, "and Susannah can be the filling."

"I will hold Quicksilver," said Susannah.

They took their positions on the swing. Suddenly something sprang out of the darkness and landed on Anatole's shoulder. It was Plumpet.

"Don't say a word," she purred in his ear. "Didn't I promise to take care of you?"

The Great Dane, who did not notice Plumpet, sprang forward barking, and began to push the swing in long loping strokes, to and fro, to and fro. Now it was rising so swiftly that the dog could run under it. The air felt chillier. The swing was flying away from the earth. How faint his barking sounded! Glancing down, Anatole was astonished to find that the dog had shrunk to the size of a toadstool. On all sides, the stars drew near, like friendly lamps hanging from dark chains. They gave off a pleasant smell of hot wax.

"Hold my paw, please!"

Anatole worked his hand up the ropes till he found the rabbit's paw. The rabbit's eyes were closed and his mouth was moving. Over the whistle of the wind, Anatole heard him shouting,

> "Sunset and evening star,
> And one clear call for me!"

The ropes were lengthening like shadows at dusk, unleashed from an endlessly turning spool.

Anatole was filled with a terror so total that he nearly let go the ropes. Then the swing gave a tremendous jerk, flipped over, and threw its passengers into the sky.

"Then the swing gave a tremendous jerk, flipped over, and threw its passengers into the sky."

a, ha, ha!"

Anatole sat up. Who was laughing at him? The thick fog rolling lazily around him opened to reveal Captain Lark close by, sitting up and feeling himself for broken bones. Then it closed like an eyelid, before blowing away completely.

They had landed in a green field. Susannah was turning Quicksilver right side up. Plumpet's fur stood on end, and she had fluffed her tail to three times its usual size.

"Ha, ha, ha!"

At the far end of the field grew an orchard, and in the middle of the orchard stood a white house, and on the veranda sat an old man and an old woman who leaned back in their rockers and roared with laughter.

"It is vexing to be laughed at in adversity," said Plumpet.

The old woman wiped her eyes and shouted, "BREAK-FAST!"

The old man watched them coming, then he rolled a bit of his beard into a thread, and called out, "Stop when the grass stops, and I'll throw you a line."

The grass ended at a broad band of glass, laid down in rainbow stripes like ribbon candy, which sloped away on either side of the house. Over this the old man tossed a line, and when they had all laid hold of it, he pulled them across as if he were reeling in a fish—and a good thing too, for the rainbow was so slick no one could keep a footing on it.

"Throw nothing away," said the old woman, taking the thread from him and tucking it into her pocket. "Save everything."

They were, thought Anatole, the oldest people he had ever seen. Their hands and faces were furrowed, like snow after children have played in it. The old woman wore a long dress of white wool, and the old man's suit was so white that his beard blended into his clothes; you could not tell where one started and the other left off. But even more curious, both the man and the woman wore roller skates instead of shoes, and the roller skates had wings. Wings the size of crocuses sprouted from the rockers of the old couple's chairs, and a pair of wings no bigger than thimbles fluttered on each side of the old woman's mobcap.

"And what can we do for you?" she asked, wiping her eyes with the back of her hand.

"We would like breakfast," said Plumpet.

"Please," added Anatole.

"Have you lost your way?" asked the old man.

"Did you have a road?" asked the old woman.

"And did it say anything to you before it left?" asked the old man.

"And was it wearing roller skates?" asked the old woman eagerly.

Anatole shook his head, astonished.

"They were, thought Anatole, the oldest people he had ever seen."

"Now that's a pity." She sighed. "If it were wearing roller skates, it could easily find its way home."

"But roads don't wear roller skates," cried Captain Lark, who could hardly believe his ears.

The old woman nodded.

"Isn't that the truth now? I've seen roads out in the worst weather without their roller skates, and I tell them they'll never get anywhere in this world, they'll lose—"

"Friends, money, memory, everything. Ha, ha, ha!" shrieked the old man.

The old woman drew Anatole and Susannah toward her and said, "We're not laughing at you, my dears. It's the air up here that makes us so merry. If you stay long enough, it'll happen to you."

"I'm sorry we can't stay," said Anatole.

"Except for breakfast," added Plumpet.

"Breakfast!" the old woman called and clapped her hands. "Come here this instant!"

Out skated a little table, loaded with hotcakes and butter and three cruets of maple syrup. You could see that it had hurried. The wings on its legs were still pulsing.

"Naughty," scolded the old woman. "You've forgotten your chairs again."

Three big chairs and one small chair scooted out of the house and arranged themselves around the table. They scuffled for places next to the old woman, but it was wonderful to watch them settle their differences at last and wait politely to be sat on. It was even more wonderful to watch the small chair tread the air with its wings at the level of the table so Quicksilver could enjoy his breakfast.

"Don't they mind nicely, though?" The old man grinned. The dishes, fluttering their wings, passed themselves. The pot of cocoa obligingly poured itself into cups. A blue cup flew to Quicksilver, who dipped his spout into it like a beak and slurped joyfully. Susannah ate nothing; glass has no appetite. The others were so hungry that the platter went back twice for more hotcakes, round and white as buttered moons.

"Do you always wear roller skates?" inquired Plumpet. And forgetting her manners, she dipped her paw in the maple syrup. The old man and the old woman took no notice.

"Always," answered the old woman. "Our house sits at the very top of the rainbow, and if we went about in shoes, we'd slide off. So roller skates with wings are the best way of getting around."

The old man, who was absorbed in counting first the dishes and then the guests, turned to Anatole and said, "Time to pay up. You ate three rounds of hotcakes and a pot of hot chocolate. Butter is free but syrup is extra."

"I'm sorry," said Anatole. "I didn't know we had to pay. We haven't any money."

"Neither have we," said the old woman, laughing. "Where on earth would we spend it?" She turned to Plumpet. "I suppose you know how to wash windows? You cats are great washers."

Plumpet sniffed at the nearest window and drew back in surprise.

"But your windows have no glass."

"Certainly not," exclaimed the old woman. "It's hard enough to keep my windows clean without having to keep the glass clean as well."

"Then how am I to wash them?"

"You must leap in and out of the windows and keep them distracted. They love to dream, and when they dream, they spin clouds. Woolgathering, I call it. Nothing beats leaping for cleaning windows."

"Do *you* leap in and out of the windows?" asked Plumpet. It struck her as a sight worth watching.

The old woman shook her head. "No, I send my sparrows to do it. They'll be glad of a day off."

Plumpet stretched herself and yawned; she did not like heavy work. Nevertheless, she began to leap in and out of the windows as briskly as any sparrow while the others watched admiringly, and soon not a cloud could be seen. When she leaped through the last window, there was a burst of applause.

Anatole turned to the old man and the old woman. "Will you help us now?" asked Anatole. "We are going to Mother Weather-sky's garden—"

"I know where you're going," said the old woman. "My eyes see all roads, even invisible ones. Is it her golden key you want?"

"Yes, but the Keeper of the Roads said she wears it at her waist night and day," said Anatole.

"The Keeper of the Roads is mistaken," said the old woman. "He sleeps too much. He gets things muddled. The Magician hid the key. He never gave it to Mother Weather-sky."

"Oh," cried Susannah, "do you know where to find it?"

"No. Only the four great winds know that, for all the lost keys in the world pass through their hands at one time or another, and they know where everything is and where it belongs and who took it, and not even my sister Mother Weather-sky knows that much. So you must go to the four great winds and ask them."

"Are they good or bad?" inquired Plumpet.

The old woman stopped rocking her chair and considered the question carefully.

"Some call them thieves, others call them peddlers," she said at last.

"But if the four winds don't like you, nothing in the world can help you find the key," added the old man.

Suddenly the old woman jumped to her feet.

"My animals are running to their pastures!"

On the eastern horizon a great door, such as Anatole had seen on very large barns, began to take shape in the sky. Slowly it swung open, and out ran the animals, as pale as smoke and broken, as if they'd come from the bottom of a box of animal crackers. The zebra had only three paws, the elephant had lost its head, the tiger broke into four pieces before their eyes. In the next instant the zebra turned into a whale, the elephant dissolved into a thousand mice, the mice gathered themselves into a sheep. Anatole found he could not look at the same animal twice.

"Tomorrow I shall send one of my animals with you, and that will please the winds. They are very fond of my animals," said the old woman. "But tonight you shall all sleep in our house at the top of the rain."

And taking Susannah and Anatole by the hand, she led everyone up a back staircase to a loft filled with clouds. Anatole had only time to think, as he crawled into one of them, how odd it was to sleep in a bed that had no frame, in a house that had no roof. Or did the roof only go away at night?

"Downstairs it was morning. How is it I can see the stars?" he asked her.

The old woman laughed.

"This is where we keep the night. We have rooms and rooms of it, and every evening we let it out and every morning it comes back."

When Anatole felt Plumpet curling at his feet, he closed his eyes and did not open them till he heard the old woman calling him for breakfast.

After they had eaten, the old woman gathered Anatole and his friends close to her as if she were going to tell them a story.

"Are you ready to meet the four winds?" she asked.

"What if they won't see us?" asked Captain Lark.

"They'll see you," said the old woman. "They're my husband's brothers, and they never turn away our friends."

And pulling a handful of wool from her apron pocket, she tossed it and turned it between her palms and nudged it here and tugged it there till she had stretched it into a huge fish. Its skin was so thin that you could see right into its empty heart.

"That's a rare one," observed Captain Lark. "It has wings instead of fins."

"I'm glad you like it," said the old woman. "I meant to make a bird."

With one finger she outlined a door on the fish's scales and opened it.

"Hurry inside," she urged, "before it changes into something else. Nothing I make lasts very long, you know."

When they had taken their places, she closed the door and smoothed the scales back into place and called the old man. He was leading the animals back to the great door. Spying the fish, he laughed and puffed up his cheeks and blew.

Wheee! The grass laid itself flat as a cat's ears, and the fish swam into the air like a kite. Through its pale skin, Anatole watched the clouds that roared past with the faces of horsemen, riding the old man's breath. They let loose such a shouting and crying that the travelers in the fish were obliged to hold their ears, except Quicksilver, who couldn't find his.

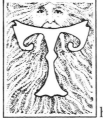hey came to rest on an island in the middle of a lake, close by a small house, which was cobbled with seashells from top to bottom. The shutters were thrown open, and there was an awful row going on inside. Before Anatole could find the door in its side, the fish flew straight up to the roof and dived down the chimney and landed softly in the middle of an enormous room.

A piano whistled past them. Books circled the room like lost birds. Gravestones, steeples, lanterns, armchairs, and fishnets flew over the heads of four men whose white hair streamed around them as they stood in the four corners of the room and shouted. You could tell who was the North Wind, for he was the biggest and strongest; and you could tell the East Wind, for he was the youngest and smallest; and you could tell the South Wind, who was very handsome and looked as if fighting really did not agree with him at all. That left only one more, a rather mysterious figure dressed entirely in black, who Anatole concluded was certainly the West Wind—since the others had been accounted for.

"The cupboard belongs to me! I found it!" shrieked the East Wind.

"Then give me back my suitcase," the West Wind hissed.

A suitcase sailed across the room. The West Wind snatched it out of the air and inspected it.

"You've torn the hinges!"

"You tore them yourself!"

Suddenly the four winds caught sight of the fish.

"Brothers," shouted the South Wind, "our sister has sent us a present."

They all wanted to have it, of course, and they began tumbling the fish to and fro about the room. Hearing shrieks from inside, they turned it upside down and shook it till the passengers came rattling out like peas in a shooter, and then the four winds grew still with astonishment. In all their travels they had never seen a company exactly like this one. The East Wind pulled Captain Lark's ears, the South Wind picked up Anatole and Quicksilver and juggled with them, the West Wind balanced Plumpet on his thumb, and the North Wind set Susannah gently on his palm and brought her close to his great eyes, for he was very shortsighted.

"This creature's made of living glass," said the North Wind, raising Susannah like a goblet, "so we mustn't throw her about. Be careful with the others as well, brothers. They, too, may be alive."

At once the South Wind set Anatole and Quicksilver on the floor, and the East Wind stood Captain Lark beside Anatole, and the West Wind arranged Plumpet between them, as if he were setting up pieces for a game of chess.

"You should have told us you were alive," scolded the

North Wind, and he shook his finger at Susannah, who was huddled in the palm of his hand. "Those who ride our breath seldom arrive with any of their own. I can see that our sister sent you. Why?"

Anatole, still reeling, stepped forward, and the four brothers turned their ears toward him, so that they would not miss a word. Then he explained why he had left home and how he had met Susannah and Captain Lark and how they escaped from the dogs and how he meant to find the key and free the King of the Grass, unless Mother Weather-sky found it first, only he didn't know where to look for it. When he had finished, the North Wind spoke.

"You're a plucky fellow, and I like plucky fellows. I know where the key is. Maybe you're the lad that's to have had it?"

Anatole did not know what to say to this, but the North Wind did not wait for an answer.

"Not even my brothers know where the key is. And all sorts of folks come to me asking for it. They've heard of a golden castle, you know, and they want to get rich. Do you want to get rich?"

"I want my grandmother to get well."

"Well, you're the right one," said the North Wind. "The golden castle was nothing but one of the Magician's illusions. However, I never give anything away, not even to heroes. It's bad for business. What have you got to trade?"

"What do you want?" asked Anatole.

"Look around. What do I need?"

Anatole looked around. So did Plumpet and Captain

Lark and Susannah, and even Quicksilver turned slowly around, so that the wealth of the winds was reflected in his bright side. It seemed to Anatole that the winds needed nothing, except perhaps a housekeeper to tidy their belongings.

"You have everything," said Susannah.

"Never mind that. What can you offer me?" asked the North Wind.

Susannah's whistle began to glow, and Anatole hastily stepped in front of her, for fear the North Wind would ask for it. Then he put his hand into his left pocket, hoping to find his harmonica, but to his great disappointment he found nothing but a yellow card.

The North Wind drew forward eagerly.

"What's that?"

"That's my YMCA card."

"What does the writing on it say?" demanded the North Wind.

"It says I belong to the YMCA."

"And what is the YMCA?"

"It's the place where I go swimming with my friends on Saturday mornings."

"And of what use is this card?"

"I show it to the lady at the door and she lets me in."

"Glory and onions!" shouted the North Wind. "All my life I've wanted people to let me in. They lock their doors. They button up. They won't listen. Did you say she'll have to let me in?"

Anatole read the card once more. It said nothing about not admitting the wind.

"If you show this card, she'll let you in."

"It's a trade!" The North Wind blew the card into the air, caught it between his teeth, rolled it up, and tucked it into his ear, which looked as if it were smoking.

"And now I'll tell you all I know about the key. It's hidden in Mother Weather-sky's garden, and I can take you there. But you must wait till I load my pack and put on my skis."

The South Wind and the East Wind were riding the fish around the room, while the West Wind ran after them, clamoring for his turn and shouting that the fish was growing fainter and fainter and would soon disappear. But the North Wind fetched a large leather bag from a hook on the wall and strode around stuffing various articles into it, including the West Wind's suitcase. He never liked to keep things long anyway; it was the getting and the getting rid of them that pleased him most. Next the North Wind put on his cape and took down his skis from their rack over the door and strapped them on his feet.

"Time to go," he said. "Jump on my pack."

"We'll be blown away," protested Susannah.

"Hold fast to my hair, then," said the North Wind. "I shall not feel it."

First Anatole climbed up, holding Quicksilver. Then Susannah got behind him with Plumpet in her arms. And last of all was Captain Lark, because he was the tallest and his arms reached around everyone else and kept them in place like the sides of a ship. The North Wind opened the door, took a deep breath, and pushed off.

What a fine figure he made, skiing down currents of air and shouting to himself.

"Look down," he called over his shoulder. "Once upon a time those trees were towers and cloud-capped palaces. On still days, when I'm not around, you can hear bells ringing in the ground."

"Bells ringing in the ground?" repeated Anatole.

"The Magician couldn't change them, so he buried them. Below us is Mother Weather-sky's garden. Jump off now."

But his passengers clung to his hair like burrs.

"Jump off! Or I'll shake you off."

And since they would not let go, the North Wind arched his back and sent them flying into a holly bush. They had hardly landed when lightning exploded all around them, bushes were ripped from the earth and hurled into the sky, branches rushed through the air like bits of paper, and a huge tree lurched in front of them and fell, screeching like an animal. The storm did not touch the holly bush where they lay, but the forest around them was being laid waste. A thunderous baying of dogs made Anatole glance up in terror. Through the leaves of the holly bush, he saw a pack of dogs running through the air overhead, and he recognized them as those dogs that had taken them prisoners. On the back of the Great Dane rode an old woman in a green cloak,

"What a fine figure he made, skiing down currents of air and shouting to himself."

and she was braiding whips of lightning and tossing them into the trees. The dogs sank lower and lower and raced yapping around the holly bush.

And then, just as suddenly, the air was so still that Anatole could hear the pounding of his heart. Cautiously, he peeped out and what he saw in that deep silence astonished him. The broken trees were mending themselves, standing up and putting forth new leaves and new boughs. Moss and partridge berries and wild mint were covering the forest floor once again.

"Who saved us?" whispered Susannah.

In the silence that followed, a small voice said, "I did. Though I am smaller than Mother Weather-sky, my spells are stronger."

"Who are you? Where are you?" cried Anatole, glancing around but seeing nobody.

"Look down," murmured the voice. "I'm resting on your shoe. Just a moment, I'm changing. Now you'll see me."

Across his left sneaker a tenuous shape appeared, a small green flame that grew brighter and brighter but gave off neither heat nor smoke. Anatole stooped and put out his hand, and a chameleon glided over his wrist and arranged itself on his palm.

"It's always hard for me to make myself different from what keeps me. Can you see me now?"

"Oh, yes!" everyone exclaimed. They could not take their eyes off the tiny lizard. It had silver claws and iridescent skin, and when Anatole lifted it for the others to examine, it turned its head this way and that and blinked its ruby eyes at them and darted its tiny blue tongue, fiery and forked, like a bolt of lightning.

"How lovely you are," exclaimed Susannah. "But how do you know Mother Weather-sky?"

"I can't tell you that," answered the chameleon. "I can only show you the road to her house."

"If your spells are stronger than hers, won't you make us good and wise and strong?" pleaded Anatole. He was certain the chameleon could make them invincible if it wanted to.

"What gifts can I give you that you haven't already got?" asked the chameleon softly. "Haven't you escaped the dogs and traveled on the wind? Haven't you survived Mother Weather-sky's storms and darknesses?"

This was true. But just then it did not seem enough.

"To reach Mother Weather-sky's house," continued the chameleon, "you must stop at her sister's."

"We've already met her sister," said Plumpet.

"You met her older sister. You haven't met her younger sister. The door to her house lies in the stream. You must go back the way you came."

Anatole set the chameleon down. Feeling solid ground under its feet, it slipped away into the darkness, but its skin gave off a trail of sparks, which flared up for an instant— long enough to light the path—and then died away and flared up again farther on. The travelers followed till the earth grew soft underfoot and the rushing and tumbling of water sounded close by.

"Stop," cautioned the chameleon. "I don't want you to fall into the stream."

"What must we do now?" asked Plumpet, who disliked getting wet paws under any circumstances; she always caught cold afterwards.

"You must wait for the full moon," answered the chameleon.

"Heavens," exclaimed Captain Lark, "we may be stranded here for a month."

Nevertheless, he sat down between Anatole and Susannah on the banks of the stream. Susannah was nearly invisible, like a window in a dark house, and Quicksilver was all darkness, but the others could hear him stamping happily in the mud. Plumpet alone waited with grace and goodwill. Years of waiting at mouseholes had given her great patience.

Suddenly Susannah glowed with a lacy radiance; her glass body held the silvery branches of trees. Anatole scanned the sky for a full moon.

"You're looking in the wrong place," said the chameleon. "Go down."

They looked down. The full moon shone clear and pale in the water.

"I see a door," said Susannah.

"That's not a door," Anatole corrected her. "That's the moon's reflection." But the moment he said it, he was not so sure. Behind the gauzy circle on the water he saw a long stairway that led down into the stream, and he was quick to point it out to the others.

"I suppose I must take the plunge," said Plumpet with a sigh.

"I can't swim a stroke," said Captain Lark.

"That's odd for a pirate," observed Anatole.

"It is, isn't it? But it's so."

"I'm afraid I shall simply sink," said Susannah.

"Can none of us swim?" asked Captain Lark. "We need someone who can save us. Anatole, can you save us?"

"I can swim," said Anatole, "but I can't save anyone. I'm still in the beginner's class."

"You can swim," said the cat. "I vote Anatole go first."

"And I'll go next," volunteered Susannah, "and I shall hold your paw, Captain Lark, if you'd like me to."

The cat, the rabbit, the glass girl, and the coffeepot lined up on the bank. Anatole took a deep breath and held his nose and jumped—he had not yet learned how to dive—into the white circle.

he water was so cold that it took Anatole's breath away. The next instant he got it back again, and he found himself on the stairway he had seen from the shore. He was quite dry, even his clothes, which smelled as fresh and clean as on the day his mother had bought them. Through the skin of water over his head, he saw his friends peering anxiously down at him, and he waved encouragingly.

"Come in! It's all right!" he shouted. But he could tell from their faces that they didn't hear him. He waved once more, then turned and started down the stairs. The darkness would have frightened him if the stairs had not reminded him of the ones that led to the fruit cellar in his grandmother's house.

"I wonder if there'll be old fruit jars and canned pears and boxes of Christmas ornaments," he said to himself. He listened for an echo but heard none, and it relieved him to know that the passage was not very large and that he was not likely to meet anyone in it. The stairs turned and ended abruptly at a wooden door, under which a yellow light shone on the stone landing. Anatole knocked twice. Nobody opened the door.

"Perhaps she's asleep," he said, and he lifted the latch and, finding it unlocked, went in.

The room into which he stepped was not at all like his grandmother's cellar but more like his mother's sewing room. A long worktable in the middle of the room was heaped with mending, and the young woman seated there was sorting, just as his mother did, and talking to herself.

"This is usable. This can be saved. But this is worn clean through. This I can use for patching. This I can piece together. But nothing can be done with this one—it's all holes. Well, nothing I mend lasts forever."

She did not look like his mother. She wore a brown robe made of dead leaves stitched close together, one on the other, and at first glance, she seemed to be wearing scales. Her hair was tucked out of sight under a lace scarf, cut and stitched from leaves that had been eaten away by insects so that only the veins remained. And now he noticed she was not sorting old clothes. Through her hands passed skins, feathers, claws, horns, antlers, fins, bones. They littered the floor. They covered the table. She ran her fingers over them, rubbed them, and held them up to the lamp. The lamp made Anatole shudder. Three serpents, twisted into a knot, hung from the ceiling, and the mouth of each serpent held a candle.

"A little more light over here, please," ordered the lady, and the snakes shifted obligingly, and lit up, briefly, a huge fireplace on the far side of the room, where a large soup pot hung, not over the fire but over a phosphorescent log, such as one occasionally finds in very damp forests.

"No, over *here*," urged the lady, and again the snakes shifted. This time the light from their candles fell directly on her hands and their strange business, but it also caught the dark corners of the room. And now Anatole gave a little cry of surprise—he had thought the room empty. He saw it was full of creatures kneeling on the floor and perched on the rafters overhead. There were otters, shrikes, stoats, deer, hawks, owls, woodchucks, crows, mice and moles; there were creatures that hunt and creatures that are hunted, and they were all waiting together quietly at the edge of the light. Some had lost a wing or a foot, others had not so much as a leg to stand on, a few were torn beyond recognition. Those that had heads to turn, turned them toward Anatole.

Suddenly the door sprang open, and Susannah, Captain Lark, Plumpet, and Quicksilver tumbled noisily into the room.

The Mender started from her chair, and Anatole noticed what an elegant chair it was, carved with shapes of the very animals that hovered in the darkness at her feet.

"Come here, please," she commanded, "one at a time. My sight has grown bad from working in the dark. But at close range, I can see everything."

Her fingers were darning a crow's wing as she spoke, and they never missed a stitch. Anatole came forward, and she brought her pale-blue eyes close to his green ones. Her face was as smooth and white as a mushroom.

"So my chameleon found you, after all," she said.

"We came for—" began Anatole, in a quavering voice, but she stopped him.

"I know what you came for," said the Mender. She nodded at the cat. "Next!"

Plumpet, who had grown faint in the presence of so many incautious moles and mice, crept to the Mender's feet and crouched there. The Mender stroked her fur appraisingly.

"You don't need mending," she said. "Your coat is in excellent repair. Next!"

At the sight of Quicksilver rolling across the floor, the Mender laughed.

"Little pot," she said, "you've nothing to fear from me. Go make friends with my big iron kettle in the fireplace. Oh, the stories it could tell you! Next!"

Captain Lark thumped forward, his wooden leg clattering on the stone floor. The Mender shook her head at him.

"I only mend creatures who are what they always were. You're an enchanted being. Now, if you were a real rabbit—"

"No, thank you," said Captain Lark hastily, and he hurried to take his place next to Anatole, for fear the Mender might magic him into a real rabbit.

"Next!"

When Susannah stepped out, the light from the serpents

*". . . the light from
their candles fell directly on her hands and their strange business, . . ."*

set her golden whistle sparkling. The Mender looked long and hard at her.

"My servant the adder told me about you," she said. "She tells me what treasures lie under the earth."

"Where is the adder?" asked Anatole. He remembered how he discovered Susannah by tossing a stone at just such a snake.

"She's gone to Mother Weather-sky's house," said the Mender. "So you want to go there, too, do you?"

"The chameleon said you could show us the way," said Anatole.

"I can show you the way," said the Mender, "but I've got to find it first. Help me clean up the workroom. You could lose your own name in this mess."

And she patted Susannah on the shoulder, for the glass girl had already found the broom and was sweeping the floor. Everyone set about straightening, picking up, and putting away. The room reminded Anatole of a barbershop; feathers and fur lay in little piles underfoot, like hair clippings. In the dark corners, the animals stirred; there was a flutter of broken wings, a light shifting of broken bodies.

"That'll do," said the Mender. "Now come to my worktable, so I can see you under the light."

Susannah stood the broom in the corner, where she had found it. Plumpet picked a feather from her claws, and they joined Anatole and Captain Lark and Quicksilver around the Mender's marvelous chair. She put her arms around them, as if she intended to mend them, too.

"Tonight you shall sleep here, and tomorrow you shall find yourself in Mother Weather-sky's garden. My meals are informal; pick what you would like from my chair."

At these words, the ornaments on the chair woke up, and the carved animals slipped out of sight, leaving behind the branches of the remarkable tree on which they had been perched. Oranges, grapes, melons, pears, peaches, apples, and pomegranates grew there, ripened to perfection. Anatole ate two apples and three pears and was sure he had never tasted better. Plumpet, who generally did not touch fruit, batted a peach with her paw and to her delight it divided itself into two saucers of cream.

When they had eaten all they wished, the chair went back to sleep again; the carved animals returned to their branches, which grew still and dark and hard once more, and the chair behaved like any chair in the ordinary world.

The Mender pointed to a wall in which could be seen a pair of closed shutters.

"From this window I cast my nets each evening and gather what needs to be mended. Tonight while you are sleeping, I will throw my nets over you. Whatever they touch travels in its sleep. You will wake up in Mother Weather-sky's house."

"Do the nets ever make mistakes?" asked Captain Lark.

The Mender shook her head.

"The way to Mother Weather-sky's house is so cleverly hidden that no one can possibly find it with his eyes open."

"But when we arrive," said Anatole, "how can we find the key?"

The Mender smiled.

"You must see to that yourself. I will give you the one other thing that's needed to free the King of the Grass. But mind Mother Weather-sky doesn't take it from you, or you are lost."

She reached under her apron and brought forth a small brown book. The leather cover was so plain and so tattered that it scarcely looked worth the trouble of opening it.

"This is the *Red Calfskin Book of Magic* that belonged to the Magician, who enchanted this island."

Anatole gasped; the others stretched forth their hands timidly to touch it.

"But the Keeper of the Roads said it was lost!" exclaimed the boy.

"Nothing is lost forever," said the Mender. "Everything under the earth and in the sea comes back to me, one way or another. This book was a long time in coming. It has traveled in the guts of a fish, in the body of a bird, in the fourth chamber of an elk's stomach. It has given its leaves for the nests of ravens. It has fed wasps, it has shaped cocoons. It is a much better book than when it was first made, for it was a proud thing then, and now it's part book and part animal. It feels pain, it is wary, and it is mortal. You'll find the spell you need on the last page, the only page that is left."

She handed the book to Anatole, who opened it at once.

"The last page is empty!" he exclaimed.

"No, it's not. The words of the spell are there. But they are invisible."

"Then how am I to read them?" demanded Anatole.

"I am sorry to tell you that only one living soul can read those words," answered the Mender, "and he is not very friendly. The wild boar who lives in Mother Weather-sky's garden can read all languages, even the invisible ones. But capturing him will be very dangerous. Above all, remember to take nothing from Mother Weather-sky's garden."

"Of course we won't," said Captain Lark.

"Not a thing," agreed Plumpet.

"If you do, you will be in Mother Weather-sky's power, and she will most certainly destroy you."

The Mender waited till Anatole had tucked the magic book into his back pocket. Then she rose and deftly plucked a snake out of her lamp and coiled it around her arm.

"Come. I'll show you to your room."

The travelers followed her into a small room, even darker than the first one but less crowded, for it had no worktable and no fireplace, and nothing on the floor except half a dozen wings scattered about like rugs. They shimmered gold and silver, as if the feathers had been worked in metal.

"Did angels leave these?" whispered Anatole.

"Not angels," replied the Mender. "Basilisks and dragons. Their wings are so warm you will not need a cover."

Anatole sank sleepily into the nearest wing, and Plumpet curled herself at his feet, for she had promised to take care of him and she always kept her promises. It seemed to the boy that he heard bells ringing far under the earth and that the bells had voices, deep and muffled:

> "Three women sailed out of the watery dark,
>   and who do you think they be?
>   The Mender, the Maker, the Bender-and-Breaker,
>   Wise women, all three!"

The harmonica in his pocket hummed quick and high, which frightened Anatole very much, till he remembered the Roadkeeper's words: "Don't be afraid. The island is full of noises. Sometimes a thousand twangling instruments will hum about your ears, and sometimes voices. And if you've waked after a long sleep, they'll make you sleep again."

The music ceased as suddenly as it had started, and the last voice he heard belonged to Plumpet, who declared herself so moved by the spectacle of the wounded creatures in the workshop that she would never go hunting again—at least not till the next full moon.

CHAPTER TEN

The next morning the Mender and her creatures were nowhere to be seen, and the travelers awoke to find themselves surrounded by a queer throng of folk who stood perfectly still with their feet in the sand and their eyes raised to heaven, as if they were praying for deliverance. Many of the women wore wings like angels, though they had caps instead of haloes, and they were waving flags, from which the colors had long been weathered away, so that you could not tell what countries they came from. The men wore periwigs or stovepipe hats or sailor suits; a few were dressed as Indian chieftains. The ladies who did not look like angels wore long gowns and bonnets. Scattered among this solemn crowd were eagles, lions, unicorns, mermaids, and a large robust figure who might have been King of the Sea, for he held a trident and wore a crown, both badly in need of paint. And nearly everyone carried banners inscribed with such names as *Constitution* or *Glory of the Sea* or *Clara Belle* or *Polar Star* or *Dashing Wave*.

Anatole felt anxiously in his pocket for the magician's book. Yes, it was quite safe.

"What funny names these people have," whispered Susannah. "They don't seem to notice us at all. I believe we can walk right past them."

"Bless me, they're figureheads," exclaimed Captain Lark. "Many's the time I've admired such things on the prows of passing ships. But how odd to find them all heaped together in a field."

A narrow flagstone path wound through the crowd of figureheads in Mother Weather-sky's garden. The garden was laid out in beds, but no flowers grew in them. Sextants and compasses glittered in one, broken crockery shone in another, chests empty of treasure—their lids open or gone entirely—lay in a third. The path led past a jumble of weathervanes—roosters and archers and fish and horses— that had long ago lost their sense of direction; motionless, they pointed to the earth.

Then the path turned abruptly. At last, and to Anatole's great delight, it entered a bed of toys. Model ships, steam engines, trucks, cars, cradles, puppets, dolls, like the stock-room of the biggest toy store in the world, except that everything was broken, everything had been battered by the sea. Anatole paused to finger a small ship that had lost its sails. Its ivory hull felt smooth as butter, and its brass spars shone.

"Do you think a sailor made this for his child back home?" he asked Captain Lark. But the rabbit only shook his head.

"Remember what the Mender told us," he warned. "Take nothing from the garden."

Anatole did not mean to take the ship, only to hold it. But the instant he picked it up, he felt a blow on his head that knocked him to the ground. He was back on his feet at once, and again something struck him, this time on the shoulder. He looked up. A stick twice the size of his baseball bat at home was dancing over his head. Now it pummeled Captain Lark on the back, and now it darted after Plumpet and nipped her tail, so that she mewed dreadfully. Fortunately it did not touch Susannah.

"Run!" the glass girl screamed.

They ran down the path, the stick bobbing after them, as if it rode an invisible wave. In their haste to escape, nobody noticed that the end of the path was near and that it led straight into the side of a broken ship, which somebody had patched up to make a house. In the doorway stood a little woman wrapped in a green cape, like an ear of corn, and she was puffing on a pipe. She blew out a great cloud of smoke and said, "Stick, lay off."

The stick stopped in mid-blow and leaped obediently into her hand. Anatole glanced round to see who had saved them.

"Don't move," said the woman. "My ash stick can split a rock if it chooses."

"Who are you?" cried Susannah.

"I am Mother Weather-sky," came the reply.

Anatole stared at her. She was without doubt the same woman he had seen riding the dogs and throwing lightning bolts during the storm. But by the calm light of a windless day how small she looked! She might have been one of the plaster dwarves at the back of his grandmother's garden. Her

*"The stick stopped in mid-blow and
leaped obediently into her hand."*

cape needed mending, her boots were split at the toes, and her blue apron, faded almost to gray, was smudged with ashes. Her hair was tangled with burrs and branches and—could it be? A sparrow had actually built its nest and was sitting on top of its eggs, fast asleep, just over her left ear.

"I'm not afraid of you," said Anatole. "You aren't much taller than my cat."

"Smaller is stronger," said Mother Weather-sky, and she stalked over to Plumpet and shook the ashes from her pipe over the cat's ears and tail.

What happened next made Anatole regret his words. Plumpet's honey-warm fur grew hard and bright, her whiskers began to shimmer, her claws shone, and where the lively cat had crouched a moment before he saw a cat of pure gold.

"She shall be my bench," said Mother Weather-sky, puffing on her pipe. Then she walked from Anatole to Susannah to Captain Lark, her wicked green eyes peering at each of them in turn. Before Anatole could stop her, she took the pipe from her mouth once more and threw a shower of ashes over Captain Lark. Without a sound he curled up like a leaf in a bonfire, smooth and still, stretched in a golden sleep.

"A very serviceable table," said Mother Weather-sky. Then she turned to Quicksilver.

"Down the path that branches to the right, you will find a well. Take the rope and climb down and fetch my water. Do not take the other path or things will go badly for you."

The coffeepot marched away sorrowfully, dragging its silver feet.

Mother Weather-sky grabbed Susannah by the wrist and asked, "Can you cook? If you can cook, I shall keep you for a little while longer before I break you to bits and take that whistle."

Susannah shrank behind Anatole, but Mother Weather-sky yanked her out and pushed her toward the open door, which was so low that the girl had to crawl through it on her hands and knees.

"My kitchen lies to the back," called Mother Weather-sky after her. "I like tea with my meals and I'm very fond of currants."

Susannah disappeared into Mother Weather-sky's house. It had not a single window; even the portholes were sealed up. Mother Weather-sky folded her arms and cocked her head at Anatole.

"My vegetable garden wants weeding. I am fond of vegetables, but where I walk weeds spring up. The center path will lead you to the vegetable plot. Pull every weed by sundown or I shall change you into a turnip and eat you for supper."

Anatole did not wait to be told twice. He ran down the path and almost immediately found the vegetable garden. It was so overgrown with burdock and thistles that ten men could not have cleared it in a week, and he knew he could never clear it in a day, for he had no spade and no rake, nothing but his bare hands.

But even worse than the weeds were the stones. He kept stubbing his toes on them. Soon he was so weary that he had to sit down, and when he remembered Susannah in that dark little house, Plumpet and Captain Lark changed into furniture, and his own fate if he didn't finish, he burst into tears.

Something splashed, not far from where he sat. He looked around startled and was very surprised to discover among the weeds a clear pool, perfectly round, just to his left. He ran to it eagerly and leaned over the rim to drink and saw, at the same moment, two golden fish—one large, one small—gliding slowly through the water, their tails fanning gently back and forth. Then he spied something else gleaming in the darkness at the bottom of the pool, and he drew in his breath and gave a cry of delight.

It was the golden key.

Before he could reach for it, a blossom sailed down from the tree overhead and glided to the water. The touch of the water turned the blossom to stone and it started to sink. But now a strange thing happened. The water, so still and clear, began to churn and stir itself, foaming and frothing, until at last the waves leaped up like hands and flung the stone flower out of the water.

Anatole jumped back in a hurry.

"It's a good thing I didn't drink from that pool."

A snorting and crashing among the trees at the far side of the pool made him freeze in his tracks. Something was charging toward him, heaving dirt into the air as it came. There flashed across his mind his mother's lullaby about the boy who played the harmonica so well that all the animals lay down around him, even the fiercer kinds, and in desperation he felt for his harmonica in his back pocket, pulled it out, and tried to play his old standby "Yankee Doodle." To his surprise it began to play his mother's lullaby instead:

> "Everything that heard him play,
>   even the billows of the sea,
>   hung their heads and then lay by."

The crashing and snorting among the trees stopped, and a husky voice supplied the rest of the words:

> "In sweet music is such art,
>   killing care and grief of heart,
>   fall asleep or hearing, die.

Into the sunlight trotted a wild boar. It was as big as a horse, and its tusks curled over its snout like two nicely matched scythes. Humming to itself, it sat down beside Anatole and then it said, "Leave off and catch your breath."

"Aren't you going to run me through?" quavered Anatole, who was almost too frightened to speak.

"No sense in running you through," replied the boar. "I've few enough folk as it is. What brings you to this dreadful place?"

So Anatole told the boar how he and his friends had fallen into Mother Weather-sky's power and he had little hope they would ever get home again. And he added that he

"Humming to itself, it sat down beside Anatole . . ."

wanted to free the King of the Grass, but he did not mention the Magician's book. The boar listened gravely.

"I am well acquainted with the King of the Grass. I was his gardener."

"Then you know where to find him?" asked Anatole eagerly.

"No. I won't see him till I carry five and sink alive. That's part of the spell. What do you think it means? Five of what? Sink into what? And where's the lost key to be found?"

"The key is in the pool," Anatole exclaimed, pointing, "but if you touch the water, you'll turn to stone."

The boar squinted into the water. "As I live and breathe! Now if we only had the lost book of spells, we'd go straight to the door."

"Could you read the lost book of spells?" asked Anatole.

"I can read all languages," said the boar, "even the invisible ones."

Hearing this, Anatole brought the book from his pocket and handed it to the boar, who sniffed it all over and raised his head slowly so that his tiny eyes met Anatole's.

"How did you come by this?"

"The Mender gave it to me."

"Wonderful!" exclaimed the boar. "Hey, my dears"—he called out to the two fish, who flamed through the dark water—"bring us the key, won't you? You know I can't reach it myself."

The biggest fish leaped out of the water, spat the key out

into Anatole's pocket, turned a somersault, and disappeared again into the depths.

"That's a good fellow," said the boar. "Now let's see what the book advises."

He opened it to the last and only page. When the light struck it, the letters began to fade in, like invisible ink before a candle. Anatole could make nothing of the words, but the boar read in a low voice:

"One for the rook, one for the crow,
one to die, and one to grow."

And now before Anatole's eyes, the strange words shifted and slowly changed themselves into the words he knew. In the R of *rook* crouched a rabbit, in the C of *crow* dozed a cat, in the G of *grow* stood a girl. The D of *die* opened up into a door, through which something had just passed, for you could see part of its shadow, but you could not tell what it was.

The boar continued:

"When bells ring clear,
summer is near."

At these words the page faded into smoke and the cover of the book crumpled into a handful of dry leaves.

"Well, well," said the boar, brushing off his paws. "I've come to the end of the spell. Do you hear the bells ringing clear?"

Anatole heard nothing. Then it seemed to him he did hear something—was it the wind? No, it was the bells, some deep and sonorous as church bells, some high and brilliant as chimes. The boar pricked up his ears.

"They're ringing from over that way," said Anatole, pointing east.

"Let's follow them," said the boar, and he trotted away so briskly that Anatole had to run to keep up with him.

he bells led the boy and the boar into a eucalyptus grove so dense that even the path could not find its way and simply disappeared under broken branches. The hulls of ships, half sunk in the mud, jutted through the underbrush. Enormous vines spread like nets at their feet, and when Anatole heard something crackling in the bushes, he called out, "Is there another boar in the forest?" just as the boar exclaimed, "I shall charge at it, whatever it is," and the branches burst apart and out tumbled Susannah, Captain Lark, Plumpet, and Quicksilver.

There were shouts of astonishment and cries of joy.

"How did you escape?" demanded Anatole, who could hardly believe his eyes.

"Quicksilver saved us," said Captain Lark. "When he brought the water from Mother Weather-sky's well, he saw her sprinkle it on a stone. The stone turned into a quail, which she ordered Susannah to cook for supper. So he took some of the water and sprinkled us back to life again."

"And then I crept through the kitchen door and found Susannah," added Plumpet.

"And I jumped out and we ran away." Susannah laughed, clapping her hands till they rang like crystal.

Suddenly she caught sight of the boar, who had concealed himself in the foliage and now came forward to introduce himself. She gave a little shriek, and the others spun around in a panic.

"Don't be afraid," said Anatole. "This is my friend, Mr.—Mr.—"

"Toby," said the boar. "The name's Toby."

"This is Toby," continued Anatole, "and he has gotten us the golden key and he has read the spell in the Magician's book, and we were following the bells through the forest and looking for the golden tree."

"Bells?" inquired Plumpet.

"Let's listen again for the bells," said Toby. "I am sure they will lead us to the King of the Grass."

They stood still and listened. The bells had stopped ringing, but another noise could be heard very distinctly, a *thwack, thwack*, which came from the direction of Mother Weather-sky's house.

"Somebody's chopping down trees," said Plumpet.

Toby let out a howl.

"She's found us," he bellowed. "That's her stick we hear, and it's marching through the forest after us. We must run for our lives."

"But where can we go?" wailed Susannah.

"To the river at the back of Mother Weather-sky's garden," answered Toby. "She can't swim. Climb on my back. I can push aside the branches with my tusks."

There was a mad scramble for places. They could hear the stick coming closer—*thwack, thwack*—and though Toby was running as fast as he could, the stick was running faster. Sitting behind Captain Lark, in the last place, Anatole looked back and saw the stick springing among the trees. And riding on the stick was Mother Weather-sky herself.

"She's right behind us!" shouted Anatole. "Hurry!"

Susannah began to laugh.

"The river! I see the river! We're saved!"

Toby rushed toward it and plunged down an embankment so steep that he nearly pitched his passengers over his head. Mother Weather-sky, whipping her stick, was bounding right after them. When Anatole looked back once more, her hand brushed his arm, and it felt cold as snow, just as Toby reached the water and waded in.

Behind them, Mother Weather-sky was dancing on the muddy banks and shouting, "May you turn into stones and sink! May the fish swallow you! May you never find your way home!"

"She's casting a spell on us," yowled Plumpet.

"No, she's not," said Toby. "She has no power over the river."

The boar, who had been walking on the river bottom, now felt it give way under him, so that he was obliged to swim. The weight of so many passengers pushed him lower.

"I'm so glad you joined us, Toby," said Susannah.

"Unfortunately," choked Toby, "when I step out of

Mother Weather-sky's garden, I shall disappear. Magician's orders, you know."

He could go no farther. His head bobbed under the water, just as those on his back gave a joyful cry.

Before them glittered the golden tree. Its fiery leaves shimmered; its golden bark dazzled their eyes. Golden bells sparkled and chimed on every branch, and there, in all that blinding brightness, gleamed the golden door.

"Have you got the key?" gasped Toby as he struggled for footing on the roots that glowed under the dark water.

Anatole scrambled off, and trembling with excitement, he fitted the key to the lock. The hinges gave a musical sigh as the door sprang open. Sunlight streamed over the threshold and down a green corridor.

"Give me your hand, please," called Susannah.

She was struggling on the slippery roots, trying to reach the door. Behind them on the riverbank Mother Weather-sky stopped shaking her stick and hurled it straight at Susannah. As Anatole stretched out his hand, he heard the shattering of glass. Mother Weather-sky gave a terrible laugh, and he found himself holding a hand as warm as his own.

He saw before him a little girl who looked exactly like Susannah. But she was not made of glass. She wore a green velvet gown and a green ribbon in her hair, and the whistle around her neck was a real blade of grass looped on a chain of forget-me-nots.

"Where is Susannah?" asked Captain Lark, bewildered.

"Here," said the girl. "Don't you know me?"

"Don't dawdle over miracles," called Plumpet's voice from beyond the threshold, "for I think we have found the King and Queen at last."

Everyone, even Toby, followed the cat down the corridor into a round green room, so magically furnished that Anatole thought that of all the marvels they met on their travels, this was the very best. Moss and wild strawberries tapestried the walls, which gave off a delicious scent of wild thyme and freshly cut grass. From the ceiling hung a small green castle cut from a single emerald, in which a light shone and lit up a company of dancing couples within, each a different-colored jewel given human shape, just as a real castle might appear to shepherds gazing at it from a distant hillside.

But the most remarkable sight was the fragrant bed of rosemary that grew in the middle of the room, on which lay a man and woman elegantly dressed in green robes, their hands folded, their eyes closed. On the man's head grew a crown of fennel, as green as if it had seen nothing but sun all its days.

Susannah rushed to them, knelt down, and kissed them. Then she rubbed their hands. And the others, seeing that she could not wake the sleepers, greeted them with "Time to rise" and "Top o' the morning to you" and other cheerful expressions, but all their efforts failed.

"The whistle," said Anatole. "Blow the whistle."

Susannah put the blade of grass to her lips and blew a loud clear note.

Nothing changed. She blew a second time.

Then the walls of the tree began to grow lighter and thinner. The man and the woman opened their eyes and sat up and looked at each other.

"I had such a peculiar dream," said the man, helping his wife to her feet.

"And so had I," she told him.

"Mother! Father!" cried Susannah. Then she turned to her companions. "*These* are my true parents. The spell is broken!"

Now the tree was gone and they were all standing together on a bridge over the river in the open air. The Queen of the Grass put her arms around Susannah.

"Are these friends of yours, Daisy?" she asked.

"My name isn't Daisy now. My friends gave me a new one," answered the girl gravely. "My name is Susannah."

And she began to tell her father and mother the whole story. But when she mentioned the rabbit, she paused in surprise.

"Why, what has become of Captain Lark?" she asked.

Where the rabbit had been leaning on his wooden leg only a moment before, they saw a man in a sailor suit, examining his two sound legs and rubbing his short brown hair and carefully touching his pale, modest ears.

"I am Captain Lark," he said, "and I'm as hale as the day I set forth on my maiden voyage. Look sharp, children. I've my own face at last."

Behind him a handsome young man in green doublet

and hose stepped forward. First he embraced the King, then the Queen, and then Susannah.

"Toby, at your service," he said. Tears of joy shone on his cheeks. "Come into the garden. The spell is broken."

It was marigold time in the garden, and on both sides of the river stretched a sea of gold, dotted by men and women, all in green, who moved slowly toward them, as in a dance. Behind them rose a golden castle.

"Where are the figureheads? Where are the broken ships?" Anatole whispered.

The King pointed to the sky, blue and clear save for one gray cloud in which could be seen, very faintly, the shape of a tiny woman in a green cape, beating the air with her stick. When the cloud broke into pieces, she disappeared.

"Is she gone for good?" asked Anatole.

"From our island, yes," said the King of the Grass.

"And where is her house?" asked Captain Lark.

"She hasn't one," replied the Queen. "She never did have one till the Magician came."

"Papa, who are the people coming this way?" asked Susannah.

"They are the people who live in the garden," said the King. "Let's go and meet them."

Then there was such rejoicing that it seemed to Anatole as if everyone on the island were celebrating a birthday. The castle of the King and Queen was built entirely of sod, planted with flowers, so that every wall and turret was a garden in itself. Marigolds covered the castle from top to bottom. Hedges of silvery green artemisia, taller than Anatole had seen it growing at home, led from the main door into an intricate labyrinth of terraces and fountains. Exploring the grounds at the back of the castle, Anatole came upon a row of marigold kennels and was at first alarmed to see Mother Weather-sky's dogs taking their ease in the yard.

"You'd better not try anything funny," he warned the Great Dane, keeping a safe distance from his old tormentor. "The King and Queen are back, you know."

The Great Dane only wagged his tail.

"So you've changed too," said Anatole. "You've gotten smaller somehow. And more friendly."

In front of the castle, tablecloths had been spread on the grass and laid with platters of apples and grapes, and bowls of butter and cream, and loaves of bread that steamed when you cut them open. The men and women of the court came eagerly forward to pay their respects to the King and Queen and the guests of honor. Captain Lark sat at the Queen's right hand, Plumpet sat at the King's left, so that she could have a good view of him, because as she said later, "A cat may look at a king, and I don't know when I shall ever have another opportunity." Quicksilver padded to and fro, snuffling up a little of everything, to the great amusement of Toby. Anatole and Susannah walked among the courtiers, greeting them; everyone wanted to hug Susannah and to shake Anatole's hand.

When Captain Lark saw the two children coming to join him at last, he bowed and said, "I have decided to stay here forever. The King of the Grass has made me Captain of the royal navy."

"We haven't a navy yet," said the King, laughing, "but if we should ever need one, Captain Lark will be in charge of it. Tell me, Anatole, would you like to be my son and live on our island? It is always summer here, and though you will grow up, you will never grow old."

Stay here on the island? Anatole tried to imagine such a life, warm, pleasant, but without his mother to sing him songs, his father to play soccer with him in the front yard, his grandmother to tell him stories of when his mother was a child and of her own childhood, so many years before he was born.

"Thank you very much," said Anatole, "but I would like to go home. What I really want is some of the fennel that grows in your crown. We had a hard winter, and my grandmother's fennel didn't come up this year."

"So my daughter tells me," said the King.

He reached up, lifted a fragrant clump from his crown, and handed it to Anatole.

"Oh," said the boy, "you've made a great hole in your crown!"

"It will grow together again," the King assured him.

Even while he was speaking, a new shoot appeared, unfolded its leaves, and closed the gap.

"Plant it as soon as possible when you get home," said Toby.

"How do I get home?" asked Anatole.

The Queen leaned toward him and pointed to a row of silvery green hedges that wound from where they sat toward the horizon.

"In the Magician's labyrinth, people lost their way. In ours, they will find it again. Take the path that starts from the castle."

"How long should I follow it?"

"Till you reach home," answered the Queen.

"I wish very much you could stay with us," said the King.

"And so do I," said Susannah. "Don't forget me, Anatole." She took from her neck the grass whistle on its chain of forget-me-nots and put it around his neck. "When you whistle on the grass, I shall hear you and know you are thinking of us."

Captain Lark was too much overcome to say a word. He whisked a large handkerchief from his pocket, blew his nose fiercely, and hugged first Anatole and then Plumpet. He even hugged Quicksilver, who wiggled all over with pleasure, for never in his life had anyone shown him so much affection.

Plumpet offered her paw, rather solemnly, to the King and Queen and Susannah, and then to Toby, who presented her with a bouquet of catnip. This moved her so much that she forgot the fine speech she had prepared for the occasion and could only say, "I shall include you in my memoirs. Your names will be household words among cats."

"I shall miss you," said Anatole, "all of you."

Holding Quicksilver, he started down the path the

"She took from her neck the grass whistle on its chain of forget-me-nots and put it around his neck."

Queen had shown him. Glancing over his shoulder and waving as he walked while Plumpet scampered at his heels, he saw his friends' hands waving back, like the bright crests of waves moving farther and farther away from him, until the hedges grew so high that he lost sight of them altogether. Before he had time to regret it, a tiny bird, feathered in gold, darted out of the hedge and lighted on his shoulder.

"Good-bye, Anatole," it chirped. "Thanks to you, I'm free again."

"Have we met before?" asked Anatole, puzzled, for he did not remember ever having seen such a bird.

The bird laughed.

"How could I meet you when I've never left you? I am the road to Mother Weather-sky's garden, and nobody will ever need me again."

"You don't look much like a road," said Plumpet.

"I almost never look like a road," sang the bird. "Sometimes I look like a lizard, leading you into moonlight. Sometimes I look like a blossom turning to stone on the water. Good-bye!"

Before Anatole could say thank you, the bird flew off. But the boy could hear it singing, "This way! This way!" and he ran after it, his eyes scanning the sky for a last glimpse of it, so that he hardly knew where his feet carried him—

—until he ran straight into his grandmother's clothes-line.

Grandmother was walking in her garden.

"Look here—the fennel's come back after all," she said, pointing to it. "And I've a nice surprise for you. Your parents sent you a kind of barometer from London. It's called a 'weather house.' Where have you been all morning?"

Anatole did not answer, only followed his grandmother into the dining room. There on the table stood a little house with two doorways. In one doorway stood an old woman, in the other doorway stood an old man. The man wore a crown of leaves and carried a staff wound with flowers and crowned with a grasshopper. The woman carried a quiver of lightning bolts on her back and leaned on a stick. Both figures were nicely carved and painted green, except for their faces, which were so hastily done you could scarcely make out the expressions.

"It says on the bottom of the house that *she* comes out when it rains and *he* comes out when it's fair," said Grandma. "Tomorrow let's change their places, out of fairness to the old woman."

"It's no use changing their places," said Anatole. "Mother Weather-sky always brings storms."

Beside the weather house stood Quicksilver, one side bright, the other side dark, waiting for somebody to polish him. Plumpet was asleep in the middle of the table.

"We'll have a late lunch today," said Grandmother. "We can't use the table until Plumpet wakes up. But I found a bird's nest in the lilac bush while you were gone. And the snake grass has come up. When I was a girl, we used to whistle on snake grass. I wonder if I can still do it since I lost my teeth?"

The whistle! Anatole looked down. There was nothing around his neck but a smudge of dirt, which did not escape Grandma's notice.

"Did you wash up before you went to bed last night?"

The last thing Anatole wanted to do was wash up. Through the French doors the sun was shaking lights like coins over the honeysuckle bush while the cardinals whistled to each other in the pear trees.

"Mother Weather-sky is in, and the King of the Grass is out," said Anatole. "Come on, Grandma. It's a perfect day for exploring."